CHARM

HELEN WHITCOMB
FORMERLY MANAGING EDITOR
OF "TODAY'S SECRETARY"

& ROSALIND LANG
LECTURER AND TEACHER AT
ALBANY BUSINESS COLLEGE,
MILDRED ELLEY SECRETARIAL
SCHOOL, MERCY SECRETARIAL
HIGH SCHOOL, AND NEW YORK
TELEPHONE COMPANY

GREGG DIVISION   McGRAW - HILL BOOK COMPANY
NEW YORK CHICAGO DALLAS SAN FRANCISCO TORONTO LONDON

CHARM

THE CAREER GIRL'S GUIDE TO BUSINESS AND PERSONAL SUCCESS

Acknowledgments: The authors wish to thank the following companies for their help and cooperation: Elizabeth Arden; Hazel Bishop, Inc.; Chesebrough-Pond's, Inc.; Helene Curtis Industries, Inc.; Clairol; Max Factor; Dorothy Gray, Ltd.; Richard Hudnut; Lanolin Plus, Inc.; Helen Neushaefer Cosmetics; Helene Rubinstein; Shulton, Inc.; Tussy Cosmetics; Lugene, Inc.; Scarves by Vera, Inc.

DESIGN BY BARBARA DU PREE KNOWLES

·

DRAWINGS BY NANCY REYNOLDS GAMAR

2 3 4 5 6 7 8 9   ROL–64   2 1 0 9 8 7 6 5 4   69641

Every girl has within her exciting potentialities that can be discovered and nurtured to help her become a more attractive, more interesting, more appealing person. *Charm* has been designed specifically to help her make the most of these potentialities so that she can achieve success and happiness, both in her work and in her personal life.

The advice of experts in many fields has been brought together in this book and carefully tailored to the needs of the career girl—to her problems, time limitations, financial status, and interests. The book is divided into six parts, each covering a specific area.

PART ONE considers posture and figure improvement, for these basic charm factors require time to develop. So much of a person's physical beauty depends on good posture and graceful movements that precise detailed explanations have been furnished for positions and actions. Figure analysis, from the standpoint of correct proportions, is supplemented with advice on exercise and diet to remedy any unsatisfactory measurements.

PART TWO fully explains various beauty and cosmetic techniques and how they can be used to accentuate natural beauty and to cleverly camouflage any imperfections. Because inner beauty is so necessary for a lovely countenance, personality improvement is also treated in this section.

PART THREE concentrates on the development of a personal flair for fashion. The reader is shown which styles, which colors, and which combinations of wardrobe elements will produce the flattering fashion sense that marks a woman of taste.

PART FOUR explains in detail how to develop a lovely voice and colorful, correct speech. Because so much of a person's charm is due to what she says and how she expresses herself, both on-the-job telephone techniques and social conversation are fully covered.

PART FIVE discusses the place of a girl in the business world. The reader is advised how to analyze job opportunities to find the one for which she is best suited, how to obtain this job, and how to please both her boss and her fellow employees.

PART SIX deals with the out-of-the-office aspects of a career girl's life. Her home life—whether with family or roommates—is considered, and the various problems of city living are evaluated. The reader is advised how to choose a good place to live; how to select compatible roommates; and how to manage her time, energy, and money. Dating is discussed, and special attention is given to the delicate handling required in the case of an office romance. An extensive chapter on etiquette equips the reader with the poise that enables her to handle difficult situations—introductions, dining out, table etiquette,

PREFACE

v

tipping, and so on. Since increased charm often leads to matrimony, suggestions have been included for happily blending marriage and a career.

In short, *Charm* is a book that shows career girls how to bring out the best in themselves, how to be admired and liked by the people they come in contact with—a prescription for happiness and success.

Helen Whitcomb

Rosalind Lang

CONTENTS

A PERSONAL PREVIEW

In the offices of the Bingham Company there was an air of suppressed excitement. The supervisor of the customer service department had announced her intention to resign.

There was great suspense as the staff waited to hear who would fill her place. Several girls hoped secretly that they would be chosen, but almost everyone felt quite sure the job would go to Nancy. Nancy was an attractive girl who, while not exactly pretty, had a contagious warmth and friendliness that made her seem almost beautiful. It was so genuine it attracted everyone in the office, both men and women.

Grace was one of those who hoped she might be selected. On the basis of seniority she had it over the other girls. Grace worked fast—perhaps even a bit faster than Nancy—and she could carry out orders efficiently. She was extremely conscientious and responsible. But as good a worker as Grace was, everyone admitted she hadn't half the personality Nancy had, or the imagination and initiative that a top post demands.

Marie was another leading contender. She was a gay, friendly girl who was also well liked by everyone. She was a good worker and could be counted on to do important jobs without supervision. Somehow, though, Marie didn't quite look the part. She wasn't always as neat as she should be, and she lacked the wonderful clothes sense that made Nancy such a standout. At times Marie was also a little too loud in her good-hearted way and, although she was considered the life of the department, she sometimes displayed a lack of discretion that would not go well in an important position.

When the news came that Nancy had been selected, almost everyone agreed that the best possible choice had been made. Not only did Nancy look the part of the clever career girl, she acted it too. She could placate customers and soothe office strife with equal ease. She was a lively, alert person whose many varied interests made her an intelligent worker and a fascinating companion.

When Nancy first came to work at Bingham, she wasn't of executive caliber. Inexperienced and unsophisticated, she didn't know her way around the office or the city. She was even a little shy and timid. But this didn't hold her back. Nancy set out to learn what she felt every successful girl should know. She studied the clothes that smart women wore and, bit by bit, built herself a beautifully coordinated wardrobe. She filled in the chinks in her social and cultural background by reading, studying, and observing. With her improved appearance and background, she gradually developed the poise and quiet assurance that enabled her to deal with others so well.

So many of the plums of modern life go to those who, like Nancy, have charm and

A CHARMED LIFE

personality. While you are learning business skills, you should also consider personal skills. In many instances, appearance, personality, sophistication, and thoughtfulness make the difference between the girl in the private office with her name on the door and the back-office drone who is always bypassed at promotion time. Out of the office, these qualities can also mean the difference between loneliness and a full and happy life.

In this course you are going to study the most intricate and fascinating subject in the world—yourself. You are going to learn how to turn yourself into the attractive, appealing person you've always dreamed of being. Already you possess the basic ingredients. You're a girl with many good features, a supply of special talents and abilities, and a certain individuality. All of these can be tended and encouraged, explored and enlarged. Being only human, you probably have your quota of imperfections, too, and these you will learn to correct when possible. Or you can learn to make them less conspicuous by spotlighting the attractive qualities you already possess.

Unfortunately, the transformation isn't a presto-chango matter. It requires considerable work—as almost everything worthwhile does—but it is the kind of work that is probably more fun and more rewarding than anything you've undertaken in your whole life.

As your charm barometer rises, admiration will be reflected in the eyes of those you meet. Life is *fun* for the charming, attractive girl. She delightedly finds that by making herself more attractive, success and happiness crowd around her. As she learns to make herself more interesting, her whole life becomes fuller, richer, more exciting. Best of all, she feels proud of herself—confident, assured, poised, *free*.

The girl who fears her clothes don't look right, knows her hair isn't at its best, or isn't sure of her manners can never be free to enjoy herself. She's so tangled up in her own insecurity that she feels self-conscious and uneasy. She actually shuts herself out from much of the fun of life. Fortunately, with improvement confidence rises. The person who is confident and assured succeeds easily. Because she's relaxed and at ease, she's able to put others at ease and so can bring out the best in them—and the best in herself as well. Her relationships with others are rich, warm, and satisfying.

Soon you will learn how to make yourself into a natural glowing beauty—how to perfect your figure, how to make cosmetics, hairdo, and clothing work a special magic for you. You'll also learn how to improve your voice and your speech and how to charm others with your lively conversation and gracious manner. You'll study how to be well liked by everyone, from personnel interviewers to handsome halfbacks, from distinguished employers to messenger girls. Because the way a business girl lives often has an important bearing on her success, both as a person and as an employee, you'll also study ways to make your life easier and more fun, and ways to make your time and money do the most for you.

You've an exciting course ahead, where good effort is clearly registered in your charm and beauty. Work well, for the subject is YOU. The reward: A charmed life.

PART ONE:

YOUR SILHOUETTE

How you stand and move can be almost as expressive of your character as your mouth and eyes are. The person who stands tall and straight and moves with fluid, easy grace seems to proclaim to the world her confidence, efficiency, and alertness. The slouch who moves like a marionette with a broken string seems inept, defeated, at odds with herself and at odds with the world.

The secret of graceful, queenly movements is Posture—with a definitely capital P. How we carry ourselves has more effect on our appearance than any amount of expensive clothing, cosmetics, dieting, or camouflage. Posture is the foundation on which all good looks depend. It makes a tremendous difference. The girl with perfect posture has a beauty of motion that can make her appear far more attractive than another girl with a pretty face who hasn't learned to move well. She is also likely to have better health, because poor posture can lead to backaches, digestive troubles, and chronic fatigue.

Particularly nasty are the things poor posture can do to figures. Even the girl with perfect proportions looks dumpy if her chest is caved in and her abdomen protrudes. With time, poor posture leads to disfigurement, because certain muscles are stretched while others do not receive enough use. Bad posture can lead to such ugly silhouette saboteurs as secretarial spread, dowager's hump, and spare-tire middle. Many a woman wonders why she is plagued by such unattractive lumps and bulges, unaware that they were brought on by incorrect posture.

1

BEAUTY IN MOTION

YOUR BEAUTY LINEUP

How is *your* posture? Take a look at your side view in a full-length mirror. Stand as you naturally do. Be honest now—your usual posture, not better. Now: Pull your abdomen in and tuck your hips under as you lift your rib cage high and straighten your spine. Let your knees flex slightly so that your body weight is forward over the main arch of your foot. Your shoulders should be so straight that in this side view your shoulder blades are not visible but are concealed by your arm. Better? No need to tell you!

The average girl can usually add at least an inch to her bust dimension and subtract as much from her waist, hip, and abdominal measurements by standing properly. Correcting your posture can make a dramatic improvement in your figure. One girl who improved her posture actually went from a size 14 dress to a size 10, even though she gained five pounds during the time.

If an imaginary yardstick were placed against your reflection from your ear to your foot, the line should pass (1) through the tip of the ear, (2) through the center of the shoulder-arm joint, (3) slightly behind the center of the hip, (4) slightly in back of the center of the knee, (5) in front of the ankle joint.

To get the feel of perfect alignment, stand with your back to a wall, your heels about two inches from the baseboard. Now press your head and back—shoulders, waist, and hips—flat against the wall. You should be able to get your entire torso flat. If you have difficulty flattening your shoulder blades, or if there is space between the small of your back and the wall, you'll want to correct this by doing some of the exercises described at the end of this chapter. You'll find that this wall position is in itself an excellent posture exercise.

In order to get the small of your back flat against the wall, bend your knees and slide down the wall until you are touching it all the way down your back. Then slowly move up the wall, digging as hard as possible with your waist to keep your torso hugging the wall as you come up. Try to keep this perfect alignment as you move away from the wall and walk around.

Any posture correction begins with acquiring the feel of good posture. Become truly conscious of how it feels to stand with your body aligned. Then practice assuming this good posture until it becomes a habit.

Envision your body as a column of blocks, each of which must nest perfectly atop the other. When one block is thrown out of line, the others are tipped, too. This is why good posture involves every inch and every muscle—and why one small bad habit can spoil your total appearance.

If you walk with your head jutting forward like a duck after minnows, you have one of the most common posture problems. If you remember to keep your ears in line over the center of your shoulders and your chin in (but parallel to the floor), you'll avoid this unbecoming tendency—and the dowager's hump it can cause.

Rounded shoulders are most unattractive. If you stand with your arms folded, you will have to be especially careful, because this position pulls the shoulders around and forward. From time to time throughout the day check the position of your shoulders. Perhaps you can't always stop to align your back against a wall, so instead try this: Rotate your shoulders forward, then up and back as far as possible, then let them drop suddenly. They will fall into a natural, attractive position. This is an inconspicuous movement, easy to do anywhere.

Another beauty destroyer is a protruding abdomen and its corollary, the jutting rear (the forerunner of weight accumulation in the waist and abdomen). These difficulties can be corrected if you remember to:

1 Raise the top part of your body as high as possible (lift the waist up from the hips, the ribs up from the waist, the neck up from the shoulders, and hold your head up high).

2 Keep your hips tucked in and under. Remember that column of blocks, each nesting perfectly atop the other, and see that your rib cage fits directly above the pelvic area (hips and abdomen).

Columnist Robert Ruark once wrote that New York models look as if they are afraid they'll be kicked in the rear. Perhaps this is a good picture to keep in mind if you're tempted to sink into a swayback position. You can't go to extremes if you remember to keep your body's column of blocks centered along an imaginary yardstick running down your side.

3 Keep your knees loose and properly centered. Often, poor alignment of the pelvic area is due to the habit of standing with the knees back in a stiff, locked position. Unless the knees are slightly flexed, the pelvis will tip out of line. When wearing heels, you will probably find it necessary to flex the knees just a bit more than you would in flats.

4 Center your weight over the main arch of your foot. (This applies no matter what heel height you are wearing.) If your weight is properly centered, you should be able to slide your heels slightly from side to side and, at the same time, wiggle your toes. This is possible because your heels and toes are free of weight.

Correct posture may feel a bit strained at first, but you should keep working at it. Don't try to keep your body rigid. Hold the proper alignment, but let your body relax.

If poor posture isn't corrected overnight, please don't become discouraged. You have misused your muscles all these years, and it will take some reeducation to make them behave properly. Soon good posture will be a habit and will be a completely natural part of the graceful new you.

TAKE A STAND FOR BEAUTY

How do you place your feet while standing? Take a tip from actresses and models. They stand with one foot slightly behind the other, the back foot turned out at a slight angle. This is a pose designed to show your legs at their prettiest—equally flattering to plump or slim legs. It also provides a long, lean stem for the body, as pretty for you as for a rosebud.

If you allow one foot to carry the body weight—always maintaining correct posture alignment—you have a lighter look than if your weight were plunked evenly on both feet. For development of a graceful stance, practice this movement: Assume that you are standing within a 16-inch square (average shoulder width), one foot a little behind the other. Imagine that your posture must remain correctly aligned and that your body must stay in the exact center of this 16-inch square. Now practice letting first one foot and then the other bear the body weight without allowing your body to shift from its center in the square or from its posture-perfect alignment. When you do this, your position can't help but be becoming. If you watch yourself in a mirror, you can see how the body automatically has more "lift" when the weight is on one foot. Your whole appearance will seem lighter and more graceful.

SITTING PRETTY

Because most white-collar girls spend a good part of their nine-to-five hours seated, correct sitting posture is more important to them. It adds to their comfort and good looks.

Attractive and healthy sitting posture depends on:

Sitting tall—lift the whole upper part of your body out of your pelvic area.

Sitting well back—your lower back should be touching the back of your chair.

Sitting straight—sit directly on your pelvic bones, not slumped on the end of your spine or perched forward on your thighs.

When you are seated, your feet should touch the floor comfortably. If they don't, see what you can do to remedy the situation. A girl whose legs are so short that the edge of her seat presses against the back of her thighs is asking for circulation troubles and spreading thighs. The tall girl whose chair is too low must sprawl to be comfortable, and that isn't very ladylike. If you're lucky enough to have a posture-type desk chair, you can custom-fit it to your height by turning a couple of knobs or push-pulling a couple of plugs. Most posture chairs allow you to regulate the height of the seat, the position of the back support, and the flexibility of the back support. If your chair can't be regulated and is too low, perhaps you can sit on a cushion. If it's too high, find something to use as a footrest—maybe an unused mail tray or an old catalog.

A pretty pose for your nonworking moments is the diagonal sitting position models use. Place your legs diagonally across the seat of the chair toward the left or right. For example, arrange your feet at the right, with the left foot behind the right. This shows off your legs at their curvaceous best. It is also especially good for solving the problem of low-slung chairs or low car seats, where your knees would be too high for modesty.

Positions to avoid (especially if you have an open-front desk!):

SITTING with knees apart.
SITTING with legs strung out, grandpa-style, in front of you.
SITTING with feet hooked around chair.

SITTING in the morning glory tangle, in which one leg crosses and entwines itself around the other.
SITTING so that your skirt pulls up.

If you want to sit with your legs crossed, cross them either well above the knee or at the ankle. Crossing them directly at the knee flattens the calves, making them look fat and unattractive, as well as presenting a hazard to anyone forced to walk in front of your protruding foot.

TAKE A SEAT

The art of sitting down gracefully is easy to acquire. When you walk up to a chair, turn and place the back of your leg against the seat (this helps your balance and serves to guide you). With one foot slightly ahead of the other, lower yourself into the chair in one *smooth* movement. Keep your hips tucked under and your body erect. Put your calf and thigh muscles to work so that you go down evenly and gracefully. Your torso merely follows; it does none of the work. Nothing is worse (for beauty or the chair) than bouncing into a seat as if you'd been heaved for a forty-yard pass.

When you rise from your chair, make the same movements in reverse. Put one foot against the chair (or slightly under, if possible) and keep your head and torso erect as you lift your body, following the surge of calf and thigh muscles. Again, these muscles should do the work. Never lift yourself up using the arms of the chair. That makes you look like an old lady.

14

A good walk depends—once again—on good posture. It consists merely of moving about with as little unnecessary motion as possible. To walk gracefully, do this:

Line yourself up properly—chin in and level, shoulders back and down, tummy pulled up and in, hips tucked under. Maintain this good alignment, keeping your body erect and your torso as free from movement as possible. Neither your shoulders nor your hips should sway. Your arms should be relaxed.

Step forward swinging your leg from your hip joint (not from your knee). Your knees should be loose but not noticeably bent. They should absorb the bumps so that you don't bob up and down like a fisherman's float.

• As you move, center your body between the forward and back foot. (This is especially important and is where many walkers go wrong. The milers on a track team throw their weight forward to gain momentum. You shouldn't.)

15

• Take a stride which is just long enough to allow you to place your forward foot flat without moving your body. The distance between your feet should be about equal to the length of your foot.

• Aim your weight at the middle of your foot rather than at your heel. Your heel will then touch lightly and you will ride off it instantly. Your weight should pass along the *outer* border of the main arch to the ball of your foot, with a final push-off from the big toe.

• Keep your feet parallel and close together, as if your footprints were to follow alongside a center line.

• Point your toes *straight* ahead.

• Walk with a minimum of up-and-down movement. Keep your feet close to the ground as you move, but avoid any tendency to shuffle. Flexed knees will help absorb shocks.

• Make your arm-swing a natural rhythmic accompaniment to your stride. It should not be too long, however. The maximum desirable swing is the width of your side. This keeps your profile neat.

• Keep the entire movement natural and easy. If the body is tense or the movement too vigorous, the effect of lightness and grace cannot be attained.

Here are some bad habits that are very common. You'll want to avoid them.

Don't swing your shoulders. How ungainly is the person who seems to use her shoulders as an up-and-down or back-and-forth propeller to push herself along!

Don't sway your hips. Pretend your middle, from hips to armpits, is a concrete slab.

Don't lead with your head. It won't get there any sooner than the rest of you. Hold it up proudly, like a princess.

Don't lean back as you walk. This makes your legs seem to be running away from the rest of you.

Don't bounce up and down on your toes. You want smooth, continuous, fluid movement. In modeling, the smoother and more natural a girl's walk, the more accomplished she is considered and the higher her rating. Top models seem almost to be gliding on wheels, as if pulled by invisible strings.

Don't come down heavily on your heels. How horrible is the loud clap, clap, clap sound of heels coming down the corridor!

Don't take too short a stride. A tiny, mincing gait makes you look prim and priggish and tends to give you the appearance of a mechanical doll.

Don't take too long a stride. It looks mannish.

Don't stare at the floor. Keep your head erect. The person who studies the floor as she walks sees only the dirt and the dust. Look up and you'll be surprised at how many smiles you'll see.

Don't pump with your arms. Keep them relaxed, palms turned in, and let them swing loosely in rhythm with your step. You won't look as if you're chugging along by means of their power if you practice a natural narrow swing and keep your arms close to your sides. Soon a wide swing will feel sloppy to you and the pumping habit will disappear.

FEET FIRST

A graceful walk begins with your feet. No one who is plagued by painful feet has an attractive walk. Weak feet can throw your entire posture out of line. And, conversely, poor posture can ruin your feet. Many common foot disorders arise from overtaxed muscles—the result of poor posture or poor walking habits. If you have any serious complaints about your feet, be sure to see your doctor.

Shoes that fit poorly also destroy good posture. When you purchase shoes, let comfort be your prime consideration. If high spike heels are painful, save them for your sitting-down occasions. Foot specialists urge the wearing of the lowest heel acceptable on the job. Flats, of course, are frowned on as office attire, but often an attractive mid-heel or a slightly lower heel will satisfy the dictates of both fashion and comfort.

Any girl who wears heels all day should switch to flats when she gets home. A change of heel heights helps prevent leg cramps and keeps muscles more flexible.

The girl who isn't used to wearing high heels is wise to put in a little practice before she makes her public debut in spikes. You will notice that in order to keep good posture alignment when wearing heels, you must bend your knees slightly.

You can do much to strengthen your feet if you use odd moments for inconspicuous foot exercises. Just stretching and wiggling your toes is helpful, and this is an exercise you can do with your shoes on, even while making a phone call or riding in a bus. Another exercise for odd moments is rotating your foot at the ankle, pointing your toes up as high as possible and down as far as possible as you make the circle. On pages 31–33 you will find some excellent foot exercises that will help develop strong foot muscles for a lithe, attractive walk.

STRATEGY FOR STAIRS

In climbing stairs, your objective is to look as if you were gliding upwards smoothly and effortlessly. Here is where those built-in shock absorbers, your knees, become your most important asset. Just like the springs in a car, which take up the jolts in a rough road, they convert the angles of the stairs you climb into a smooth incline—at least it will look that way. The line of your head and body coming up or down stairs will be along the banister line; it will not follow the zigzag of the steps. And you will feel as though you were gliding!

How is it done? By keeping all the action downstairs, in your legs. Upstairs, you'll keep your chest high, back straight, and hips tucked under. When climbing stairs, move that erect posture ahead, over the foot on the next step, before pushing up with your calf and thigh muscles. Your knee is bent, and as you push up from below, it will straighten out smoothly in one continuous motion. When almost all the weight is transferred, bring the lower leg up, place it on the second step above, and repeat the process.

Place your entire foot, not just your toes, on each step. Perching only the toes on each step is hazardous (especially with spike heels and a full skirt—all too easy to catch a heel in your hem). Besides, it gives an ugly appearance to the back of the leg. Lift your foot lightly into position each time. Don't slide it onto the step.

When coming down stairs, keep your erect posture and step softly with your feet pointed straight ahead. If your foot is long and the step is narrow, you may find it helpful to turn your body slightly so that each foot touches the step at a right angle rather than pointing directly forward. You needn't look down at each step; your brain will respond properly, judging the length and depth of the steps. Drop each leg to the next lower step, making a smooth transition from one foot to the next, using those knees and keeping your torso erect.

Practice going up and down stairs (good for the figure, you know) until you can achieve an attractive floating motion.

BEAUTY IN BALANCE

Balance plays an important part in graceful movements. Some girls appear awkward merely because they have difficulty keeping their balance. With improved muscle tone, balance should improve.

Here is an excellent exercise that dance studios suggest to help their pupils develop the good balance so important for smooth dancing. Stand on your right foot with your left foot hooked behind your right ankle. Place your hands on your hips and slowly move up and then down on the toes of your right foot. Do this ten times; repeat, using your left foot. You'll find it easier to keep your balance as you move up and down if you concentrate on a spot on the wall at about eye level.

CARRIAGE FOR CARS

Getting into and out of cars is one of the most difficult movements to make gracefully. Take your cue from the automobile commercials on television—watch how the models do it.

When climbing in, use the sideways method. Stand beside the open door, facing forward. Rest your outer hand on the door handle or window if you wish, and bend your knee as you slide your nearest foot in sideways. Then slide the rest of your body onto the seat. Pull in your other foot and move back on the seat. Avoid the forward lunge with its unattractive rear view. If you are carrying bundles, put them in first. It's difficult to make a graceful entrance when you're encumbered with packages.

Getting into the back seat of a two-door car is a rather difficult maneuver to perform gracefully; but if you use the same sideways approach and put your nearest foot back and in, it will be easier. Support yourself on the back of the front seat, if necessary, as you step in.

When you are coming out, a sideways movement is more graceful. Slide over to the end of the seat. Put your nearest foot out and a little behind and touch the ground with your toe pointing toward the front of the car. Pushing against the foot on the ground, let your body and other leg follow smoothly as you clear the door and stand erect.

Buses are a different problem. When entering a bus with a high step, rise as high on your toe as possible while you lift your other foot. This is especially important if you are wearing a straight skirt. Disembarking is safer if you hold on to the rail at the side of the door and turn your body sideways toward this railing as you step down.

Why are there times when our hands seem to be unnecessary appendages that we wish we could take off like a pair of gloves and park in a purse for a while? Actually, they needn't be a source of trouble. The secret of graceful hands is to keep them *still* and to keep them *relaxed*. The fidgeter who twists a ring, toys with her gloves, or pats at her hair appears nervous, whether she is or not. The poised person learns to place—and keep—her hands in her lap (palms up, one hand on the other, is most attractive) or she rests them quietly on the arms of her chair.

When standing, you will find it comfortable and attractive to bring your arms across the front of your abdomen, resting your forearms on your pelvic bones as you clasp your hands loosely. Hold your elbows in close to your body. Another graceful position is keeping the hands down at your sides, with the insides of the wrists brushing your hips. Or, perhaps, you may prefer to keep one hand down at your side and to hold the other in front at the waistline. Your hands should always be relaxed, never stiff as if you were standing at attention in a military lineup.

Many people stand with their arms hugging their waists. It is comfortable and easy—but it looks unattractive and can lead to rounded shoulders. If you *must* cross your arms, try this trick to make yourself look graceful and maintain good posture while you do it: Cross your arms at or above the waist, bending the elbows slightly and turning one hand up along the inside of the opposite arm. The other hand clasps the opposite elbow loosely (see illustration). This gives your whole body a more pleasing line and relieves the pull on your shoulders.

Your hand movements will have grace and beauty if you concentrate on making the major motions with your wrists. Don't grab! For instance, if you wish to pick something up, lead with your wrist, keeping your fingers relaxed until they are just about to touch the object. This is much prettier to watch.

BENDING WITH BEAUTY

Some business girls find their jobs require quite a bit of bending and squatting—there are the files in the bottom drawer, the needed book is on the lowest shelf of the boss's bookcase, and so on. *Down* may seem to be your major motion some days. Take cheer: all this squatting can do very nice things for your hip and leg muscles if you do it correctly. Keep your back straight and erect, and bend your knees when you want to pick something up. Make your leg muscles push you up again, as they do when you mount the stairs. Not only is this more attractive than a bottoms-up stoop, but it prevents the back strain that can easily occur when heavy items are lifted incorrectly.

When carrying something heavy, be kind to your back. Carry packages in front of you just below the waist—not at chest level—so that the strong muscles in the lower part of your torso can share the work.

If you must frequently tote books, groceries, or any similar parcels in your arms, carry them well up on your arms and to the side, so that you can keep your shoulders and back straight. Carrying parcels on your hips drags your posture out of line. You'll be wise not to carry things on the same side each time. The girl who does this may end up with one shoulder slightly higher than the other.

EXERCISES FOR GRACE AND POSTURE

To correct rounded shoulders · Two groups of muscles must be retrained to improve the position of the shoulders. Rounded shoulders are caused by a stretching of the back muscles between the shoulder blades and also by a shortening of the chest muscles at the front of the shoulders. The following exercises will help to remedy this imbalance.

· ELBOW TWIRL (1).　Place your fingertips at the back of your neck just below the hairline. Keep the middle fingers touching.

Slowly circle the elbows forward, up, back, and down. Do five circles forward, five circles backward. Work up to a total of fifty circles—they only take about a minute.

You should feel pressure at the back in the neck muscles, a squeezing together of the shoulder blades, and a stretching of the front shoulder muscles.

· HAND FLING (2).　Stand with good relaxed posture, your arms crossed at the wrists in front.

Swing your arms up, out, and back as far as possible. Use brisk movements and keep the arms straight. Return to the starting position. Repeat ten times; increase to twenty times.

(1)

(2)

(3)

- SHOULDER BLADE PRESS (3).   Stand against a wall, body erect, knees loose.

Press your back in, pushing the shoulder blades flat. Concentrate on getting the entire shoulder area flat on the wall. Repeat at least three times and often throughout the day.

To correct a protruding abdomen or a swayback • The two go together. When there is an incurve at the small of the back (swayback), there will be a compensating bulge of the abdomen. It is impossible to be sure whether the weakened back muscles or the weakened abdominal muscles cause the trouble. (Incidentally, fat on the abdomen may not always be the cause of the bulge—the bulge may be flabby muscles). To correct this condition, both the back muscles and the abdominal muscles must be strengthened. These exercises will help to bring the body back into good posture.

23

a

b

(4)

• ELEVATOR HIP LIFT (4). Lie on your back on the floor with your knees raised and bent, your feet flat on the floor, your arms down at your side.

    With the abdominal muscles, pull up and in, flattening the small of your back to the floor. Hold. Slowly raise the hips off the floor, concentrating on making the end of the spine lift itself, one vertebra at a time. (Do *not* arch your stomach up, keep it as flat as it was.) Hold. Keep your back straight, and very slowly lower it back to the floor, one vertebra at a time. Dig in with the small of your back so that the tail bone touches last. Repeat twice at first; work up to eight times.

a

(5)

b

● LEG LOWERING (5). Lie on your back on the floor with your knees raised and bent, your feet flat on the floor, your arms down at your side. Relax your back muscles and your abdominal muscles.

Bring the right knee back towards the chest. Straighten out the knee as you raise the foot up; then, pulling up and in with the abdominal muscles to keep your back flat, very gradually lower the leg to the floor. Return to the starting position. During the exercise, keep the other leg in position. Repeat three times with each leg. Do not alternate legs. Increase to ten repeats for each leg.

(6)

a

b

● KNEE SLIDE (6). Lie on your back on the floor with your knees raised and bent, your feet flat on the floor, your arms out at shoulder level, the elbows bent so that the backs of the hands touch the floor opposite the head.

Force the spine to lie flat on the floor all the way from the neck to the seat, tensing the seat and abdominal muscles while relaxing the upper torso. This will give you the feel of perfect posture, so that you will be able to assume it when you are upright. Slowly lower both knees to the floor (by sliding the heels forward) until the point where you feel the arch returning to the back. Stop and bring the legs back to the starting position, still pressing down with the lower back. Repeat three times, later increasing to ten.

26

(7)

Exercises for more graceful arm and hand motion • Tenseness is usually the cause of awkward arm and hand motion. If the arms and hands can be taught to relax, their movements will be more attractive.

• ARM DROP (7).   Stand erect and raise your arms above your head.

Keeping the hands relaxed, tense your arms and push up hard at the ceiling. Hold. Suddenly release your muscles and let the arms drop down and swing freely.

This exercise is helpful in loosening any tenseness in the shoulder joint. Doing this even once will relax the muscles.

27

(8)

• PENCIL PICKUP (8). Sit in front of a table with a mirror facing you. Place a pencil on the table.

Reach for the pencil with your right hand, concentrating on moving your wrist rather than your fingers. Keep your fingers relaxed and still until you are ready to pick the pencil up. Pick it up and hold it loosely. Reach out with your left hand and take the pencil. Return the right hand to your lap. Continue transferring the pencil ten times, checking your movements in the mirror.

Exercises for lovelier leg movements • To enable us to have graceful control of our bodies while walking or dancing, or while raising or lowering the body for sitting, climbing or descending stairs, the muscles of the legs, thighs, and feet must be strong. These exercises will strengthen and rehabilitate any muscles weakened through lack of use.

• DEEP KNEE BEND (9). Stand with the torso erect and balanced. (Be sure that your weight is properly centered over your arches. Try swinging your heels and wiggling your toes without a shift in position.)

Slowly drop to the floor, bending the knees (and raising the heels) gradually until your seat rests at ankle level. Raise slowly to the starting position. Repeat five times,

(9)

increasing to ten. Keep the torso relaxed and balanced throughout the exercise, the leg muscles should do the work. You should feel the tensing of the muscles in your calves and thighs.

The movements in this exercise are the same as those used to a lesser degree in all the various leg motions that involve lifting or lowering the body. The deep knee bend is one of the most valuable exercises in improving balance, grace and coordination—and also in producing shapely legs.

(10)

• KNEE BEND GLIDE (10). Walk around the room with the knees partially bent, torso upright.

As you walk, gradually unbend your knees until you are in a normal walking posture. Reverse the process, gradually walking down into the starting position. Repeat three times, increasing to six.

This exercise is helpful in adapting to the feeling of walking smoothly and gracefully and in teaching you to employ the knees as shock absorbers to keep the body gliding evenly.

(11)

Exercises to strengthen your feet · Tired, aching feet can make your whole outlook sour. These exercises will relax tense muscles and improve their tone, so that you will have stronger feet. They do lovely things for legs, too.

· TIPTOES (11). Stand barefoot with your feet parallel, the weight slightly to the outside of the feet.

Slowly raise your body high on your toes; then return as *slowly* as possible to the starting position. Do this slowly so that the arch muscles control the movement. This will give you the full benefit of the exercise. Repeat twenty times.

(12)

(13)

(14)

- FOOT ROLL (12).   Stand barefoot with your feet about an inch apart.

Raise the inner sides of the feet, rolling as far as possible over onto the outer sides. Curve the toes inward at the same time. Hold. Return to the starting position. Repeat twenty times. Then walk across the room and back on the outer sides of your feet.

- MARBLE PICKUP (13).   Sit on a chair and practice picking up a marble or a pencil with your toes. Alternate feet. Repeat five times for each foot.

32

• TOE LIFT (14). Stand barefoot with your feet flat on the floor about an inch apart.

Slowly raise the toes upward and backward as far as possible. Hold. Lower toes back to the floor as slowly as possible. Repeat ten times.

When this exercise is done properly you should be able to count to ten as you lift the toes and again as you lower them.

 FOLLOW-UP

1 Line up three or four chairs with varying seat heights, some with legs, some with solid bases. Practice sitting and rising from these until you can manage them all gracefully.

2 Sit in front of a full-length mirror and devise five different comfortable and becoming ways you can place your hands and feet. Practice these until they become second nature. Then you will never feel ill at ease or awkward.

3 Before a full-length mirror practice five graceful hand positions to use while standing. Practice these until they become a natural part of your posture.

4 If you have a car available, practice sliding in and out until you can do it in a smooth, attractive manner. Or use a low chair without arms, and simulate all the problems entering and leaving a car create.

5 If you are a business girl who is lucky enough to have a posture desk chair, see if you can regulate yours for greater comfort. Even if it seems satisfactory now, experiment with different positions. Perhaps you can make it even more comfortable. You will also learn what to do in case you are ever switched to a chair adjusted to someone else's size.

6 To help remind yourself of good posture, resolve to check your posture each time you comb your hair, wait at a crossing, or walk through a certain doorway. Make good posture a habit for the future.

33

One of the most significant factors in appearance is general size and shape. We immediately notice whether a person is tall or short, but a far more important factor in determining attractiveness is weight—and how that weight is distributed. A girl with a slender silhouette has a good start on beauty. Clothes always look best on a well-proportioned figure, and a slim girl has a wide range of becoming styles from which to choose.

Few of us are constructed according to an ideal pattern. But even the girl whose proportions are a far cry from the ideal will look much smarter if the dial on her scale hovers near the proper spot and if her body is firm and supple. In cases where body structure is a problem, correct weight is of prime importance. More often than not, excess poundage tends to lodge right where it does the least good.

2 SHAPING UP

CHECKING YOUR STATISTICS

To see how your figure compares with the averages, let's do some measuring. In order to determine your ideal weight, you must first decide what type of bone structure you possess. Someone with delicate bone structure should necessarily weigh less than someone with a heavier body frame. To check on yourself, measure your wrist at the joint, just forward of the bone. Hold the tape snugly and note the figure to the very last fraction of an inch. Then determine your structure from the chart on page 37. Mark this (and all other measurements that follow) on a personal record chart. Next, measure your height in stocking feet, being careful to credit yourself with every fraction of an inch. With these figures in hand, compute your ideal weight, using the weight chart appearing on page 36.

Now bring out the tape measure again and compare your statistics with the ideal measurement chart. All measurements are to be taken over the fullest part of the area. Check your side view to be sure the hip measurement is taken where your circumference is largest. Measure over a bra, but without a girdle, remembering to keep the tape measure straight and taut but not tight. The ankle is measured just above the ankle bone. Ideally, your bust and hips should measure the same, and your waist should be ten inches smaller.

If, after making allowance for your particular bone structure, you find that your weight is approximately correct and your pounds are properly distributed—lucky you!

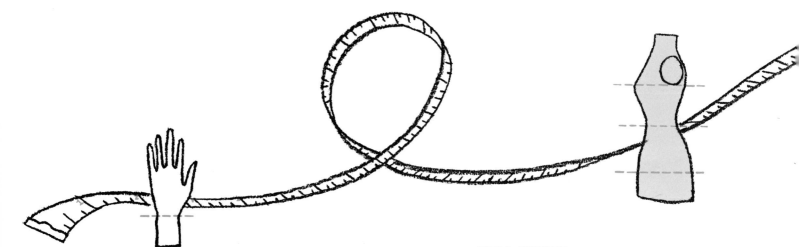

IDEAL WEIGHT

Height	Small frame	Medium frame	Large frame
4'10"	89–97	94–106	102–118
4'11"	92–100	97–109	105–121
5'0"	95–103	100–112	108–124
5'1"	98–106	103–115	111–127
5'2"	101–109	106–119	114–131
5'3"	104–112	109–123	118–135
5'4"	107–116	113–128	122–139
5'5"	111–120	117–132	126–143
5'6"	115–124	121–136	130–147
5'7"	119–128	125–140	134–151
5'8"	123–133	129–144	138–156
5'9"	127–137	133–148	142–161
5'10"	131–141	137–152	146–166
5'11"	135–145	141–156	150–171
6'0"	139–149	145–160	154–176

NOTE: This chart is based on figures from the Metropolitan Life Insurance Company. It shows ideal weight for girls of eighteen dressed in indoor clothing. If you are over eighteen, add one pound for each year up to the age of twenty-five, at which point ideal weight remains stationary.

36

BONE STRUCTURE

Height	Wrist measurement	Bone structure
Short (5' to 5'4")	(a) 5¼" or less (b) 5¼" to 5¾" (c) 5¾" or more	(a) small (b) medium (c) large
Average (5'4" to 5'7")	(a) 5½" or less (b) 5½" to 6" (c) 6" or more	(a) small (b) medium (c) large
Tall (over 5'7")	(a) 5¾" or less (b) 5¾" to 6¼" (c) 6¼" or more	(a) small (b) medium (c) large

IDEAL MEASUREMENTS

	Your height			
	UNDER 5'4"	5'4" TO 5'7"	5'7" TO 5'9"	OVER 5'9"
Bust	32–33"	34–35"	35–37"	38–39"
Waist	22–23"	24–25"	25–27"	28–29"
Hips	32–33"	34–35"	35–37"	38–39"
Thigh	19"	19½"	20"	20½"
Calf	12½"	13"	13½"	13¾"
Ankle	7¾"	8"	8¼"	8½"
Upper Arm	9"	9½"	10"	10½"

NOTE: This chart is for the medium bone structure. To obtain ideal measurements for:
Small frames, subtract 1" for bust, waist, and hips; ½" for thigh, calf, and upper arm; ¼" for ankle.
Large frames, add 1" for bust, waist, and hips; ½" for thigh, calf, and upper arm; ¼" for ankle.

Guard your good figure jealously. If your weight is a few pounds below the suggested amount and you feel fit and healthy, don't feel obliged to try to gain. Modern medical research indicates that it is beneficial to be slightly underweight. Gaining weight is all too easy for most of us. Without realizing it, we develop careless habits—the scale reading starts to creep up before we know it.

GOOD HABITS, GOOD FIGURE

Ann Sawyer was a tiny girl who wore a size 9 dress and had a most enviable waistline. Her mother always prepared well-balanced meals, not too heavy in sweets and starches. When Ann went to work, she no longer ate lunches at home under Mother's watchful eye. A hamburger with French fries, a malted, and devil's food layer cake became a typical lunch, followed by a midafternoon snack of Coke and pie and possibly a candy bar. Of course, Ann's skin wasn't quite as clear as it should have been, but she didn't worry. She still didn't worry when she discovered a couple of her skirts were a bit too snug or that her new dress had to be size 11. But the woeful day arrived when even a size 15 was tight. Ann realized that something had to be done—she was rapidly slipping into the fat-girl category.

Fortunately, Ann had the wisdom to realize that her eating binge wasn't worth the toll in good looks. She also had the willpower to pass up the high-calorie foods until she had whittled her figure back to its former desirable proportions. When Ann's dieting days were over, she was quite pleased with herself for the strength of mind and stick-to-itiveness she had shown. But she was well aware of how easy it was for her to gain weight, and how important it was to continue to eat wisely and moderately. She realized the shortsightedness of eating more than she really wanted, and she learned to substitute low-calorie treats for the routine of scale-sagging snacks she had formerly indulged in. When the gang stopped off for banana splits, Ann often voted in favor of raspberry sherbet. Instead of malteds, she ordered orangeade, limeade, or milk. She nibbled fruit instead of candy, celery instead of potato chips or peanuts. By eating properly, Ann not only regained her slim figure but also improved her skin. Her hair gleamed, and her fingernails lost their brittleness. She had more pep and energy, too, because her well-balanced meals gave her a good supply of all the food essentials—proteins, vitamins, and minerals.

If you want to stay slim:

1 Eat slowly and chew your food well. The speedy eater may not realize how much she is consuming, and she always has time to be tempted by seconds before others are finished. Besides, we get the most flavor and satisfaction out of food that is eaten slowly and chewed thoroughly.

2 Begin lunch and dinner with bulky foods (such as a salad) to help you feel more full.

3 Eat crisp leafy salads—your figure's best friend. Salads with fresh fruit, meat, cottage cheese, or seafood are also excellent for dieters. Choose these rather than the soggy, heavily dressed varieties like coleslaw. Use a diet dressing or lemon juice, which is an excellent calorie-free dressing. If you prefer the richer dressings, use only a teaspoonful.

4 Avoid fried foods. The butter or fat used in cooking them adds enormously to their calorie count.

5 Don't eat just because everybody else does. Perhaps you can become a bit of a gourmet snob about snacks—adopt the attitude that you don't really want to be bothered to eat unless you're offered something definitely out of the ordinary. This is rather helpful in passing up the mundane potato chips, pretzels, and so-so snacks that tempt us.

6 Don't eat while watching TV, reading, or studying—and skip the popcorn and ice cream at the movies. When your attention is diverted, you may consume more than you realize.

7 If you must tackle rich foods, eat only a little—a small taste of the chocolate cream pie, a sliver of seven-layer cake, and so on. When you are served rich foods while dining out, don't feel that you must finish your entire portion.

8 If you pal around with big eaters (boyfriends can be particularly detrimental), don't let yourself unconsciously match their consumption. Quit before you have that full feeling.

9 Get enough rest. When you are too tired, you often try to counteract your weariness by overeating.

10 Eat at regular hours. Delaying a meal may make you so famished that you will tend to eat more than normal.

11 Never skip a meal—breakfast, for instance. You'll only be tempted to fill up on dough-nuts and similar nutritionless high-calorie snacks later on. Start the day right by refueling with a sound breakfast. It's been a long time since dinner and your body needs something to go on.

12 Get enough regular exercise. Walk to work (or part of the way) if you can. Join a bowling team. Swim, play tennis, ski, go biking whenever possible.

TRIMMING EXCESS POUNDAGE

If your weight is ten pounds or more above what it should be, you ought to slim down while it's still relatively easy. Excess poundage not only sabotages your good looks but it also creates an undesirable impression on others. Lack of willpower, laziness, self-indulgence, and slowness are attributed (although often wrongly) to stout people. The hefty girl may find it difficult to get a good job, and she is less likely to be considered for promotion to the more interesting meet-the-public jobs. Businessmen want attractive, smartly-turned-out workers whose appearance will be an asset to the firm.

The only way to lose weight, let's face it, is to EAT LESS. You'd have to walk about thirty-six miles to lose one pound—exercise alone isn't enough. You must diet, in some way.

If the idea of dieting sounds like a torturous ordeal, take heart. There's no need to starve yourself. No fasting. It's merely a matter of substituting low-calorie foods for high-calorie ones. Many of the best-loved foods—steak, watermelon, cheese, strawberries—are ideal for dieters. Magazines and cookbooks contain many low-calorie versions of popular desserts so that you need not deny yourself the pleasures of good eating.

Although it's true that reducers must usually eat less, it's amazing how appetite adjusts to habit. As you eat less, your appetite shrinks. Within about a week, you will probably feel just as full, just as satisfied, on your sensibly trimmed-down diet as on your usual fare. You may wonder how you ever managed to stow away so much before.

Before you undertake any diet, you'll be wise to check with your doctor and let him suggest what is best for you. For the sake of your health, steer clear of fast, fad diets. You need well-balanced meals every day. The wild dieter who goes on a crazy banana-and-hard-boiled-egg diet sheds pounds quickly. But her success may be short-

Breakfast

1 serving of fruit

1 egg (preferably boiled or poached)
  – OR 1 cup *whole grain* or high-protein cold cereal
  – OR ⅔ cup hot oatmeal or other whole grain hot cereal (use granulated or liquid sugar substitute)

1 glass of skimmed milk
  – OR 1 thin slice of toast (preferably whole wheat) with ½ tsp. butter

1 cup of coffee or tea, if desired (use sugar substitute or skimmed milk, not cream)

Lunch

1 small serving of lean meat, fish, poultry, cheese (for example, ⅔ cup cottage cheese),
  – OR two eggs

½ cup green vegetable
  – OR yellow vegetable (without butter or sauce)

1 serving of tossed green salad, with low-calorie dressing if desired

1 serving of fruit for dessert (preferably fresh fruit)

1 glass of skimmed milk or buttermilk

1 cup coffee or tea, if desired (use sugar substitute, skimmed milk)

Dinner

1 small serving of lean meat, fish, poultry,
  – OR two eggs

½ cup green vegetable and ½ cup yellow vegetable (without butter or sauce)

1 serving of tossed green salad
  – OR tomato salad (low-calorie dressing)

1 serving of fruit
  – OR two small graham crackers
  – OR two gingersnaps

1 glass of skimmed milk

1 cup coffee or tea, if desired (use sugar substitute, skimmed milk)

41

lived. In order to prove her tremendous willpower, she may have to have it engraved on her tombstone!

There are several food concentrates on the market that serve as low-calorie meal substitutes. While these products, with their 900-calories-a-day total, bring about a quick weight loss, many medical men consider them too drastic. They suggest using these concentrates for one meal a day, lunch perhaps, accompanied by a small salad. Then eat a normal, but low-calorie, breakfast and supper.

Appetite-chasing pills will fortify your willpower if you have trouble getting started on your diet. You'll be wise to take these only with your doctor's blessing. And don't let them become a crutch. When you feel the urge to nibble, choose something that won't shatter your diet—celery, carrot sticks, fruit, unsweetened fruit juice. Even a drink of water can sometimes save you from disaster!

Whenever you use dieting aids, try to work away from them gradually. Your aim is not only to get a good figure but to *keep* it, and this means developing new, wiser eating habits that will let you retain your slim figure after your dieting stint is over.

Try to keep mentally and physically active as you diet, for the lonely, bored individual is the one who beats a steady path to the refrigerator door. Keep your life so filled with absorbing activities that you haven't time to think of food. Keep your mind on your goal of charm and beauty, and you'll easily shun the tempting figure-destroyers.

HOW MUCH DO YOU EAT?

Make a list of everything you ate yesterday. Include not only what you ate at meals but also any between-meal snacks like cookies or soda. Every bite, and every sip, counts. Then check your calories. Most cookbooks contain sizable calorie charts; and dieting books with calorie charts are easy to find in libraries, dime stores, and supermarkets. Using such a chart, determine the caloric value of the various foods you eat and the total number of calories you consume in an average day. (You should also include the little extras, such as butter when you list bread or potatoes, cream and sugar with your coffee, and dressing for your salad.)

How many calories does *your* body actually require? To obtain this amount, multiply your ideal weight by 15 (your body needs 15 to 20 calories per pound per day). If you wish to lose weight, reduce your calorie requirements by one-third. If you wish to gain, add on one-third. This gives you your calorie quota for one day.

The results of your mathematics may be surprising. It isn't until we actually take the time to figure out our caloric intake that we get a clear picture of our eating habits. By counting calories and holding to a certain quota, most people can lose or gain as they choose.

	Quantity	Calories
Malted milk	average glass	400
Cocoa with all milk	8 oz.	235
Cola	8 oz.	105
Coffee or tea—plain	8 oz.	none
—with 1 tsp. sugar	8 oz.	25
—with cream and sugar	8 oz.	50
Doughnut—plain	1	135
Coffee cake	average slice	150
Iced cake	average slice	300
Chocolate eclair, custard	1	315
Pie—mince, apple	average slice	400
English muffin	1	175
Butter	1 pat	50
Jelly or jam	1 tbs.	50
Egg—fried, omelet, scrambled	1	100
—poached, boiled	1	75
Sundae	average	400
Ice cream—vanilla	1 scoop	150
—chocolate	1 scoop	240
Pretzel	1 medium	70
Peanut	1 (!)	5
Candy bar	average	255
Whipped cream	1 tbs.	50
Mayonnaise	1 tbs.	100
Gravy, thick	2 tbs.	100
Peanut butter	1 tbs.	125

43

HOW TO GAIN WEIGHT

A slim figure may be the ideal today, but no one is attractive if she is too thin. Gaining weight is often more difficult than losing it. But it is well worth the effort, particularly if you have high hopes for your career. Girls who are extremely underweight may find themselves crossed off the list for desirable jobs, because many employers feel that such girls are a health risk and lack the physical stamina needed to meet the day-to-day demands of the work.

To put more meat on your bones, you need some calories to spare. This means eating more and burning up less energy. Easier said than done, perhaps. If your appetite is fickle, it may be due to a combination of things—faulty nutrition, irregularity of meals, or fatigue. If you frequently feel tired out, consult your doctor. You may have an iron or vitamin deficiency that prevents you from putting on weight.

Here are some suggestions for adding pounds:

• Develop a healthy respect for good nutrition. Because your appetite is limited, make sure you eat a sufficient supply of the beauty-building essentials, such as milk, meat, green and yellow vegetables, fruits, and whole grain cereals. Indulge in the high-calorie desserts if you wish, but only after you've packed away a good meal.

• A between-meal pickup, such as a milk shake or ice cream, is excellent. Schedule snacks so that they won't interfere with meals, preferably two to three hours before your next meal. Too much nibbling of rich or starchy foods can spoil the appetite and fill you up to such a degree that you haven't room left for the vitamin-packed foods you need most.

• Don't skip a meal. Curiously enough, the only way to build up an appetite is to eat. If you eat three meals a day at approximately the same times, you become the victim of habit and your appetite responds. Another factor is that the B vitamins in food tend to spark your appetite and prepare you for the next meal. If you've been breakfasting on coffee only, try to educate your palate to better things. Perhaps at first you'll find that a milk shake with an egg in it (flavored with coffee if you wish) will give you early-morning nutrition you can enjoy or at least tolerate. Gradually, as you become accustomed to a morning meal, you can move up to a more substantial breakfast.

• Learn to relax. The girl who is tense and keyed up burns calories at a terrific clip. Avoid tension by trying to minimize crises—allow yourself enough time so that you are

44

never rushed, don't let little things annoy you, steer a wide berth around unpleasant people whenever possible, and make an effort to remain calm and to keep your emotions under control. If you don't squander your energy on trifles, you'll have more left for the fun of life.

- Get plenty of rest—eight or nine hours a night without fail—and don't allow yourself to become overtired.

- Allow plenty of time for your meal. Eat slowly and chew your food thoroughly.

- If you smoke, do so moderately. Don't smoke before meals; it will tend to kill your appetite.

- Develop an interest in food. Occasionally treat yourself to unusual exotic dishes at foreign restaurants. Try to learn more about cooking. Look for unusual recipes and learn to use herbs and spices to bring out flavors. Perhaps you'll become such a culinary artist that you won't be able to resist your own cooking.

45

(15)

EATING FOR BEAUTY

A good diet consist of more than calories. Its primary function is nourishment. Beautiful skin, sparkling eyes, glossy hair, steady nerves, stamina, and often a good disposition and a cheerful outlook on life are strongly affected by what we eat. To maintain health and beauty, our bodies need a balanced diet with a full quota of proteins, vitamins, and minerals. Each day your diet should include the following beauty foods:

Milk—at least two glasses

Protein foods—(meat, fish, poultry, or cheese)—two servings

Eggs—preferably one a day, at least three to five a week

Fruit—two servings (one a citrus fruit or tomato)

Vegetables—two or more servings, especially leafy green and deep yellow vegetables

Whole grain bread or cereal—two servings. For better health and beauty, acquire a taste for the whole wheat, oatmeal, and other dark, whole grain breads that contain many vitamins and minerals lost in processing flour for white bread. Choose whole grain cereals—whole wheat, oat, or high-protein varieties—rather than corn flakes, puffed cereals, or rice crisps, which have a low nutritional value.

ADJUSTING THE CURVES

Although you don't lose much weight by exercise, you can speed up the loss of inches in some places and build up curves in others rather than just losing pounds but retaining the same old shape. If your measurements are out of proportion when you *start* dieting and you don't exercise, you will end up smaller but *still* out of proportion. To put and keep the proper curves in the proper places, make exercise a habit. Many a slender girl still needs to flatten her tummy or improve her posture or tone up her thigh muscles. Even the girl who is attempting to gain weight may find that unless she exercises, her extra pounds all settle unbecomingly around her waist and tummy.

Before you begin a routine of exercises, have your doctor check your heart and blood pressure—not that you plan to undertake anything terrifically strenuous, but it is always important to know that your heart is in good condition before you undertake any unusual physical activity.

If you manage to get regular exercise of the bowling-swimming-tennis-biking variety, this may be sufficient to keep your muscles in tone. But just about every girl needs to do at least one waist and hip exercise, one shoulder and bust exercise, and one posture exercise each day. Set aside five or ten minutes each morning or evening for a few exercise quickies. Once you get into the habit of exercising, you'll find it so relaxing and refreshing that no day will seem complete without your daily half dozen.

To get the most out of your exercises, go at them s-l-o-w-l-y and rhythmically, stretching gracefully as far as possible. The girl who madly flails about like a propeller does little more than wear herself out. Pretend you are a ballet dancer. Kick and swing as smoothly and gracefully as a prima ballerina. If you can do your exercises to music— even humming a tune to yourself—so much the better. It's fun to kick around when you have peppy ballet music or show tunes playing in the background to heighten the illusion.

In order to have exercises perform their toning and beautifying magic, you must keep at them regularly. A few minutes' worth each night is better than an hour's rugged workout every week or two. Keep up the good work and in a few short weeks your tape measure will indicate the pleasing results.

(16)

SPOT REDUCING EXERCISES

Waist whittlers · These will help to reduce your midway dimensions and are good for posture too.

• BALLET BEND (15). Lift your arms overhead, holding them limply. (The stretch should be felt only through the midriff, not in the arms.)

Hold the tension as you stretch high. Then relax and bend directly to the left, letting right arm drop as far over the head as possible. Hold. Come back to position. Stretch high, tense, relax, and bend to the right, with the left arm over your head. Your knees should be kept straight and you should feel a good pull at the sides of your waist. Repeat five times on each side, increasing to ten.

• FORWARD AND BACK BENDS (16). Stand erect with your feet a foot apart.

Drop forward, bending at the waist. Keep your knees straight and try to touch your hands to the floor. Hold. You should feel the stretch in your midriff and in the back of your thighs, not in your arms. Rise to the original position. Then bend backward as far as possible. Hold, then return to position. Repeat four times, increasing to eight.

You may not be able to touch the floor in the beginning, but make a good try.

47

(17)

• TORSO TWIST (17). Stand erect in good posture, with your arms out at the sides and your feet about eighteen inches apart.

Keeping the feet firmly in place, twist the upper body as far to the left as possible. Try to follow your left hand with your eyes. Then reverse and swing to the right, following your right hand with your eyes. Repeat four times on each side, increasing to eight.

The effort should be felt in the waistline, which is only possible if you stand erect.

• FORE AND AFT LEG SWING (18). Lie on your left side with your head on your outstretched left arm.

(18)

Keeping your left leg in position, swing your right leg forward as far as possible. Hold. Then swing it backward as far as possible. Hold, and return to starting position. Repeat four times with one leg; roll over and repeat with the other leg. Increase to eight times.

Your torso must be straight throughout and the pull should be felt only in the waist, hip, and thigh areas (all of which benefit from this exercise).

For a trim tummy · The exercises suggested at the end of Chapter 1 for correcting a protruding abdomen or swayback will also trim excess fat while they improve posture.

49

(19)

• SITUP (19).   Lie on your back on the floor, legs straight, hands clasped at the back of the neck.

Sit up, letting your abdominal muscles do the work. When you are fully erect, straighten your back and hold your head high as you give your elbows a good backward push. Then, rounding your back, *slowly* roll down to the floor, trying to touch each vertebra in order as you go. Repeat twice, gradually increasing to ten times.

This is *the* best exercise for the abdomen and should be done regularly. If you have difficulty the first few times, tuck your feet under a low piece of furniture so that they stay on the floor.

(20)

• ROCKER (20). Lie face down on the floor with your arms extended overhead.

Raise the right arm and the left leg simultaneously. Then alternate, using opposite arm and leg. Do ten times. If this is easy for you, try the more advanced version: raise both arms and both legs off the floor simultaneously—a few inches will do at first but lift higher as you become more supple.

Hips, hips away · One of the most common figure problems is heavy hips. A regular exercise routine can definitely trim inches from this area, so make a firm resolution and go to it.

(21)

(22)

• ROLL OVER HANDS (21). Lie on your back with your hands (palms down) tucked under your rear, your knees drawn up to your chest.

Roll sideways over your hands and touch your knees to the floor. Use your hip, leg, and abdominal muscles (not your hands) to roll your body back to position. Then roll to the other side and back. Repeat eight times for each side.

• BICYCLE RIDE (22). Lie on your back and roll up on your shoulders, supporting your hips with your hands.

Pedal big circles with your feet, *being sure that the inner borders of your knees touch as they pass each other*. Pedalling wide and wild does no good. Pedal a minute.

(23)

There is a three-fold purpose here: you work the legs into proper contact at the thigh joint, reduce the hips and thighs, and strengthen the muscles that keep your legs tracking properly for smooth carriage. (And good carriage automatically slims you as you walk!)

SPREAD EAGLE (23). Lie on the floor with your arms outstretched at shoulder level.

Swing the right leg across the body at hip level, stretching it as far to the left as possible. Hold. Keep the rest of the body in position. Then bend the right knee, and bring it up to touch your left elbow. Return to position and repeat with left leg. Repeat four times for each side, increasing to eight.

This gives a good pull through the hips and also tones the waist and thighs.

(24)

• HIP HOP (24). Sit on the floor with your legs extended, your arms straight out at shoulder height. Keep your torso erect.

Using your buttocks as feet, "walk" forward pointing your toes. Then reverse and back up, curling toes up toward you. Take about 25 steps forward, then return.

You literally walk off fat pads with this one. Be sure to lift your legs from the hip joints.

For shapelier legs · The deep knee bend exercise described in Chapter 1 is not only excellent for posture but firms and shapes your legs as well. To correct bulgy calf condi-

(25)

tions, do all your sitting or lying down exercises with your feet held at right angles to your legs, *not* with your toes pointed.

• THIGH SLIMMER (25).   Lie on the floor on your left side with your head on your outstretched left arm, your legs together.

Slowly raise your right leg straight up from the hip joint until you feel the pull on the inside thigh muscles. Hold. *Slowly* return to position. Repeat five times before changing to other side. Then do five times on right side. After a week or more, increase to ten times.

(26)

(27)

(28)

a

b

c

• CALF BEAUTIFIER (26). Stand with the balls of your feet on a fairly thick book, your heels on the floor.

Rise on your toes *slowly*. Hold. Then return very slowly. Repeat ten times.

This exercise can develop *or* slenderize calves.

• ANKLE SLIMMER (27). Sit well back in any straight chair, with one knee crossed over the other.

Bend the raised foot upward from the ankle as far as possible. Hold for a count of five and then relax, letting your foot fall limp. Repeat twenty times. Then switch to the other leg.

Bustline · These exercises will improve a heavy or drooping bust but, alas, nothing has yet been found that actually increases the size of a small bust. These exercises will strengthen the chest muscles, however, and will encourage better contours for a small or large bosom.

• PUSH-UP, LADIES' STYLE (28). Lie face down with the hands, palm down, at shoulder level.

(29)

(30)

Hold your torso rigid as you push away from the floor, straightening your arms so that your body is supported by your hands and knees. (Your knees should never leave the floor.) Next sit back on your heels. Hold. Then move your body forward and lower it to the floor. Start with two or three push-ups and work up to ten.

• ELBOW CHUG-CHUG (29).   Stand in good posture. Raise your arms chin high and grasp the *inside* of each forearm just below the elbow with the opposite hand. Then push the elbows together as you resist by grasping hard with the fingers. Hold, then relax to first position. Repeat fifty times—it won't take much more than a minute.

• CRISS-CROSS (30).   Lie on your back across a low stool or hassock so that your shoulders and upper back are supported by the seat and your feet are resting on the floor. Start with your arms on the floor.

Raise your arms up and cross them over your chest. Slowly drop arms straight back to original position. Repeat ten times.

To make this exercise more effective by offering more resistance, hold heavy books of equal size in your hands.

EXERCISES FOR ODD MOMENTS

Unlike the daily dozen variety, the following exercises involve only muscle stretching and contracting, and can often be sneaked in during ordinary activities. While you are riding in a car, talking on the phone, standing in line, or even seated at your desk, you can put your idle moments to work for muscle toning.

❦ When you wake up in the morning, recharge your muscles by giving them a good hard stretch before you struggle out of bed. Hold on to the headboard with one hand and push hard with the heel of the opposite foot. Stretch hard and push down as far as you can. Then switch to the opposite hand and push with the other foot.

❦ While toweling yourself dry after a bath, loop the towel behind your neck. Pull your chin back as you tug forward on both ends of the towel, resisting the towel with your neck as hard as you can to a count of ten. Relax. Then slide the towel down to the small of your back. Again pull forward on the towel, resisting by contracting your abdomen and buttock muscles. Push back hard against the towel as you count to ten. Now loop the towel under your toes and pull up with both ends while you push your toes down. Hold for ten counts, release, and do the other foot.

❦ Abdominal and hip muscle contractions are so inconspicuous that they can be done any time. Just tense the muscles tightly, hold for a count of ten, then relax. Do this whenever you think about it throughout the day. Contracting the buttock muscles is especially effective if it is done while you are walking.

❦ When you are standing in bare feet, try this variation to firm inner thighs as well as buttock muscles. Stand with your heels about two inches apart and the weight on the balls of your feet. Concentrate on slowly bringing the buttocks close to each other so that you feel their contraction. Also exert tension through the inner thigh by attempting to press your knees together. (Don't bend your knees, and be sure to keep your ankles straight and inner arches high.) Hold for a count of ten. Slowly release the tension. Do at least six times during the day.

❦ Twisting your hip while you stand creates a front-to-back hip stretch. Stand on your left foot and turn the right foot in as far as possible toward the inside of the left leg. At the same time try to look over your right shoulder at your right heel. Then turn that

58

same foot outward and back as far as you can. Repeat with the left foot and look over your left shoulder.

🌸 To flatten the upper back and to overcome round shoulders, stand in perfect posture and put both arms behind you, thumbs turned out, elbows straight. Lift your arms up behind you as far as they will go, which will not be high. Hold while you count to ten. Release tension and relax.

🌸 For correcting a double chin, a dowager's hump, or a problem of head posture, try this. Sit erect and slowly rotate your head in a circle—forward, around to the left, to the back, to the right, to the front. Then reverse the direction. Be sure to keep your neck and spine erect. You'll get the correct feeling if you imagine that you have a basin of water strapped on your head and that you are going to spill out a few drops in a complete circle around you.

🌸 During a phone conversation use your opposite hand to do an arm twist. Keeping your arm extended straight out to the side, rotate your hand back and forth. Do each arm separately, slowly at first and then doubling the tempo.

 FOLLOW-UP

1 After you've determined the calorie quota needed to maintain or change your figure, plan complete menus (plus snacks, if desired) for three days. Choose foods that you like, but be sure that your meals are well balanced and that your calorie tally is approximately correct. Each day's set of menus should include foods from each of the beauty-food categories.

2 If you need to reduce:
   a Find recipes for at least two low-calorie dishes you would like to try.
   b Prepare a list of at least twenty high-calorie items that you eat frequently but that are taboo for reducers.

3 If you wish to gain weight:
   a Find at least two recipes for unusual dishes that tempt your appetite.
   b Make a list showing at least twenty high-calorie foods that you enjoy. Include not only desserts but also meats, fruits, vegetables, dairy products, and other foods.

PART TWO:

IMPROVING ON NATURE

There are many pretty girls whose features, if examined closely, are not the most perfect; but because of a clear, glowing complexion their faces seem beautiful. Lovely bright skin adds a radiance that magnifies beauty. A good complexion is so important that even a set of movie-queen features will never add up to beauty if the skin is poor. Very often complexion care is the vitally important detail that can turn a so-so face into an especially attractive one.

Taking good care of your skin is the only way to achieve a beautiful complexion. No makeup can create this glow nor truly compensate for the lack of it. It comes only from the healthy condition of the skin itself. Fortunately, skin is a living, growing thing that responds to proper care. Because the top layer is continually being washed or worn off and replaced by new cells, even neglected skin can be made to bloom. As we grow older, however, skin responds less easily to efforts to improve it. Now, while you are young, is the time to bring your complexion to its peak of beauty and to guard it carefully so that it can better withstand the ravages of wear and age.

3   COMPLEXION CARE

BASIC CARE FOR ALL SKIN TYPES

Proper care of your skin involves three important steps: cleansing, stimulating, protecting.

1   Keep skin clean, clean, clean. Cleanliness is the most important factor in obtaining and retaining lovely skin. Most of the lasting damage that is done to young skin is the result of insufficient cleansing. Blackheads, whiteheads, blemishes, enlarged pores, and muddy complexions can usually be traced back to that arch villain—DIRT. For the sake of your beauty, promise yourself that you will never go to bed without first thoroughly cleansing your face. No matter how weary you are, take the extra few minutes to clean off all makeup and dirt. During the day remove old makeup before applying the new, whenever possible. Many business girls keep a cosmetic bag of cleansing and makeup essentials in their lockers or desk drawers for easy makeup changes. When you can't do a complete new makeup job, rub a moistened tissue (or your *clean* moistened hands) over your face to remove some of the previous makeup and accumulated grime before applying new cosmetics.

Do you know how to cleanse your face properly? Today's clinging cosmetics require thorough methods to remove them. Depending upon your type of skin, you will want first to use some sort of cream or lotion makeup remover and follow that with a second cleansing—soap and water (for oily skin) or a second cream or lotion cleansing if more gentle care is indicated. Particularly good are the clear, deep-cleansing lotions that contain germicidal ingredients. Just a single cleansing with soap and water was all right for the girl who never ventured near the cosmetic counter, but it can't do a good enough job of removing modern makeup. To cleanse your face, gently massage cleansing cream or lotion all over your face and throat. A dab of cream about the size of a dime should be sufficient. (Most people throw away a good part of the jar by using too much). Start with the throat and chin area, using upward and outward movements (see diagram). If your skin is blemished, pay particular attention to the chin, mouth, and any blemished areas. Allow the cream to set for two or three minutes. Tissue off lipstick and eye makeup first. Then use upward and outward strokes to remove the rest of your makeup. Avoid dragging the skin downward and be particularly gentle in the area beneath the eyes. Age and the elements do enough to pull our faces out of shape and to cause wrinkles without our contributing to the damage.

If you wash your face with soap for your second cleansing, work up a good lather and rinse well with warm water. Then follow with a stimulating cold splash.

If you use two cream cleansings in place of soap, it is important that you finish off with skin freshener (sometimes called skin lotion) that will remove the last vestiges of dirty cleansing cream that would otherwise remain in the pores to cause trouble. After tissuing the cream off, moisten a wad of cotton with skin freshener and wipe it all over your face. Skin freshener has an additional cleansing action, helps to remove any remaining cream, and gently tones your skin.

You probably know the old saw about the ounce of prevention. In regard to your face it's certainly worth several pounds of cure. Protect your skin as much as possible from contact with dirt. If you tend to prop your chin with your hand or have any other habits that involve touching your face, better adopt a hands-off policy. You know how dirty your hands become during an ordinary day of reading, writing, and typing. When you transfer this dirt to your face, you're only inviting trouble.

Everything that comes in contact with your face should be immaculately clean. Always use a separate washcloth for your face, and change washcloths frequently. Your washbasin should be scrubbed and shining, your face towel fresh and clean. Girls with blemished skin are wise to boil their washcloths and to dry linens in the sun to help prevent the spread of infection (which is what a pimple is). A soiled powder puff is another trouble causer. Using disposable puffs or tufts of cotton to apply makeup is the most sanitary method.

2 ✿ Stimulate your skin to beautify itself. Even the most expensive creams can do but very little for complexions. Skin is nourished primarily from within. The bloodstream brings the important health nutrients gleaned from food (showing the importance of good diet for beauty). Poor circulation means that the blood delivery system isn't working at full capacity—the skin is being deprived. You can improve your circulation by getting plenty of exercise, especially outdoor exercise, and also by giving direct stimulation to the skin.

Stimulate directly by massaging the skin as you apply cream or soapy lather. Gently patting your skin with quick little slaps will also bring the blood rushing to the area. Exercise of facial muscles—pretend you are a man shaving, or blow your cheeks out—not only tones these muscles up but provides stimulation as well.

Cosmetic aids to stimulation include skin fresheners and astringent lotions (the latter for oily skins only) and facial masks, which, in addition to their cleansing benefits, are especially good for encouraging a pink and pretty glow for big date nights.

Also good is plain cold water. After washing try this stimulating finale to prod lazy circulation. Take two washcloths. Put one in warm water and then press it against your face for a few seconds. Meantime, place the other washcloth under the cold water tap and then exchange this for the warm cloth, pressing the cold cloth against your face. Continue alternating with warm and cold cloths three or four times. You'll love the tingle you feel in your skin and the healthy glow that results. Just don't let the water become too hot or too icy. Neither extreme is wise for delicate skin.

3 🌷 **Protect your complexion.** Protection is, of course, most important to those with dry skin. Lubricating creams and lotions that contain lanolin and other rich emollients can help compensate for the lack in natural oil production and keep dry skin soft and smooth. They can be used on dry skin nightly after cleansing and also under makeup for protection during the day, if necessary. In addition to the heavy lubricating products, there are also moisture creams and lotions, which soften skin and add moisture. If your skin is normal or oily, one of the greaseless moisturizers will be best for softening any chapped or rough areas; the rich lubricating products are intended only for dry skin. Moisturizers are effective because moisture is needed on the surface of the skin to help spread the oil that is pumped up by the oil glands. Normally this moisture comes out through every pore, but cold air outdoors and hot dry air indoors tend to retard this process, as well as hold down oil production. Incidentally, after applying skin freshener in wintertime, it's a good idea for those with dry or normal skin to wait fifteen minutes before beginning their makeup, in order to give the new supply of oil and moisture time to spread and to create a fresh base for makeup.

Although lubrication is usually the concern only of the dry-skinned girl, there is one very important area that needs regular protection even by girls with oily skin—the area around the eyes. Most girls over twenty-one—and some that are younger—begin to notice tiny lines forming beneath and at the corners of the eyes. This may occur even though the rest of the skin is oily. The eye area is generally the first to wrinkle. A tiny bit of eye cream or oil used nightly can help ward off the development of permanent crow's feet and lines. An eye cream is a heavy clinging cream especially designed to penetrate the pores in the eye area. These pores are almost totally closed and are not capable of absorbing regular creams. Only the tiniest touch of cream or oil is needed, and it should be patted on *very* gently so that the skin is not pulled or rubbed.

WHICH TYPE OF SKIN IS YOURS?

Normal and nice · If you have a fresh peaches-and-cream complexion that is soft and smooth with no flaky patches, no dry tight-feeling areas, greasy shine, or blemishes, thank your lucky stars. You have normal skin; make every effort to keep it that way.

Oily skin · Oily skin is usually easy to define. The most noticeable clue is its greasy shine, which may reappear within an hour or so after washing. This is because the oil ducts are overactive and the pores cannot get rid of the excess oil. When oil remains on the surface of the skin, it acts like flypaper to hold dust and dirt—the perfect setting for the formation of nasty blackheads and pimples. Unless a vigorous battle for cleanliness is waged, blemishes are likely to be a problem.

Oily skin is usually most troublesome during the teen-age years. Gradually, as we grow older, the secretion of oil lessens. One pleasant prospect is that this type of skin usually resists wrinkles better than others.

Dry skin · Dry skin is characterized by a tight feeling and a tendency to develop little lines, particularly around the eyes and lips. Pores are small and fine. The skin may look drawn over the cheeks and may be rough and flaky in places.

Dry skin needs the gentlest of care. It must be pampered and protected or it will wrinkle at an early age.

Combination skin · If your skin type doesn't fit neatly into one of the preceding categories, you may be one of the multitude of girls who have combination skin. Many girls have skin that is normal or dry in some sections and oily in others. Usually the middle portion of the face is oily—the center forehead, nose, chin—while the cheeks may be normal or even a bit dry. In such cases, each section must be treated according to its type; gentler cleansing and protection for the drier areas, vigorous cleansing and no lubrication for the oily areas.

HOW TO CARE FOR YOUR OWN SKIN TYPE

Normal skin • Your aim is to keep your skin just the way it is—healthy, lovely, and normal. You should use makeup sparingly and should choose light nongreasy products that allow your natural beauty to show itself off. By all means don't overtreat your skin. You needn't waste money on so-called "high-powered" lubricating creams and lotions. You already have the skin that the ads extol, and rich creams are only likely to cause harm. The one exception is an eye cream. If your skin seems slightly dry in winter, you can use a moisture cream or lotion under makeup. Other than this, the best rule for normal skin is to leave well enough alone.

Cleanliness, of course, is most important in maintaining your normal complexion. Cleanse your face twice, perhaps using a cleansing cream the first time and a deep-cleansing lotion or wash-off cleanser the second time. If soap doesn't cause your skin to feel tight, you may use a gentle facial soap after your cream cleansing. If you prefer to use only cream on your face, finish up with skin freshener to remove the last vestiges of cleansing cream. This is important, for the cream that remains in the pores has the same effect as excess secretions and will clog pores and attract dirt. Your morning cleansing routine can be a washup with either soap or a cleansing lotion.

Oily skin · When oil glands are overactive, skin usually loses its fresh, young look and becomes sallow and flabby. It is also the ideal site for the formation of blackheads and blemishes. Your aim is twofold: to help control this excess oil and to get rid of any over-supply before it can do damage.

Good care can help alleviate an oily condition.

• Be a demon for cleanliness. By frequent cleansings you can remove excess oil.

• Eat a nutritious diet, avoiding greasy foods that stimulate overproduction of oil as well as blemish-causing rich or spicy foods. Some complexions register every gooey dessert or candy bar in the form of a pimple. Chocolate and nuts are particularly troublesome. The best prescription for overly oily skin is a well-balanced diet based on plenty of meat, milk, leafy vegetables, fruit, and whole wheat breads.

• Maintain regular elimination habits. The experts advise drinking six to eight glasses of liquid (noncarbonated) each day. It's also a good idea to include in your diet some raw fruits and vegetables (apples, whole oranges, and green salads) for roughage.

• Perk up your circulation. The overactivity of oil glands is often due to sluggish circulation. Both exercise and cosmetic stimulants should be part of your beauty campaign.

• Bask in the sun. Sunshine is especially good for oily skins and a great boon in drying up blemishes.

• Use cosmetics sparingly. Naturally, you'll avoid all greasy creams and bases. If skin is blemished, a medicated lotion should be used as a makeup foundation. Any areas that become chapped or rough can be treated with a greaseless moisture cream or lotion. Oily skin may flake off slightly at certain times of the year. This should not be considered a sign that lubrication is needed. Oil secretion has merely lessened sufficiently so that the *normal* scaling off of dead skin is occurring.

• Keep your hair scrupulously clean. Many infections on the face arise from dust and dirt transferred from the hair.

Cleansing routine for oily skin • To help counteract excess oil, you'll need to cleanse your face thoroughly at least three times a day, more if your condition requires it. A quick cleanup is in order whenever your skin begins to look dull and greasy, and all old makeup should always be removed before applying new. A light cleansing cream (one that liquefies easily) or a creamy cleansing lotion is best for you. Follow this with either a medicated cleansing lotion or a soap-and-water scrub. If you use soap, try a soft-bristled complexion brush for extra stimulation. Finish off with an astringent lotion. An astringent provides the stimulation oily skin needs and also helps to tighten pores and to delay the return of a greasy shine. Pour a little on a bit of cotton and wipe it all over your face. An economical version you can concoct yourself is a half-and-half mixture of witch hazel and rubbing alcohol.

Your morning routine can omit the cream cleansing. You went to bed with a sparkling-clean, makeup-free face, didn't you? A soap-and-water sudsing followed by astringent lotion will remove excess oil and wastes excreted during the night and will get you off to a shine-free start.

For exceptionally oily or blemished skin you may want to try washing with either a tar soap or tincture of green soap. Each has a helpful drying effect and can be used about twice a week. Calamine lotion applied to blemishes after your cleanup is helpful in drying up pimples.

If you are troubled by blackheads, you can use a cleansing grain preparation once or twice a week. Grainy cleansers have a gentle scouring action that tackles blackheads far more safely than your squeezing could. If you like to mix up your own beauty aids, you can make quite acceptable cleansing grains by combining equal parts of uncooked corn meal (or almond meal) and mild granulated soap (soap beads). Take a teaspoonful in the palm of your hand and mix it to a soft paste with warm water. Spread this over your face and work it well into any blackhead areas. Rinse thoroughly.

Dry skin • Dry skin, with its fine texture and delicate translucence, can be beautiful. It is seldom the victim of blackheads or blemishes. But it must be preserved carefully to keep it lovely. Cold winds, steam heat, or hot summer sun will rob the already scant supply of natural oils and moisture your skin has. If nature is not given some assistance, your complexion may become rough, dull, and coarsened.

• Avoid, as much as possible, the things that dry your skin—overexposure to sun, wind, water, or hot indoor air. Dry, overheated rooms are a beauty menace. Try to keep the thermostat at 70 degrees.

• Eat a well-balanced diet. A poor diet not only means neglect for your skin, but it also means neglect for your nervous system. A nervous condition is often the cause of skin disorders—and there you have double trouble.

• Use cosmetics that contain plenty of lubricants. You need the heavier cleansing creams, the rich lubricating and moisture creams, and the creamy foundations that protect your skin under makeup during the day.

• Step up your circulation with exercise. Improved circulation helps a dry skin as well as an oily one, for it can do much to correct any imbalance in oil production.

Cleansing routine for dry skin • Cleanliness is important for dry skin. Pores must not become clogged, as that would interfere with the secretion of whatever oil is present. Your cleansing methods must be very gentle. Avoid soap and harsh cleansing agents.

Cleansing cream will be kindest to your skin. Use two applications, massaging while you apply the cream but tissuing it off very gently. Cleansing *twice* is important. You may be surprised at how much dirt and makeup still shows on your tissue following a second creaming. Finish off with a skin freshener. If your skin is very sensitive, look for a skin freshener especially designed for dry skin. Never use an astringent or other drying, highly alcoholic product on dry skin.

Your morning routine can be a single cream cleansing plus skin freshener. During the day try to remove makeup completely at least once.

Pamper and protect dry skin · Dry skin needs plenty of lubrication to protect its loveliness. If skin is very dry, a lubricating preparation can be used nightly after cleansing. A tiny dab of lubricating cream goes a long way. No need to slather it on—a light film will do. The cream should be gently massaged over your clean skin—using upward and outward movements. (See illustration on page 64.)

Lubricating creams are best used during your daily bath time. The warmth and steam open the pores and help your skin absorb the cream. Occasionally you may want to give yourself a hot cream treatment. A heating pad is wonderful for this. Just place a sheet of waxed paper over your creamed face and hold the pad against it.

Don't butter your face with cream before going to bed at night. You get full benefit from a lubricating product in about fifteen or twenty minutes. Then you can blot off any residue and hop into bed without fear of smearing sheets and pillowcases. Your skin should be allowed time at night to breathe—free of cosmetics or treatments.

If your skin is very dry, a moisturizer should be used after your morning cleansing to protect your skin under makeup during the day.

When choosing a lubricating preparation, pick one intended for your age category. Young girls, for instance, will steer clear of hormone or estrogen creams and other products designed for aging skin.

Combination skin · Combination skin, with its normal-to-dry areas and its oily patches, must be treated as two separate complexions. For cleansing you can use cream followed by either soap or a wash-off cleanser. If this is too harsh for the dry areas of your face, you would do better using two cream cleansings and scrubbing only the oily areas with soap and water. Your aim is to guard the drier areas of your skin but to give the oily areas the vigorous cleansing they require so that blemishes and blackheads will not be a problem.

At times the dry areas may need a little lubrication. You will be careful, of course, that none of the cream reaches the oily sections of your face, where it might cause skin eruptions.

❀ Cleanliness, we can't overemphasize, is the key to complexion beauty. Keep your skin clean and it will be bright, clear, and fresh.

❀ Get sufficient rest. Sleep, all too often neglected by busy young misses, is vital to good looks. A girl can manage to drag herself around and get by with too little sleep, but the dark circles under her eyes and her chalky countenance give her away all too easily.

❀ Give your skin a vacation from makeup whenever possible. On at-home Saturdays and during your private hours, clean your face and let your skin breathe freely.

❀ Whenever you're tempted to squeeze a blackhead or pimple, *don't*. Treat yourself to a facial instead (see page 70) or apply medicated lotion. In a few days a blemish will probably cure itself, but squeezing is likely to spread the infection and may also injure the blood vessels, causing permanent unsightly red marks.

❀ Choose treatment products for specific needs. A cleanser is not a substitute for a lubricating cream, nor should a hand cream be used for a face cream.

❀ Adapt your beauty routine to the seasons. Temperature and humidity have such a strong effect on our skin condition that it can vary with the weather. A girl whose complexion seems normal or even a bit dry in winter may find that she has an oily shine to contend with in summer. As more and more seasons go by, and you get older, your skin type can undergo several changes.

TREAT YOURSELF TO A FACIAL

When you want to look especially pretty, treat yourself to a facial! After your regular cleansing, apply a light film of cleansing cream to your face and give yourself a steam treatment to open pores. Steam treatments are an important part of a facial in the famous beauty salons. An at-home version can be created by leaning over a steaming pot of boiling water (or run hot water in the basin). Cover your head completely with a towel to form a tent that will direct steam to your face, and lean over the steaming water. Continue this for five minutes and then wipe with tissues. Your pores will open, wastes will be excreted, and your skin will be receptive to further cleansing.

Next comes a deep-pore cleansing mask. A mask is an excellent pickup for a sallow complexion. Not only does it help draw out wastes, remove blackheads and whiteheads, but it stimulates your skin and leaves it rosy and glowing, with a soft silky texture that is sure to invite compliments.

74

Homemade versions • You can buy excellent facial masks at cosmetic counters, but if you wish to experiment with a homemade variety, you can try one of the following:

- OATMEAL MASK. Cook about half a cup of oatmeal. (The instant varieties are ready as soon as you add hot water.) Allow oatmeal to cool to a comfortable temperature. Hold your hair back with a kerchief or makeup band and apply a thin layer of the oatmeal to your thoroughly cleansed face, avoiding the eye area.

The mask will dry in about ten or fifteen minutes, but better results are gained by leaving it on for a total of twenty or twenty-five. Remove the mask with lukewarm water, followed by a cold splashing.

- EGG WHITE MASK. Use only the white of an egg. Beat it lightly with a fork and apply to the face, avoiding the eye area. Leave it on and rest with your feet propped up for about fifteen or twenty minutes, until the mask dries and begins to pull and draw your skin. Rinse with cool, then cold water.

Use the waiting period for a beauty catnap. Moisten two cotton pads with cold water and place these over your eyes as you lie down to rest. The cool pads help soothe your eyes so that they will be clear and sparkling. If you place two pillows under your feet and one under your fanny—none under your head—this inclined position will stimulate circulation in your face for extra beautifying.

FRUSTRATED BY FRECKLES?

Don't be! Freckles can be delightfully charming. They can create an interesting pixie-like quality or set you off as the all-American outdoorsy type. If you are concerned about your freckles reaching the too-many point, shield your face from the sun as much as possible and use a makeup foundation whenever you are outdoors. There are special sun protection products that coat your skin so that *none* of the sun's rays reach you. Use these at the beach.

If you feel disturbed by your freckles, you can lighten them by applying a bleaching face cream or by doing a little freckle painting with lemon juice. Apply the lemon juice with a paint brush or cotton swab to each freckle. Leave it on for half an hour; then rinse off with warm water. Lemon juice has a drying effect, as well as a bleaching one, and you will probably want to apply a lubricating cream afterwards.

SKIN DISCOLORATIONS

Birthmarks, red marks, and eye shadows can often be masked by one of the heavy covering agents especially designed to hide discolorations. These are applied under a regular foundation. With these products, you choose the color nearest to your own skin tone and apply according to directions. Some companies make a stick form of covering agent for use on small spots.

Too much suntanning sometimes produces a yellow or brownish shadow around the mouth and nose area or along the upper lip, a shadow that lingers long after summer tan has faded. Gradually this shadow should disappear, but use of a bleaching face cream or lemon juice, as described above, will help. In the future, keep this area shielded by hat or sun cream or adhesive-taped patch. Using a lighter foundation on the discolored areas will help produce a more even coloring.

MOLES, SCARS, BIRTHMARKS

All too many people go through life feeling self-conscious about a conspicuous mole or some sort of unsightly skin flaw without realizing that it could easily be removed, or at least be made less visible. Severe scarring from acne, and similar defects in skin texture, can often be treated quite successfully by a dermatologist. Moles can be removed, and large scars or birthmarks concealed, by plastic surgery. If you are considering such treatment, consult a highly qualified specialist who can judge how your particular problem can best be handled.

FACIAL HAIR

Every now and then a girl is horrified to discover a long bristly hair growing on her cheek or chin. This is nothing to worry about. Simply apply a bit of alcohol to the area and tweeze the hair out. There are a few exceptions, however. Keep hands off if the hair is growing from a mole or if it protrudes from the nose or ear. Serious trouble can be caused by such tweezing. Straggly nose and ear hairs can be trimmed shorter with scissors. Only a physician should remove mole hair.

When there is considerable dark fuzz on upper lips or cheeks, try bleaching to hide it. Here is a simple recipe for a gentle bleach. Mix together ¾ cup of gentle-action soap flakes, 4 tablespoons of 20-volume peroxide, and 3 drops of ammonia. (Be sure to ask your druggist for bleaching peroxide and for ammonia water diluted for facial use. *Never* use household ammonia or regular hydrogen peroxide.) Coat the hairs with this paste and allow it to remain for about fifteen minutes. Wash it off with lukewarm water and apply a lubricating cream to the area.

If facial hair growth is too thick to bleach, it should be treated by a specialist. It can be removed permanently and safely only by use of electrolysis.

Never use a razor on your face; the hair will come back unbecomingly bristly and coarse. Facial depilatories are sometimes a little risky for home use and are best avoided.

ALLERGIES CAN BE ANNOYING

Certain hypersensitive skins will break out in blotches or become itchy or irritated when regular cosmetics are used. Fortunately, some excellent cosmetics are now being produced that are free from the ingredients that might prove irritating. If your skin seems to react adversely to regular cosmetics, or if your lips become cracked or swollen when you use lipstick, investigate the hypoallergenic brands. Of course, some skin disorders result from allergies of other types—allergies to various foods, to pets, to dust, and to other things we come in contact with. If the irritation persists, consult your doctor.

 FOLLOW-UP

1 Stand in good light while you examine your face closely. Based on what you have learned, decide what type skin you have.

2 Visit a cosmetic counter and study the various products available to decide which would be suitable for your particular skin. Find the items necessary for a complete cleansing, lubricating (if needed), and stimulating routine. As soon as your budget permits, purchase any of the essentials you lack so that you can soon enjoy the benefits a complete skin care program brings. Follow your beauty routine carefully. Treatment products must be used regularly to bring results. The cream that sits unused on a dressing table can't help anyone.

3 Pamper yourself with a complete beauty facial. Give yourself the "works" and see what a wonderful lift it adds to your appearance—and your morale.

Some women are born beautiful, but a much larger percentage have made themselves beautiful thanks to a skillful use of cosmetics. When properly applied, makeup can smooth and brighten your complexion, conceal or camouflage your bad features. It can even seem to change the shape of a face or the length of a nose. But it must be used with wisdom and discretion, for that little touch of color here and pat of powder there can be read like a billboard, telling the world about a girl's fashion know-how, her personal grooming habits, and her good taste. The girl who has learned to use a degree of artistry putting on makeup has beauty power that can work magic for her all her life.

Before you apply your first dab of makeup, you should examine your face and features to see what should be enhanced and what should be modified.

Start with the shape of your face. Is it oval, round, square, oblong (long and narrow), heart-shaped (wider at the top), diamond-shaped (wider through the cheek bones), or pear-shaped (wider at the bottom)? If you're in doubt, have a private study session with your mirror.

Pull your hair straight back from your face so that your *entire* hairline is exposed, and pin or tie your hair flat. Then, closing one eye and looking straight at your reflection, trace the outline of your face on the mirror with a piece of soap. Now you have the general outline of your face. If you compare it with those illustrated here, you can identify the general shape. Possibly your face isn't a perfect example of one particular shape. Few faces are. A square face, for instance, may have a little pointed chin. A widow's peak may dip into a round face. What you need to know is what general category your face shape belongs in.

4

MAKE THE MOST OF MAKEUP

THE IDEAL FACE SHAPE

An oval face is usually considered the ideal. It is two-thirds as wide as it is long and has perfect oval contours. However, one face type is as attractive as another, providing it is properly dramatized. Through makeup, hair styling, and choice of necklines, any face can be made to appear more oval.

If you are planning to lose or gain weight during this course, you will want to check your face shape again as your scale shows improvement. Weight loss can, for instance, change a square face into an oval one, while extra poundage might make a round face out of a triangular one.

A few more statistics:

• The perfect face can be divided into three equal parts: from the hairline to the eyebrows, from the eyebrows to the tip of the nose, and from the tip of the nose to the tip of the chin.

• The space between the eyes should equal the width of one eye.

• Ideally the nose, from bridge to tip, is supposed to equal the distance between the eyebrows and the hairline.

You may find it helpful in checking your facial dimensions to hold a book flat under your chin, so that you have a flat surface on which to stand your ruler while reading your measurements in the mirror. The ruler should be straight, not tipped forward or back.

Don't forget your profile in this self-study. Check both left and right sides; they can be surprisingly different, you know. Examine your nose and forehead line. Does your chin recede or jut forward? Is it firm and straight? How about any facial hollows, puffiness, or lines? Because we don't see our profiles often, we may tend to disregard this view; but others are forced to judge us from this angle, too. In examining your profile, don't search for beauty as much as for character, strength, and individuality.

Before you can begin your makeup, your face must be immaculately clean. Then, depending on your skin type, you may wish to use a "primer coat"—a lubricant or moisturizer for dry skin or a medicated lotion for blemished skin. Your steps for the application of makeup will then be as follows:

1 Tinted foundation

2 Rouge (cream or liquid—dry rouge follows powder)

3 Powder

4 Lipstick

5 Eyebrow pencil

6 Eyeshadow (if used)

7 Eyeliner (if used)

8 Mascara (if used)

FOUNDATION FOR MAKEUP MAGIC

Just as its name implies, a foundation (or base, as it is sometimes called) is the foundation of good makeup. It is the first cosmetic you apply, and probably the one single cosmetic that does the most to simulate a peaches-and-cream complexion. A foundation provides fresh, even color because it covers dark circles, minor blemishes, and skin discolorations and gives the complexion a brighter, clearer look. It protects the skin by providing a shield against sun, wind, cold, and dirt, and against other makeup that might otherwise penetrate pores too deeply. It increases the clinging power of other makeup, and the right type of base can help counteract an oily or dry condition. Truly a cosmetic to be cherished!

Which shade? · There are three major skin shades: pink (red tones), cream (neutral tones), and olive (golden yellow tones). If you are in doubt about your coloring, stand before a bright sunlit window and hold a sheet of white paper next to your cheek. When you look in a hand mirror, you should see a reflection of your skin tone on the paper. Pink and olive tones are easiest to pick out. If you can't see either of these tones, your skin is probably cream.

Once you have decided on the proper color family, you will want to choose a shade in that family that matches the deepest tones of your skin color. Be careful not to select too dark a shade, because this will be hard to blend into your natural coloring at the neckline, and nothing looks more phony than a pink or tan face perched like a lollipop on a white neck. Too light a shade looks chalky. In choosing a foundation, it is usually best to consult a reliable cosmetics saleswoman. She will probably test the shade on the back of your hand. The color in the bottle is so concentrated that it looks much darker than when it is a gossamer film on your skin. If your complexion is sallow or dull, the cosmetician may suggest a pinkish shade to add life to your skin. If, on the other hand, it is more ruddy than you wish, she may suggest an ivory shade to tone it down.

Which type of foundation? · Foundations come in many forms and have varying degrees of covering power. You will probably need to experiment a little to find the type and brand that best suits your needs. Basically there are three types:

· LIQUID FOUNDATIONS. These are easy to apply and look the most natural. They are excellent for all skin types. Different brands vary greatly in oil content and covering power. Ask the advice of a cosmetics saleswoman and test carefully.

To apply liquid foundation, place a dot of it on your chin and blend it across the jaw, using your fingertips. Then put a dot or two on each cheek and blend well so that it meets previously applied color. Be sure to carry the foundation all the way out to your ears. Repeat with another dot for the nose and mouth area, and finish with a dot or two for the forehead. Use upward and outward movements, being sure that the foundation covers the entire face. Work it gently into any tiny lines around the eyes and mouth, spreading the lines smooth so that they take up the color. Use any base remaining on your fingers to blend color down under the chin and jaw so that the color fades out gradually. Many girls like to use a foundation over the entire throat area. This is fine *if* it doesn't come down far enough to rub off on dress and coat collars.

- CREAM FOUNDATIONS. These come in tubes, sticks, cream cakes, or jars and provide heavier coverage. They are good for concealing dark circles and blending in skin discolorations. Cream foundations are especially good for very dry skin. They must be applied carefully and sparingly to avoid a "made-up" look. Cream foundations are applied with the fingertips in same manner as liquid bases.
- DRY CAKE FOUNDATIONS. These are applied with a wet sponge. They have good covering power but are apt to look artificial in daylight. Because of their drying effect, they are best suited to oily skins.

When applying cake foundation, remember that using a wet sponge will give a lighter finish. A slightly damp sponge will add more color. Cake foundations should be used very lightly and sparingly. Be sure that the sponge is kept clean and allowed to dry thoroughly. A damp sponge in a closed compact is an ideal breeding ground for bacteria.

No matter which type of base you choose, inspect your face carefully to see that you have created a smooth, even finish. There should be no puddles or streaks of color, and the foundation should be blended so smoothly that no one can tell what is natural and what is bottle-bestowed.

ALL-IN-ONE MAKEUPS

There are several products that combine foundation and powder together as an all-in-one makeup. Some come in cake form, others in a tube. The cake forms do not usually give as much covering power or hold up as long as a regular base plus powder. Tube forms are comparable to a regular base with powder. One of the chief virtues of these products is that they are quick and easy to use. They are best for oily or normal young skin that does not need much makeup and is not lined or wrinkled.

THE ART OF CAMOUFLAGE

Through clever use of makeup, any less-than-perfect features can be given the illusion of symmetry. Camouflage involves using two shades of foundation—your regular color and an extra shade that is one or two shades lighter or darker. In a nutshell, a darker shade casts a shadow and conceals; a lighter shade is a highlight that attracts the eye and makes the feature appear more prominent. For instance, full cheeks can be made

83

to appear more slender if the foundation used on the outer edges of the cheeks is slightly darker than that used on the rest of the face. A receding chin can be brought forward by applying a foundation that is slightly lighter than your regular shade over the front of the chin. It's as simple as that! In choosing shades for camouflage, try them together so that you can be sure they will blend inconspicuously. This is important, for you want to avoid a marble-cake effect in the camouflaged area.

Additional camouflage tricks · Use these hints for solving special problems.

- THIN FACE—Blend a darker shade across the jawline to cut length and therefore increase width.

- HOLLOW CHEEKS—Apply a lighter shade.

- DOUBLE CHIN—Conceal it with a darker tone.

- PROTRUDING CHIN—Blend a darker foundation over and under the chin.

- RECEDING CHIN—Blend a lighter foundation over and under the chin.

- SQUARE JAW—Use a darker shade on the extreme sides of face and jawbone.

- LOW FOREHEAD—Play it up with a lighter shade.

- HIGH FOREHEAD—De-emphasize it with a darker foundation.

- SUNKEN EYES—Apply a lighter foundation on the upper lid area, carrying it clear up to the eyebrows.

- CLOSE-SET EYES—Blend a light foundation under the brows and at the bridge of the nose.

- DARK CIRCLES UNDER THE EYES—Use a lighter shade, preferably a heavier type of foundation cream applied with a brush, or one of the stick coverups designed to lighten and hide shadows.

- PUFFINESS UNDER THE EYES—Conceal it with a darker foundation.

BROAD NOSE—Highlight the middle of the nose by blending a line of light foundation down the center; tone down broad nostrils with a darker shade.

LONG NOSE—Blend darker foundation under the tip of the nose and at the edge of the nostrils.

THIN NOSE—Create width with a lighter shade over the sides of the nostrils; cut length with a darker foundation at the tip of the nose.

HOOKED NOSE—Use a darker shade down the center of the nose (in the hooked portion).

SMILE LINES—Puff out the cheeks to spread lines flat and apply a lighter foundation, preferably a cream type, using a brush. Blend edges carefully.

ROUGE

Not every face needs rouge, and many girls skip rouge for daytime wear. In the evening, when artificial lights tend to draw color from complexions, a touch of rouge lends a soft flattering bloom.

There are three types of rouge—cream, liquid, and cake. Cream rouge gives the most natural effect and can be blended easily to give just a subtle hint of color. In applying cream rouge, take the tiniest bit on your forefinger and work it well between the finger and thumb to warm and soften the cream so that it will blend smoothly. Use the merest touch of color. Better too little than too much—you can always add more. Blend thoroughly until only the faintest suggestion of color remains. Liquid rouge is slightly more difficult to use because it must be applied quickly before the color sets. To create a softer effect, a small drop of rouge can be mixed with a drop of foundation in the palm of your hand before it is applied. For dry or normal skin, cream or liquid rouge is most satisfactory. Either type is applied directly after foundation and before powder. Cake rouge, on the other hand, is applied after powder, and to soften its appearance, you will want to finish off with an additional fluff of powder over the rouge. Dry rouge is less lasting than the other varieties and is slightly more difficult to blend to achieve a natural effect. Dry rouge is best for use over cake foundations and for touch-ups during the day. It is recommended for oily skins.

Which shade of rouge? · The shade you choose will depend on your coloring. The lighter your skin, the lighter your rouge should be. Remember that rouge defeats its purpose if it is obvious. If your skin has cream or olive tones, you will probably look best in a coral or orange-red shade of rouge. Pink complexions need a soft pink shade.

Placement of rouge · Rouge does two things: it shapes a face and gives it additional color. Where you place your rouge is most important. If you have an *oval face*, smile at yourself in the mirror and place your rouge in a little wing-shaped triangle from the top of your smile out along the cheekbones. Start the color about under the center of the eyes and let it fade out gently toward the temples.

A *broad face* can be made to seem more oval if you apply rouge fairly high on the cheekbones. Start about under the center of the eyes and blend the rouge in a tiny triangle along your smile, being careful that color does not extend too far out on the cheeks.

A *long, thin face* can gain width if you place rouge a bit lower on the cheekbone and extend the color outward toward the hairline. Start the rouge about on a line with the outer rim of the iris.

If there are shadowy circles under the eyes, blend a little rouge over the edge of the circle to make the shadow less obvious.

There are a few rules that must be followed if you want rouge to do a proper job of beautifying. A few never-nevers:

- Never apply rouge lower than the tip of the nose or it will create shadows that make your face sag.

- Never put rouge close to the nose. A point under the center of the eyes is as close as it should ever come.

- Never rouge in an obvious little circle.

- Never bring rouge close to the eyes.

- Never use lipstick as a substitute for rouge. It contains ingredients that are too strong for delicate facial skin.

- Never leave any obvious boundaries.

POWDER

Powder provides the smooth matte finish that gives your makeup a soft, glowing unity. Your powder shade should match your foundation. Always use a clean disposable puff or cotton to *press* powder gently all over your face, fluffing rather than rubbing the powder on. Brush all excess from your brows and lashes and from around your nose.

Never apply powder directly to your skin. Some type of foundation or moisturizer should be used underneath to prevent powder from penetrating too deeply into the pores. Some girls with complexions so lovely that they need little makeup skip powder for daytime wear. They prefer the fresh, dewy look of foundation alone.

Tip: After your makeup is complete, you can set it by patting very lightly with cotton that has been wrung out in cold water. This helps keep makeup intact longer.

LIPSTICK

Use your lipstick in an artful way to make the most of your mouth—to shape it, to emphasize the beauty of your lips, and to cleverly catch up the color of your costume.

Lipstick is the most obvious cosmetic, and therefore the one that requires most care—in choice of color and in application.

Which shade? · All lipstick colors fall into three basic categories: the blue-reds (from pale candy pinks to deep wine shades), the true reds, and the coral-orange reds (from pale tangerine to russet-brown red). The blue-red shades are best for pink complexions an olive complexion is enhanced by coral-orange reds. A cream complexion can wear any shade safely.

These rules are not hard-and-fast, for your choice of lipstick color is based also on the shade of foundation you wear and the color of your costume. The right shade of foundation, as discussed earlier, can alter the tone of your complexion so that you will be able to wear a lipstick color that would not be flattering if you were wearing no makeup

One fact to remember in selecting your lipstick is that you must be sure that the new color does something for *you*. Just because it is the most ballyhooed shade of the moment, has a catchy name, or looks marvelous on your best friend isn't reason enough to make it your own. Fair-skinned lasses are most beguiling in the lighter shades. (A dark, bold color is too harsh and makes the rest of the complexion fade out.) If you have vivid dramatic coloring practically the whole spectrum is open to you. Bright shades are in keeping with deeper coloring, and pale shades (when in fashion) can be a striking understatement.

In selecting the lipstick you will wear, the most important consideration is how well it goes with your outfit. To be sure of having the ingredients for perfect color harmony on hand at all times, it is necessary to own at least three lipstick shades—one in each color category. You can blend them to suit if you need to. Owning a variety of lipsticks is fun and is really no extravagance.

To help you choose the right makeup for each costume, this chart has been devised. In general terms, it gives you suggestions for making your clothes and your cosmetics a lovely blend of fashion. Colors with yellow in them (greens, browns, oranges) harmonize best with orange or true-red lipsticks or nail enamels. Colors with blue in them (blue-greens, purples, maroons, pinks) look well with blue-red shades. Off-red colors (orange, coral, rose) are very tricky to match—try to keep the color of your lipstick close to the costume shade.

MATCH YOUR MAKEUP

Costume color	Lipstick and nail polish color	Eye makeup colors		
		BLUE OR GRAY EYES	GREEN OR HAZEL EYES	BROWN EYES
Black, white, gray, beige, navy	Any shade	Blue, gray	Green, gray	Gray, blue-green, turquoise
Pink, red, orange	Closely matching shade	Blue, gray turquoise	Blue-green, turquoise, blue	Turquoise, gray, blue
Blues, purple, rose, lavender, maroon	Blue-red (including pinks)	Blue, lavender, violet, gray	Blue, lavender, violet, gray	Blue, lavender, violet, gray
Greens; emerald, olive, forest	Yellow-reds (including corals)	Blue-green, green	Green, blue-green	Green
Yellows, tans, corals	Yellow-reds (including corals)	Turquoise, blue-green	Blue-green, turquoise	Blue-green, green
Blue-greens, aqua, teal	Red-red, blue-red, or yellow-red (depending on accessory color)	Turquoise, blue-green	Blue-green, turquoise, green	Blue-green, turquoise
Browns, russets, coppers	Yellow-reds, red-red	Turquoise, blue-green	Green, blue-green, brown	Brown, blue-green

89

Paint yourself a pretty mouth · If lipstick is smeary or frayed, your whole expression seems awry. If you haven't yet experimented with a lip-liner pencil or a lipstick brush, you owe it to your pretty smile to give them a try. Their benefits: they create a cleaner, neater lip outline and are less likely to cause skid marks because their slender girth allows you to control where you're going much better than a thick stick does. You may find your hand has better control when using a brush if you rest your pinky on your chin. The most popular lipstick brushes have short sable or camel's hair bristles. (Don't expect your kid sister's paint brush to be a good substitute.)

Just a reminder—before applying lipstick, make sure the remains of the last job have been thoroughly wiped away and that your lips are free from cream or moisture so that new lipstick has a clean, dry surface to cling to. Always blot your lips first to be safe.

If you use a lip-liner pencil, shape your lip outline with it, then fill in with your lipstick. When using a brush, put plenty of lipstick on the bristles so that you can make an even line. Then, keeping your lips closed and relaxed, draw a firm outline of half your upper lip. Repeat on the other side. Then do your lower lip.

Now retrace the complete lip line with the mouth open and the lips stretched taut so that all lip creases will be filled and a sharper line will be achieved. Fill in either with your lipstick or by using vertical brush strokes. Be sure to carry color back deep enough so that no boundary line is visible on your lips.

Lipstick should always be applied to both lips. When color is merely put on the upper lip and then the lips are pressed together to transfer color to the lower lip, wearing quality is reduced considerably because not enough stain is left. Also, the bottom lip will not be shaped correctly.

A trick that many models use to make their lipstick last longer is to powder lightly over and around their lips before applying color. This helps lipstick set better and keeps color from creeping or smearing. Lipstick is allowed to set for a few minutes and then blotted gently with tissue. This is followed with another dusting of powder, another application of color, a few moments' wait, and a final light blotting. Try this method next time you're invited out to dinner—it keeps lipstick on *you*, instead of on silver and glassware.

Check the manufacturer's instructions about blotting. With some types of lipsticks you are advised to wait twenty minutes before blotting so that color will set. When you blot your lips, use gentle pressure. Biting down hard removes too much color.

Correcting your lip line · If you want to do a little revamping of your lip line—and a very little is all that you can get away with—you must proceed with caution. Lips painted out beyond their borders don't fool anybody, neither do out-of-date Cupid's bows, pointed upper lips, or exaggerated lower lips.

• THIN LIPS.   Outline with a darker shade and fill in with a brighter color, carrying it to the outer edges of your lips. Don't exceed the rim of your lips, the profile will look phony.

• FULL LIPS.   Make them look thinner by bringing foundation up over the lip edge and keeping the lip outline just *slightly* inside natural borders. Use a lighter shade to outline and fill in with a darker one.

• WIDE MOUTH.   Don't carry color into the corners; let it fade away gradually.

• SMALL MOUTH.   Extend color as far as possible.

• FULL LOWER LIP.   Color lower lip a slightly darker shade, upper lip slightly lighter (keeping in the same color family, of course).

• DROOPING CORNERS.   Let lipstick fade out before it reaches the corners of the upper lip, but extend color as far as possible into the corners of the lower lip.

Remember, too, the best beautifier for your lips is a warm friendly smile. Let an easy smile become a habit and you'll have accomplished more for your beauty than any cosmetic can.

ACCENTUATING EYES

Eye makeup has come into its own within the past few years. It can provide an attractive frame for the eyes—making them seem larger, more radiant, more alluring. It emphasizes and lends importance to eyes that otherwise pass unnoticed, and is a great asset to those who wear glasses. Girls with light brows and lashes achieve a particularly impressive improvement.

Until a few years ago eye makeup was reserved strictly for prom night and other galas; today in some parts of the country it is worn even by girls in shorts. This, it seems, is going a little too far. Elaborate eye makeup still seems most appropriate as a glamorous accent for after dark. Business frowns on anything that smacks of the theatrical. In most offices eyebrow pencil and a light, *inconspicuous* touch of mascara are permissible, but eye shadow and dark eyeliners should be skipped during working hours.

Eyebrow care • Eyebrows are the exclamation marks of the face. They add expression to the eyes and balance to the rest of your features. If they are too pale, the face takes on a blank look; too short, features look pinched; too long, eyes are overpowered. Brows that are well tended do much to intensify the beauty of the entire face.

• KEEP EYEBROWS NEAT. Eyebrow beauty begins with brushing. It's amazing how well scrawny brows and straying hairs respond to regular brushing. A mascara brush is most satisfactory, but even a hairbrush will do. Brush hairs in toward the center of the face—opposite from the way they grow—then straight up, and smooth them into place by running a comb or finger over the top edge of the arch. Every time you comb your hair take a moment to comb brow stragglers into line. Shaggy, untidy brows can make the whole face seem to droop.

• SHAPING EYEBROWS. The most flattering shape for your eyebrows is usually the one Mother Nature designed for you. Artificial upslants, high surprised-looking arches, and long thin penciled tails merely look peculiar. The natural arch usually needs a bit of sharpening and refining, however, to make it most attractive.

Tweeze only the stragglers that blur the clean outline of your brows, plucking only stray hairs at the bridge of the nose and *beneath* the arch. Please don't tweeze above the arch or pluck any but the lowest stragglers from beneath the inner third of the brow. The brow bone protrudes there and looks peculiar if it is bared. By all means don't tweeze eyebrows into a thin, unnatural line. Some girls who have gone wild with their tweezing have come to rue the day. After they saw what they had done, and how unattractive it looked, they were horrified to find that the plucked hairs didn't grow back. This occasionally happens, particularly with girls in their teens.

Your eyebrow should begin just above the inner corner of the eye. (The space between the eyes, you remember, should be the width of an eye.) If your eyes are very close-set, brows may be plucked just a tiny bit farther out—no more than one-eighth of an inch—to add width.

What is the proper length for your eyebrows? Try this: Hold a pencil against your face with one end at the side of the base of your nose and the other end at the outer corner of your eye. To be in balance with the rest of your features, the tip of the eyebrow should extend just to the line formed by the pencil. If your face is round or pear-shaped, the outer tips of the brows should point out toward the hairline. A long or oval face is flattered by eyebrows that arch down at the tips so that the curve will soften the lines of the face.

To keep eyebrows smoothly tapered, tweezing should be done at least once a week—or, better yet, whenever you spot a stray. Plucking will be quick and painless if you apply a bit of face cream to the brows before you begin. Or cream the area and do your tweezing after a hot bath. Hold the skin taut with one hand and use tweezers to grasp the hair as near as possible to the root. A quick pull in the direction the hair is growing, and out it comes! Finish off with a wipe of alcohol to guard against any possible infection.

• INTENSIFYING EYEBROWS. All of us weren't born with dark dramatic eyebrows, but thanks to a bit of eyebrow pencil, we can all arch a brow effectively. Unless you have jet black hair, avoid a black pencil. Black tends to look harsh and unnatural. Brunettes and darker blondes should use brown pencil; light blondes and redheads should choose a light brown or auburn shade. Eyebrow pencil should be applied in tiny, feather-like strokes to the hairs of the brow—never drawn in a straight line. Each line should be in the same direction as the hair is growing. Color should be sketched in lightly, as though each hair were being touched up. Do not apply pencil to the skin unless brows are extremely sparse or do not extend far enough. Soften the appearance by rubbing the darkened brow gently with your fingertip to avoid a hard crayoned line. Then blot with facial tissue. If you have lengthened your brows, check your profile to be sure that the line is not too long or too obvious.

Eyeshadow · Eyeshadow should be applied subtly and carefully. The effect should be the slightest suggestion of color. Only the added beauty of your eyes should be apparent—not the makeup.

Soft blues and greens are the most generally flattering shades; lavender adds depth to blue eyes. You'll want to experiment to see which colors flatter your particular eye coloring and the costume you plan to wear.

Just the tiniest smidge of shadow is needed. Apply it lightly to the center of the upper lid, close to the lashline. Smooth the color gently along lashes to the outer corner of the lid. Blend slightly up toward the eyebrow, never going higher than the first crease of the lid except to play down prominent eyes or deep-set eyes, in which the upper lid folds back so completely that it is not seen. In these cases shadow can be brought up to the eyebrow line. Blend the shadow lightly until color fades off into nothingness. Color emphasis should be kept in the outer corners, where the natural shadows appear. Blending color out toward temples will make close-set eyes seem farther apart.

If lids are dry, a touch of eye cream should be applied first, to help shadow spread smoothly. If you want to soften a color, blend a bit of foundation with the shadow before applying it. Girls who find the color forms crease lines on the lid may have more success with powdered eyeshadow. After applying eyeshadow, set the color with a fluff of face powder. This prevents color from collecting in the creases.

Eyeshadow is not flattering to all girls. It should be skipped by those who have naturally shadowed lids, darkly circled eyes, very little space between eyes and eyebrows, heavily-lidded eyes, or a wrinkled eye area.

Eyeliner · Outlining the eyes and drawing extended upswept corners (doe eyes, or Cleopatra eyes), enjoyed a vogue with models and with some women in highly sophisticated sets. Although it has been several years since doe eyes first made fashion history, they still have not been widely accepted. Perhaps it is because they are so frankly artificial, perhaps because men make disapproving jokes about them, perhaps because we still haven't gotten used to the idea. Eyelines, are, of course, too extreme for office wear, but for gala occasions . . . well, you know best whether or not they will be appreciated by your personal public.

A soft, well-sharpened eyeliner pencil (or a liquid eyeliner) is used, usually brown or a shade that matches the natural color of the lashes. If the pencil seems too hard, it can be softened by holding the tip under hot water. Liquid liners are harder to work with but stay on longer.

Start at the outer corner of the eye and make the little pointed upslanting extension. (Note: this extension is *always* made in a natural lash color—the blues, greens, and other fashion colors (if used) should be applied only on the lid itself.) Lift skin gently until taut. With the eye shut, draw the extension following the curve of the lid and moving upward and outward an eighth of an inch. For a more conservative makeup, keep the corner line even shorter. Be sure your extension begins exactly at the corner of the eye. Some girls get this line a little too high, which looks rather peculiar from the side. Next, draw a line (or a series of tiny dots for a more natural effect) across the upper lid as close to the lashes as possible. Start about one quarter of the way in and join it with the corner extension. The line may be widened slightly toward the outer corner but should not be overdone.

Most girls limit their eyelining to the upper lid. If the lower lid is to be lined, the best procedure is to make a series of tiny dots along the inside of the lashes, again starting about one quarter of the way in from the inner corner.

If your eyes are small, or deep-set, and you like to wear an eyeliner, be sure that the line you apply is very fine. Place it as close to the roots of your lashes as possible and use a brown shade—*not* black.

In making eyelines, accuracy counts. All allure vanishes when there are smudged edges or incorrectly drawn lines. Before a public appearance, plenty of private practice is advisable.

Remember that the idea is to draw attention to the eye, not the makeup. Eyelines defeat this purpose unless applied with great care and caution.

Curling eyelashes · Lashes seem longer if they are curved upward. You can do this with gentle pressure when you apply mascara or you can use an eyelash curler. Only the upper lashes should be curled. Regular brushing will coax lashes to curl naturally, and will also promote thicker growth. Girls who wear glasses find that the annoyance of having lashes bat against lenses is lessened if they use a curler regularly.

Mascara · Darkening eyelashes with mascara provides a flattering setting for the eyes, making them look larger, more radiant. Blondes and redheads with very light lashes find that mascara is one of their most important beauty aids. But even the darkest lashes have light tips and seem longer and more luxuriant when mascara is added.

Black or brownish-black mascara is best for most women, but brown will give a more natural effect for those with very light lashes. The blues, greens, and other exotic shades are best reserved for evening wear.

Mascara comes in cream, liquid, and cake forms. The creams and liquids are the proper consistency for use and can be put on a dry brush.

The liquid mascaras that come in tubes with roll-on or brush-on applicators are convenient but offer no way to regulate the amount of mascara on the brush. Often too much gets on the lashes, sticking them together. Be sure to use a clean brush or lash comb to remove excess.

With cake mascara you mix your own, using a clean brush barely moistened with *hot* water. Hot water dissolves the cake more quickly and allows the mascara to spread more evenly, giving a sheen that is impossible to get with cold water.

A tip to make mascara cling longer: Start with dry, clean lashes and give them a preliminary light dusting with face powder. Apply mascara with upward and outward strokes along the entire length of the lashes, from roots to tips, concentrating color on the outer lashes. If you use cake mascara, remember that the brush should not be too wet, or it will pick up so much mascara that the lashes will look blobby and artificial. Lashes should not stick together—each hair must be separate. If lashes do become matted or beaded, rinse brush well, shake dry, and brush again. Apply mascara only to upper lashes; it should never be used on lower lashes. Some girls find that a second coat is beneficial. Wait until the first coat has dried before applying a second. Be sure to clean the brush thoroughly after every use. And remember not to rub your eyes!

Beautiful eyes are healthy eyes • Your eyes deserve every bit of pampering you can give them. Business girls who spend much of their day typing, proofreading, or scanning mail are particularly susceptible to eye troubles. Try to work in good light—and this applies at home as well. When you are reading or doing close work, give your eyes a restful change by occasionally looking up and as far off as possible. For the sake of your eyes, don't let yourself be lured into reading on buses or bouncy trains. If your eyes feel strained from too much reading, dust, or sun glare, bathe them or treat them to eye drops.

One of the best refreshers for tired eyes is "looking at black." Close your eyes and let yourself relax as you imagine you are in a completely darkened room that has walls draped with black velvet. See only black—deep, rich black—for two or three minutes. When you open your eyes, they'll feel much fresher.

No makeup is complete until it has passed a careful final inspection. What might get by when viewed across a dressing table often shows up at closer range. Take a moment to check with your hand mirror. Is the foundation even and well blended? Do you have a chin line of foundation? Is there any excess powder? Do rouge and eye makeup look natural? Does your lipstick pass the profile test? A few moments' final check is a valuable investment in beauty and poise. When you know your makeup is perfect, you can forget it and concentrate on enjoying yourself.

 FOLLOW-UP

1 Using the instructions in this chapter, decide on the shape of your face. How do your features compare with the ideal specifications?

2 Examine your features to decide which is your most impressive feature—the one that has the most individuality. It may not be your prettiest feature, but it should be the one that gives the most character to your face. Ask two friends, or members of your family, if they agree.

3 After you determine the color of your skin, experiment with different types and brands of foundations to see which is most flattering.

4 Following the suggestions given earlier, check your eyebrows to see that they are the correct length to balance your features. Pluck them carefully. Then experiment with eyebrow pencil to see how the arch can be improved.

5 Experiment with giving yourself a new makeup. Do your face completely at least three times, trying different shades and camouflage tricks to see which is prettiest for you. Then try making up someone else—perhaps your mother or sister or a friend—so that you can practice other techniques.

Hair care and styling offer so many opportunities for changing and revitalizing appearance that every girl owes it to her good looks to become skilled in these techniques. Beautiful, glossy hair is a striking beauty asset in itself. And a flattering, fashionable hairdo sets you off as a clever girl with plenty of grooming *savoir faire*.

Hair is not attractive unless it is clean. When hair becomes dull and clings together in sticky strands, no hair style will look pretty. A regular shampoo schedule is the answer. How often should you shampoo? Often enough to keep hair clean and sparkling, which is probably about once a week. Every girl has to make her own decision on this because, depending on the oiliness of her hair and the amount of soot and dirt it's exposed to, washing time can vary from every four or five days to every ten or twelve days. Even if your hair is very dry, it isn't wise to put off a shampoo longer. Dirt will merely clog up the pores and prevent the oil glands from functioning properly. Bear in mind that in summer, when you perspire freely, hair must be washed more frequently to prevent a sour, dirty-hair odor.

5

BEAUTIFUL HAIR

A GOOD HEAD START

Before your shampoo, brush hair vigorously to loosen scalp scale and to sweep out loose hair and dirt. Then wash your brushes and combs, including those you carry in your purse. Why is it that some girls who are otherwise respectably groomed carry revoltingly filthy combs? For the sake of your grooming reputation, as well as hair health, keep your brushes and combs sparkling clean. A quick method to clean them is to soak them in sudsy ammonia and warm water while you shampoo. Then give the combs a quick run through the brushes, rinse, and shake out. When you dry your brush, stand it up on end with the handle in a glass or jar and the bristles exposed to the air. This prevents any weight on wet bristles, which might weaken them, and allows water to drain away from the base of the brush so that the bristles won't be loosened. Don't dry brushes on radiators; heat may warp them.

If your hair is dry, a preshampoo hot oil treatment is very helpful. This involves warming a few tablespoons of cooking oil (vegetable oil—never mineral oil) or using a special conditioning product for dry hair. Rub it well into your hair and scalp. Then a towel wrung out in very hot water can be wrapped around your head in a turban and left on for fifteen or twenty minutes to spread the oil evenly. Reheat the towel whenever it cools. If time allows, you'll gain greater benefit by leaving the oil on for a couple of hours or, better yet, overnight. In this case, make yourself a turban of aluminum foil or cellophane wrap, and cover your pillow with a turkish towel. A hot oil treatment is often helpful in conditioning hair for a permanent. It should be given a week before the permanent, however, because some experts believe that an oil treatment just before a permanent may affect the way the permanent takes.

When you shampoo, wash your hair twice with shampoo and rinse until it squeaks. Rinse thoroughly, for any soap left in will dull hair. Choose a shampoo that is suited to your hair condition and that will work effectively in the water you use. In hard water areas detergents are usually best, although some brands are drying. Consult labels and experiment until you find the products that work best for you.

If you use a soap shampoo, you can be sure all soap film is removed if you finish with a lemon juice rinse (especially good for blondes) or a vinegar rinse (for brunettes and redheads). The commercial rinses that highlight your natural hair color and provide added sheen are also good.

If your hair is dry or tends to take off in all directions after a shampoo, or if your permanent is new and a little hard to handle, try a cream rinse. Cream rinses counteract the static electricity that causes hair to stand on end. They also contain hair-conditioning ingredients that make hair softer and more manageable.

WORKING UP A SHINE

The secret of soft, glossy locks is just this: healthy hair. Your hair can only look its prettiest when it is kept in top condition. Daily massage and hairbrush sessions are the best way to keep hair healthy, bright, and gleaming. They improve circulation in the scalp, stimulating the blood to speed up its beauty work and helping to regulate the supply of natural hair oils.

Whether your hair is dry, normal, or oily, brushing is important. If your hair is oily, you won't want to brush too vigorously. Firm but gentle lifting strokes will give your scalp the stimulation it requires. Concentrate on hair more than scalp. At first your hair may seem to become more oily, because the oil is being spread throughout the hair instead of being allowed to remain on the scalp where it clogs the pores. However, brushing will, in time, help to correct this over-oily condition. To prevent the spread of oil through your hair, you can work a piece of cheesecloth over and down through the bristles of your brush. Then, as you brush, dirt and oil will cling to the cloth. Shift the cheesecloth frequently so that a clean section can be used.

A brush with natural bristles is generally recommended by hair specialists. The irregular shape of the natural bristle provides more surface to clean and polish the hair, and natural bristles have a more gentle effect. Nylon bristles are sharp and may cut delicate hair.

Do you know how to brush your hair? Ridiculous as the question may seem, many people don't know how. They merely glide a brush lightly over the top of the hair, which does little good. As you brush, use long strokes, sweeping the hair up from the roots and out to the very tips. Lean forward, holding your head down, and brush the back hair forward over your head. Then brush the side and top hair up, opposite to the way it normally lies. Don't bother counting strokes. Just do a good job, and keep at it until your scalp tingles all over. Incidentally, brushing is an excellent beauty treatment for your complexion as well.

You'll probably notice that your brush picks up considerable dirt in the process. To avoid merely transferring dirt from one section of your hair to another, wipe the bristles at intervals on a lintless cloth or tissue. Rinse your brush off whenever it becomes soiled and give it a thorough washing before each shampoo.

MAKE MASSAGE A HABIT

A young typist with gorgeous hair says she wakes up her scalp each morning by giving it a good massage. Smart gal! Morning may be too hectic a time for most girls, but perhaps in the evening you can manage three or four minutes for massage while you're reading or watching television. A massage does wonders in stimulating your scalp and in promoting general relaxation and is excellent for relieving nervous tension. Put your fingers under your hair now and rotate your scalp. Does your scalp feel loose and move easily? It should. When you massage, use both hands, one on each side of your head, and work with the pads of your fingers so that your nails won't scratch. Begin at the nape of your neck and slowly rotate your fingers, moving the scalp as you do. Then slide your fingers to a new position and rotate the scalp again. Gradually work forward up over your head to your front hairline. Then, starting behind your ears, spiral up and forward along the sides of your head. Remember that your fingers should move the scalp; they should not merely slide over the surface. Keep repeating these back-to-front spiraling patterns all over your head. Feels marvelous, doesn't it?

If your hair tends to be dry, you can obtain an extra bonus from your massage by working in one of the lubricating hair conditioners as you massage.

HAIR PROBLEMS

Dry hair · Dry hair is lusterless, brittle, often hard to manage. Among the causes: poor diet, too much sun, swimming pool chemicals, a poor permanent, use of coloring products, illness—or just plain neglect. Dry hair usually responds nicely if given proper care. This includes regular use of conditioners, frequent hot oil treatments, and washing with a mild, specially formulated shampoo. Follow up with a cream rinse or, if hair is very dry, with one of the excellent commercial after-shampoo treatments that help replace washed-away lubricants. (Lemon rinses should not be used because of their drying effect.)

Dry hair, particularly, needs the extra stimulation of massage and hair brushing to stir up lazy oil glands. Brushing should be thorough but not too vigorous. Treat hair gently by using a wide-tooth comb and avoiding tight or sharp setting implements. If hair sprays dry or dull your hair, you may find a conditioning hairdressing more satisfactory for disciplining hair because it will add sheen as well as body.

Oily hair · Even fairly soon after a shampoo, oily hair may become drab and stringy. Frequent washing is necessary to keep it pretty. Brushing is helpful, but the brush must be kept clean. Investigate the hairdressings containing alcohol and the setting lotions or sprays that are specially formulated for oily hair. For emergency cleanups between shampoos, you may want to try a powder-type dry shampoo that brushes out, taking unwanted oil with it.

Simple hairstyles are most successful for oily hair. Fashion permitting, set hair on large rollers that give bulk rather than in small curls that encourage hair to separate into sections. Sun and air will help an oily condition. Avoid snug hats that block scalp ventilation.

Limp, lifeless hair · Usually, poor hair is the direct result of poor nourishment. This may be due to an inadequate diet or it may result from an illness, an operation, a severe shock, or nervous tension that saps strength and robs hair of the nutrition it needs. Perhaps you've noticed how an illness, particularly one accompanied by high fever, can cause hair to fall out. An intense mental or physical strain or shock will also take its toll. Good nutrition, plenty of brushing and massage, and the use of lubricating conditioners and dressings will gradually restore hair beauty.

Fine hair · Fine hair is often sparse, fragile, and stubborn, developing definite flyaway tendencies in cold weather and hanging limp in heat. Try all the various props that give more body: a permanent (which should be loose and soft because fine hair tends to frizz), a hair spray, a cream rinse, setting with wave lotion or stale beer. Frequent washing will also give your hair more bulk. Keep your hair style simple and short; length pulls out waves and makes fine hair harder to keep neat.

Very curly hair · Though the envy of straight-haired females, curly hair can be too much of a good thing. It limits hair styles; it tangles easily; and it can become woolly or frowzy. Frequent professional shaping is necessary, and the most flattering hairdos are usually short curl caps. Curly hair tends to become bushy and shapeless when it gets long. To make such hair behave, use a cream rinse after your shampoo and set it while wet on very thick rollers. When your hair is dry, comb it out gently. Overworking it at this point may send it corkscrewing again. So will dampness and humidity, making it necessary to protect your hair, with a shower cap at bathtime or with a hat when it rains just as your straight-haired friends must. For girls who find curly hair too much to bear there are straightening permanents. These must be done professionally and last about three or four months, until new curly hair grows in.

Baldness · This is a problem that seems to be increasing among women. Some of the causes advanced by dermatologists include brushing hair with nylon bristle brushes which seem to tear and cut hair, wearing tight hats that restrict circulation, overteasing and pulling hair into tight pony tails. Pony tails are inadvisable not only because of the fact that the hair is pulled so tightly but also because the elastic band used to hold the hair tends to cut hair and cause it to break.

As mentioned before, an illness or shock of some sort to the nervous system may cause hair to fall out. It may take quite a while—months even—for the condition to correct itself. If it doesn't seem to be improving within a reasonable time, consult your physician. Stimulating circulation with massage is usually quite helpful, but vigorous brushing should be avoided.

Dandruff · Dandruff is *not* to be confused with the flaking off of dead scalp scales, which is a completely natural process. Real dandruff actually is rather rare. Nevertheless, we are occasionally bothered by an avalanche of white flakes on our shoulders and collars. The best remedy is to go to work with a hairbrush and massage—more stimulation is usually the best remedy. Shampoo more frequently, too. Special dandruff-removing shampoos and tonics often alleviate the situation, whether the dandruff is genuine or not.

Sun damage · While sun is excellent for brightening blonde hair and for improving oily conditions, it can play havoc with dry hair. A pretty sun hat, or a gay scarf, is the ounce of prevention that is worth many sessions with hot oil treatments and special conditioners. Once the damage is done, these treatments will gradually help hair regain its beauty

Also try cream rinses and after-shampoo treatments. They are very beneficial for damaged hair.

Split ends · Split ends are caused by anything that causes dryness—a permanent, too much sun, and so on. When hair is dry, it breaks more easily. Then, if pins or rollers are yanked out carelessly, the ends split. The only cure is to cut them off. Split ends should always be trimmed off before a new permanent. In the future, try to be more gentle in handling your hair and try to counteract the dryness.

WHICH HAIR STYLE FOR YOU?

There are several factors that determine your best hair style—the shape of your face, the various features that should be emphasized or minimized, your personality, and the type of life you lead. As a business girl, you'll naturally need an easy-to-manage style that looks crisply neat and attractive. It should be fashionable but should not be overly dramatic or so ultrasophisticated that it looks out of place with your trimly tailored business clothes.

For business, your hair should be kept fairly short, preferably above shoulder length. If hair is long, it can be swirled into a neat chignon or tucked into a stylish French twist. Long flowing manes and pony tails are out of place for office wear. They are too little-girlish, and they detract from the look of efficiency and sophisticated maturity that every business girl should strive for.

Do you know how high your hairdo should be to balance your face most attractively? Here's a guide to help determine the approximate height that should be most flattering. Once again prop a book flat under your chin as you face your mirror; then measure with a ruler. The length from the outer corner of your eye to the book should equal the distance from the eye corner to the top of your hairdo.

Styling for your face shape · Before deciding on a style, analyze your face to see if any camouflage tactics can be used for more flattery. With hairdos, the idea is to use curls and waves to create an illusion of width wherever the face is too narrow, to cover up any places that are too wide, or to disguise broadness by creating an illusion of slimness through adding height and length.

RIGHT ►

WRONG ►

- WELL-ROUNDED? If you have full cheeks and a softly curved cherubic chin, your face may look almost round. To counteract this effect, you will want to keep hair fairly smooth at the sides, perhaps allowing a few curls to come forward over your cheeks. Soft curls and high waves at the top of the head will add height, and a little below-the-ear fullness will give length. Because a center part is broadening, you will want to choose a more flattering side part.

- SQUARE? If your chin and forehead are both broad, your face probably falls into this category. Square faces have a look of strength about them, but are usually most attractive when the sharp angles are softened by curving lines and the width is slimmed down. To achieve this effect, use either high top waves or a dipping side bang. Beware of flat center parts, straight-across bangs, or hair pulled back tightly at the forehead. You will probably look prettiest if your hair is shorter or longer than chin length, with a wave or curl coming in at the cheekbone.

- LONG AND NARROW? Your aim is to cut the length of your face and to add fullness at the sides. Bangs are for you; brief, softly waved ones that dip to the side in an irregular line are especially good for shortening a high brow. Keep soft fullness at the ears. If your neck is long, allow hair to grow long enough to give background to the lower part of your face.

◄ RIGHT

◄ WRONG

HEART-SHAPED? This is often a most attractive face. If you have a pretty chin, perhaps you will want to play it up more by keeping your chin line clear. If, however, you wish to camouflage a too-pointed chin, try soft curls below and behind the ears or a loose page-boy style. If you are lucky enough to have a widow's peak, which often accompanies a heart-shaped face, you can dramatize it by combing hair high or back to show off the hairline. You need only be wary of adding width at the temples. Keep temple hair smooth, perhaps allowing a soft, gentle, inward curve.

DIAMOND-SHAPED? Many interesting faces have a diamond shape—wide through the cheekbones and narrowing at brow and chin. No serious problems are presented here. The only rule to remember is that you shouldn't completely bare your forehead. You can conceal its narrowness with a short puffy bang that is wider than your forehead and perhaps flows into short curls at the temples to add fullness.

PEAR-SHAPED? If your forehead is narrow and your jaw wide, you will want your hair to add width at the temples to balance your full chin. This is easy to achieve with a center part and curls at the temples, or use wide bangs to add breadth at the forehead. Although you will want to keep your hair smooth below the ears, you can try some of the dramatic, softly pulled-back Grecian styles with a cluster of curls at the back of the head. Short hairdos that flow up and back should also be flattering.

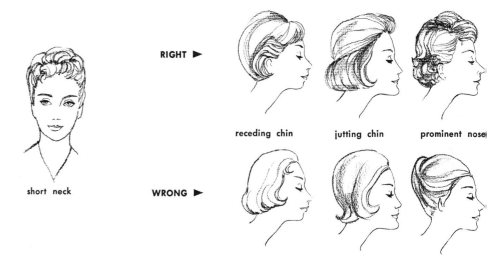

short neck

RIGHT ▶

receding chin   jutting chin   prominent nose

WRONG ▶

Consider the other angles · The front of your face is not the only view that you must consider when deciding on a hair style. Have you a special profile or figure problem? Your hair can help camouflage here, too.

• RECEDING CHIN.   Use fluffy bangs or waves at the forehead. Lift hair at temples and let sides sweep back softly, showing a flattering distance between ear and chin.

• JUTTING CHIN.   Avoid a flat line in back—no shingled styles. You will want to keep fullness at the lower part of your head and to use a soft puff above the forehead. Be cautious about trying bangs, or any style that carries the hair down over the forehead.

• PROMINENT NOSE.   Keep hair interest back and away from the nose to provide balance. Use soft waves above the forehead to break a profile line that emphasizes the nose. Avoid a center part.

• HIGH FOREHEAD.   Hide it behind soft bangs or hair that dips down over the brow.

• LOW FOREHEAD.   Add height by fluffing hair up and back from hairline.

• GLASSES.   Don't crowd your face with low bangs or hair brought forward on temples or cheeks.

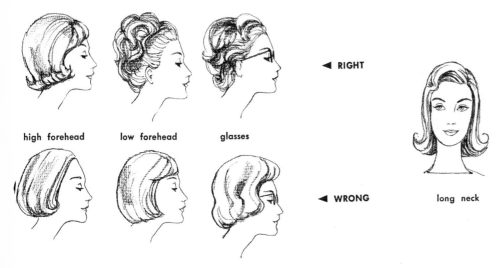

high forehead   low forehead   glasses   ◄ RIGHT   long neck

◄ WRONG

• HEIGHT PROBLEMS.   Check your coiffure in a full-length mirror before giving it your O.K. If you're tiny, steer clear of bushy styles or long hairdos and select fairly close-cropped coifs. Tall girls should avoid high top curls and cap cuts that make their heads seem too skimpy for their tall frames.

• FIGURE PROBLEMS.   *Narrow shoulders and big hips* call for a neither too wide nor too narrow hair style. Either extreme is unbecoming. *Large head, small body?* Choose a neat cap cut. *Large bosom?* Keep hair short to medium in length; avoid long bobs.

• NECK TROUBLES.   If your neck is short, keep hair short and curled up, especially in back at the nape of the neck, where you should be able to see at least the curve where the neck joins the shoulder. If your neck is long, keep back hair long enough to cover part of the neck and to fill in below the ears.

Next time you shampoo your hair, have a little fun experimenting with a variety of suds cap coiffures. While your hair is soapy, you can test the effect that will be created by a dip at the temple, a high-rising pouf, hair bulk at different heights along the side of your face, hair swirled forward onto the cheek or swept back behind the ears, and so on. Try the effect of various coiffure lines to see what they do for your features. Concern yourself only with the basic outline of the style, and check the profile and back views to determine what is most flattering.

A SHAPELY COIFFURE NEEDS A GOOD CUT

A good cut is essential for hair to look its best. The most skillful setting can't compensate for a choppy cut. Cutting and thinning your own hair is an art you can't master until you grow eyes in the back of your head. Leave this to a hairdresser. He knows the intricacies of making your particular type and texture of hair look its best.

Even if you're letting your hair grow, it's a good idea to have your hair shaped every so often so that it keeps its good line. Each hair doesn't grow at the same rate, and the best cut can become straggly. Trimming is particularly important before a permanent. All split ends and remnants of an old permanent should be snipped off before a new permanent is given.

LONG MAY IT WAVE

Unless you are blessed with hair that has a natural tendency to curl, you will probably need to give your hair body in some way. Wave set lotions and hair sprays give your set greater longevity, and a permanent is a great boon for locks that tend to go limp.

Many girls have become quite expert at using home permanents. There are many varieties available that can be suited to your hair texture, to the amount of curl desired, and to the time you have available. Whether you give yourself a permanent or go to a beauty salon, insist on a test curl first to be sure you will have no unpleasant reactions to the chemicals. Even if you have used the same brand before, take time for test curls. Your body changes continually, and you may have developed an allergy to some of the chemicals or, although extreme caution is taken by the manufacturers to keep each batch of wave lotion the same, some slight variance might affect you. Your hair is such an important beauty asset that you don't want to risk unhappy results.

The main purpose of a permanent is to give the hair body. Some women make the mistake of thinking that a tight frizzy permanent will last longer. It never will look right, for by the time the kinkiness has worn off, the hair will be too long. Most hair still needs regular setting even with a permanent. A permanent merely makes the hair more curlable, but it is the set that creates the curl.

THE SMART SET

Save up your pennies so that every now and then you can treat yourself to a good-for-the-soul professional hairstyling. Just the luxury of being prettied and pampered is enough to make any girl's spirits soar, but you can also improve your own setting technique if you watch carefully and ask pertinent questions. Any hair stylist is willing to help you learn how to maintain the lovely coiffure he has created for you, so don't be afraid to ask for setting directions. Note particularly how and where your hairdresser places curls and the direction he pulls the hair before starting to wind it.

Incidentally, when you go to a beauty salon, be punctual. Time is money to a beautician, and it isn't fair to keep him waiting. If you know you will be delayed, call the salon and let them know. They will appreciate your courtesy.

It's helpful to have some idea—but a flexible one—of the type of coiffure you would like. You already know your face shape and what styles are generally most flattering.

Some girls bring pictures of the hairdos they like and ask their hairdresser if he can adapt one to their particular features. As a busy career girl, you will probably want a style that is easy to care for and, unless you can afford to have your hair set professionally every week, you should be sure that your stylist understands that you don't want anything too complicated.

When he sets your hair, he will probably give you a box of clips or rollers so that you can hand them to him one at a time as he works. Before you go under the dryer, select a magazine to read. (You will, of course, leave the magazine in the drying room when your hair is dry.) Usually a regulator for the heat of the dryer is attached to a rubber cord that hangs down beside or behind your chair. Keep the heat set high as long as possible and stay under the dryer until an attendant comes for you. The person who bobs up every few minutes to ask if her hair isn't dry yet is a nuisance. If you have been given a robe to wear, you will change back into your own outfit before your hair is taken down.

When your hair is being combed out, avoid unnecessary conversation so that your stylist can concentrate. Notice the tricks he uses in arranging your hair. First he brushes your hair back hard. This softens the curls and puts snap in your waves. Then he carefully arranges the curls where he wants them so that your coiffure takes on line and form. Does he use light, lifting strokes when he combs your hair, perhaps taking just a few strands at a time? Does he back-comb or tease your hair to give it more body? When he arranges a wave, does he clip it in place and then give it a wisp of hair spray to encourage it to stay put? Does each curl or wave section flow harmoniously into the allover pattern? Watch his techniques so that you can duplicate his results at home.

When it comes to tipping, your stylist should receive from 15 to 20 percent of your total bill and a smaller tip should go to the person who washed your hair and to the maid who helped you with your robe. Slip the tip into a uniform pocket if they are busy with other clients. When the stylist is the owner of the shop, you are not expected to tip him, although some people do.

THE AT-HOME SET

With a little experimentation—and a few tricks in her curler bag—any girl should be able to turn out near-professional results at home.

Rolling your own · Rollers are helpful in setting high, loose curls or deep, soft waves. They are particularly desirable for removing the kinkiness from hair that is too curly. Select the size roller for the size curl you want: the thicker the roller, the looser the curl. Probably you will need two or three sizes. Plan your setting pattern beforehand—where to use little ones (short ends, sides), and where to use big ones (top waves, long ends). Section off a strand, no more than a half-inch thick and not quite as wide as the roller. Before you start rolling, stretch the hair straight up and a little back from the way you want the curl to go. The trick is to get all the ends folded neatly around the roller, so that there will be no bent or unset ends. If you have difficulty, cover the ends with an end paper or piece of tissue. Curls should be rolled evenly, in straight lines.

Pin curls · Pin curls don't provide as much lift and height as rollers, but with them you can create soft shadow waves as well as curls. To make a pin curl, block off a small lock of hair—no more than one inch square. Comb hair straight out or up, as the case may be, and place your forefinger directly in front of the strand, close to the scalp. (This curl will turn toward your face; for curls that turn away from your face, place your finger behind the strand.) Then wind the lock of hair around your finger smoothly and firmly. Slip the curl off your finger, carefully tucking in the ends so that there will be no frizzy tips. Secure the curl with a curl clip.

Curling cues • Try these ideas for a successful set.

• The placement of your finished pin curl and the direction in which it is wound determine the way your hair will go when it is combed out. For instance, if you want your hair to have a lift at the sides, pull hair high before you start to wind and place the finished curl higher than its roots.

• Wind curls toward your face if you want your hair to come toward your cheeks. Wind curls toward the back of your head if you want a swept-back look.

• To make a wave, arrange your pin curls in neat, even rows and alternate the direction in which the curls of each row are wound (one row all wound forward, the next row backward, and so on).

• Two or more rows of pin curls will produce a softer, fluffier effect than one row.

• When using rollers, crown hair will flow smoothly into back hair with no high-low dividing line if, for the last curls across the crown, the hair is pulled back at a 45 degree angle instead of straight up before winding.

116

Straight bangs can be given a soft lift by pinning a rolled facial tissue at your hairline and combing wet bangs over and under the tissue. Then pin the hair to the underside of the tissue to create a roll. This gives softer, fluffier bangs and avoids the childish straight-across Dutch boy look.

Your set will last longer if you wet your hair first and use either a wave set, stale beer, or a hair spray as you set curls. Then, after you comb out and arrange your finished coiffure, preserve its prettiness by spraying it lightly. For very dry hair, use a hairdressing instead.

If you put your hair up at bedtime, cover your curls with a kerchief or a frilly night cap to keep them in place while you sleep. Looks prettier, too.

If you were just too sleepy to set your hair the night before, try this in the morning. Whip your hair up in rollers and spray thoroughly with hair spray. In about twenty minutes it should be dry and presentable. Good idea, too, for a quick pickup when you come home after work and have an early date.

117

• Try a couple of tricks for emergencies. Sometimes teasing will give a bouffant coiffure the extra lift it needs. To do this, take a good-sized section of hair and use gentle, light strokes to comb it, layer by layer, back from the tips toward the scalp. Brush it gently into place. This draws a number of hairs out of the tangle and layers them across the top to produce a smooth look. Another trick for adding height is the lift-and-spray technique. First fluff hair as high as you want it. Then spray lightly and, before the spray dries, pick up small strands of hair with a rattail comb or pencil and lift again.

HAIR COLORING

Every brunette occasionally gets a yen to be a blonde and every blonde probably wonders how she would look as a brunette or redhead. Time was when any girl who dyed her hair was immediately marked as a fallen woman. Gradually the stigma is disappearing, but there is still plenty of disapproval—mostly from men (and from girls who don't). Anything that is obviously artificial is usually looked on with distaste.

Few girls realize what they are getting into in the way of expense and time when they decide to change hair color. Dyeing should be done by a professional. The process is expensive, takes a great deal of time, and once you've started you have to keep at it. Giveaway roots of another color just won't do.

If you want to liven up your hair color, why not experiment with improving your natural color? Blondes who want a bit of brightening will find that Grandma's suggestion of a lemon juice rinse still is a valid beautifier. Color shampoos are easy to use and will add a little temporary color; suds should be left on for at least five minutes. Semi-permanent rinses add a bit more color. Most varieties can be washed out with your next shampoo; others last through several shampoos. These products will add sparkle and color highlights that dramatize your natural color. They will not produce a drastic change of color. If your hair lacks oil, it's not advisable to use a color rinse too often. Both commercial rinses and lemon juice tend to have a drying effect.

If you are determined to change your hair color, heed the advice of the experts and go to a lighter rather than a darker shade. A darker shade will look artificial and will not flatter your complexion. Occasionally a young girl—even a teen-ager—finds that her hair is turning gray. There's nothing more striking than a young face with lovely white hair but if she is bothered by the change and wants to hide her gray hairs for a while, she should choose a color that is a shade *lighter* than the predominant color.

A note of caution: Girls with dyed hair must be wary of the sun. Too much sun will produce discolored streaks and unattractive color changes. Special hairdressings are available to help protect the color; they should be reapplied frequently when you sunbathe—every hour or so.

 FOLLOW-UP

1 Be on the alert for hairdo ideas that you can try. As you watch TV or look through magazines, study the hairstyles you see. Look closely at girls you meet—particularly those whose hair texture and face shape are similar to yours—to find flattering lines you might adapt.

2 Conduct a hairstyling session for yourself. See how your hair looks with different parts—a center part, various side parts, or a diagonal part. Then experiment with various hairdos. Can you wear your hair pulled back smoothly or do you need a softer, fluffier frame at the top? At the sides? How about bangs? If your hair is long, fold it up to see how you'd look in a short cut. Brush your hair forward at temples and ears. Experiment with many styles and study your face and profile to see which are the most flattering.

3 When you have settled on a flattering hairstyle, play with it a bit to see if your everyday wear-to-work version can perhaps be glamorized for evening wear.

119

For hands to have the lily-white loveliness that poets extol and the unchipped, color-coordinated nails that fashion decrees, frequent attention is required. But this attention is well repaid. A business girl's hands are always on display—as she types, files, operates a machine, or takes dictation. Graceful, impeccably groomed hands are a great asset to personal charm.

A little attention several times a day is the best way to keep your hands smooth and soft. Here are a few ideas to insure loveliness.

❀ Keep hands and nails immaculately clean. If they become stained from carbons and mimeograph inks, use the special cleansers that are designed to tackle these stains gently and efficiently.

❀ Every hand washing can be a beauty treatment if you push cuticle back with your towel as you dry.

❀ Dry your hands thoroughly and apply hand lotion after washing if your skin is rough. Rub it well into your cuticles to prevent hangnails. Many career girls keep a small bottle of lotion in a desk drawer.

❀ Nightly use of a hand cream prevents troubles as well as curing them. Creams are more effective than lotions because the heavy consistency of the cream allows greater concentration of lubricants. While you're at it, rub a little cream on your elbows to keep them soft and attractive.

❀ As a special treatment for chapped skin, slather hand cream on thickly and don an old pair of white gloves. Leave them on overnight. Your hands will be soft and lovely again by morning.

❀ Wearing rubber gloves saves hands during washing and cleaning chores. Fabric-lined types are most comfortable and don't cause hands to perspire. Teach your fingers to be nimble inside gloves. If a surgeon can perform a delicate operation while wearing gloves, any girl should be able to use them when she does her hand laundry—and the dishes.

❀ Cream applied before tackling a dirty job prevents grime from being ground in, makes it easy to wash off.

❀ In nippy weather put your gloves on before you go out the door. Don't risk chapping.

❀ If you smoke, hold the lighted end upward so that smoke won't drift through your fingers and stain them. Cigarette stains can usually be removed with lemon juice.

6

BEAUTY AT YOUR FINGERTIPS

File nails in one direction only—from sides to center, not back and forth. Do not file deeply into corners (leave at least one-sixteenth of an inch at each side) or make extreme points, but keep nails in rounded oval shape. This makes them stronger and gives them a more graceful appearance. ▶

◀ Then soak fingers in warm, soapy water and dry thoroughly, pushing cuticle back gently with the towel when you dry. Dip a cotton-tipped orangewood stick in cuticle remover or cuticle oil and push cuticle back gently—never press hard. Snip off any stubborn hangnails but do not cut the cuticle. Cutting merely encourages the cuticle to grow back thicker and more ragged.

If nails break easily, look to your diet. Foods rich in calcium (milk and milk products) and protein (meat, eggs, fish) help strengthen new nail growth. Many girls find gelatin, with its high protein content, helpful in improving nails—drink a tablespoonful of *unflavored* gelatin dissolved in a glass of fruit juice daily. (Don't be too impatient to see results. Only new growth can benefit, and it takes about four months for nails to grow out from roots to tips.) An incorrect filing method—filing back and forth—can also cause nails to split or peel.

GIVE YOURSELF A PROFESSIONAL MANICURE

You can easily give yourself a manicure that will rival a professional's if you follow the same procedures a manicurist does. This means using a base and a top coat as well as two coats of polish, and allowing sufficient time between coats. A manicurist allows an hour for a manicure alone, plus *plenty* of time for final drying. A good manicure should give you a week's worth of lovely nails—actually a timesaver when compared to the short lifespan of a halfway, slapdash job.

After you have removed all the old polish, follow the steps shown above.

After wiping each nail with remover to clean the surface of any oil or dirt, apply a base coat, brushing it under the nail tip as well as on the nail itself to double the protection. Do your most difficult hand first (right hand for the right-handed, left for the left). ▶

◀ Apply two coats of polish, doing fingers in the same order as with the base coat. There should be just enough enamel on the brush to create an even flow onto the nail and give good coverage. Re-dip the brush for each nail. Let the first coat dry thoroughly before applying the second. As you finish each nail, wipe a hairline of polish from the edge of the tip. This bevels the edge and makes the polish less likely to chip.

When you are finished, wipe the neck of each bottle with remover. This dissolves any hardened bits that might prevent caps from fitting tightly and postpones the inevitable thickening of the enamel. Nail polish that has thickened can be restored by adding a few drops of the *same* manufacturer's solvent. Never use remover for this purpose.

After a manicure it is important to keep those lovely nails from hard labor for at least an hour. Actually, nail polish takes several hours to harden completely so you will want to guard your nails in every way possible. If you *must* work during this time protect your manicure by being extra careful.

WHY MANICURES DON'T LAST

If even a complete manicure—base coat, two coats of polish, and a top coat—doesn't hold up for you, do a little detective work. If nail enamel chips, the trouble may be due to:

• A film of oil or moisture on the nail when the first coat was applied. (Always wipe each nail with polish remover just before applying the base coat—no matter how clean nails seem.)

123

- Polish that is too thin.
- Forced drying (putting nails under cold water, holding them before a fan or heater).

If nail polish peels, it is usually due to:
- A film of oil or moisture on nails.
- Enamel that is too thick.
- Application of a fresh coat before the preceding one has had time to dry properly.

The chief menace to manicures is, of course, rough treatment. Using nails as tools—to dial phone numbers, to pry open bobby pins, to slit letters—is murder for manicures. Make it a habit to use the balls of your fingers rather than your nails whenever possible.

Chipped or ragged polish can cancel out an otherwise well-groomed appearance. When you wear polish, it must be kept in perfect condition. Should a chip suddenly occur, remove polish and do the nail again. When such accidents happen during office hours, a bottle of "neutral" true-red polish and some remover kept in your desk drawer will come to the rescue. Apply a new coat of polish to all nails, and once again your grooming rating rises. The place for such repairs is, of course, the ladies' room—never an office desk. The time—during your break or lunch hour. No boss will appreciate even the most perfect grooming if it is maintained at the expense of vital business time.

CAMOUFLAGE CREATES LOVELIER NAILS

Occasionally a girl has nails so unattractively shaped that she doesn't want to call attention to them with nail polish. She can resort to colorless polish or one of the lighter shades, but if she uses a few tricks in applying her nail enamel an oval illusion can be created. Round or square nails, which give the hand a stubby look, can be disguised if you don't carry polish all the way to the sides of the nails. If nails fan out toward the tips, keep polish away from sides at tips of nails.

Colored nail polish does tend to make fingers look longer. But if nails are very short or bitten off, polish is a lost cause. Medium-length nails are best—short enough for efficiency yet long enough to form a gracefully tapered fingertip. Long claws make bosses and dates shudder.

Dark or bright nail polish colors should be avoided by girls with heavily veined or bony hands. Dark colors attract attention to a problem that is best played down.

No war among the reds, please · Nail polish color must be coordinated with the rest of your outfit. It must match, or at least harmonize with, your lipstick. When your nails are a luscious rose shade and you suddenly decide to wear the dress with the orange trim, take time out to whisk a coat of "Citrus Orange" polish over the offending rose color. An extra coat or two of nail enamel does no harm and actually makes your polish more chip-resistant.

 🌸 FOLLOW-UP

1 Give yourself a complete manicure, following all the steps a professional manicurist would use.

2 Start a hand care campaign today, devoting special attention to cuticle and nail health and to healing any roughened or chapped skin.

3 Are you remembering to lead with your wrists to make hand movements more graceful? Stand in front of a mirror and practice the hand-yourself-the-pencil exercise that was described on page 28. Let all your hand gestures be gentle curving motions.

4 The way in which a person shakes hands is sometimes taken as an indication of his personality. Make a conscious effort whenever you shake hands to use a firm but delicate touch.

How much joy do you find in life? Hopefully, a large amount, for your facial expressions will be taken as an indication of whether or not you're nice to know. Facial expressions and general appearance are the first clues a stranger has to go on in deciding what type of person you are. Some girls have beauty but little or no charm. Good looks won't guarantee social success. They must be accompanied by facial expressions that reveal warmth and friendliness. How emotionally flat we feel when confronted with Miss Deadpan. She may be the most beautiful girl in Oshkosh, and may have a heart of gold down there somewhere, but unless her face shows her kindly disposition her plus qualities are lost.

Attractive facial expressions add a shine that can make a plain girl stand out from the crowd. A lively smile and sparkling eyes will attract attention, and a face that mirrors a warm and kindly personality has a vivacious quality far more desirable than mere beauty.

Let the face you show the world advertise you as someone who is nice to know. Too much reserve detracts from charm. Once you really understand Miss Deadpan, you may become bosom pals; but often you haven't the time or the opportunity to dig beneath a cold exterior. Especially in the brief encounters of busy offices, the ability to project your feelings instantly with features, gestures, and movements is all important.

The girl who wants more expressive features can easily teach them to be more responsive. Just watch a movie or TV play and note how the actors express their feelings. A fascinating study can be made by turning off the sound while watching a TV play. Through actions alone you can often get the gist of the story. A good actor is an astute student of human nature. He knows that a smile comes from the eyes as well as the mouth. Some of the most intense feelings can be vividly portrayed without uttering a word.

Notice the difference between an accomplished actor and a ham—the actor is an artist who uses facial expressions and gestures with restraint. His movements are subtle, not flamboyant. Unnatural theatrical expressions and gestures only smack of affectation. Features should express *sincere* feelings or they make you look false or comic.

7

MORE THAN SKIN DEEP

CULTIVATE A SMILE

An easy, natural smile is the most important facial expression anyone can have. When you have made a happy smile a habit, you have a beauty asset that will keep your face pleasant and youthful no matter how many gray hairs the years bring. Just as good posture is a matter of good habits, a cheerful expression is often merely a habit of remembering to smile. Although we may feel quite pleased with our world, we are sometimes just so naturally lazy that we allow our faces to remain blank. How much prettier is the girl who lets her pleasant feelings light up her face!

Conversely, when your spirits are low, do your best not to advertise it by your expression. This only spreads your gloom, and can often increase it. Unhappy expressions are too costly to tolerate; if they become habits, they can actually distort features.

Teach yourself to smile easily and often. It's amazing how a sincere smile can charm others. No need to tell you that a smile is contagious. Perhaps you can promote an epidemic!

LET YOUR EYES SPARKLE

When you enjoy something, show it. Let your eyes radiate your delight. A sparkle in the eyes is something you can develop if it doesn't already come naturally. Many people forget to use their eyes in expressing themselves, but eyes can dramatize feelings with great effectiveness and subtlety. Let the sparkle in your eyes proclaim you as someone who's fun to be with.

THINK HAPPY

Trying to cultivate a smile has many benefits. Not only does it look pretty, but you are forced to develop a pleasant mood to back it up. Otherwise the smile quickly fades—or gives itself away as being merely mechanical.

The easiest way to promote a good mood is to allow nothing but pleasant, kindly thoughts to lodge in your mind, which, granted, is far from easy. It's all too human to take a certain pleasure from telling someone off mentally or secretly spotting another's flaws to enjoy the feeling of superiority. But what wasteful thoughts they are! Worse yet, they are sure to show—if not in our faces, in our actions. If we criticize, our disapproval can't help but leak through and do damage we did not intend.

The brain—marvel though it is—is unable to give primary attention to more than one thing at a time. Only one thought can be supreme. Fill your mind with a pleasant thought and the disagreeable one must fade out. Actually, you can build yourself a protective armor of happiness if you resolve not to give room to useless gripes, grievances, envy, and similar destructive negative thoughts. The disturbing trifles of life will stay in their proper perspective. The rude salesgirl, the man who shoved the door in your face, the thoughtless remark your boss made—these will be less likely to upset you or disrupt your poise and self-control.

Search for happiness in everything you do. What ideas of your own can you add to these?

❀ Make other people happy. Take a few moments each morning—perhaps while you're churning up enough energy to climb out of bed, or while traveling to school or office—to analyze the day for opportunities to be gracious and kind. Go out of your way to be especially thoughtful today.

❀ Use your senses to the fullest in your search for beauty. Develop the artist's eye for appreciating the beautiful lacy design of leafless tree branches or the pattern of city

129

streets. Notice the lovely fragrance of springtime blossoms, the aroma of morning toast and coffee, the sounds of the city at evening when the workaday noises give way to nighttime glamour. There's beauty of some sort all around you if you can learn to appreciate it.

🌷 Let yourself be inspired by those you admire most. Cultivate their acquaintance, for some of their greatness will surely rub off on you.

🌷 Ruthlessly weed out any strangling self-pity. A certain masochistic pleasure can be derived from picturing ourselves as "poor little me." Sometimes we tend to flaunt our difficulties almost proudly, and often we use them as excuses for inertia and lack of effort. All of us have limitations of some sort. It's how we surmount these limitations that reveals our strength and character.

🌼 Learn to accept others as they are and don't compare yourself with them. Concentrate instead on making the most of what you have.

🌼 Try to bring out the charm in others. Charm is merely your effect on others. If you can help them to feel more clever and important—to bring out the best in themselves—you will be cherished dearly.

🌼 Try to become deeply interested in someone or something. Perhaps it can be a hobby, an organization, charity work at the local orphanage, a little theater group—or you-know-who. Love and enthusiasm are the greatest beautifiers.

🌼 Don't criticize. Don't even let yourself think criticism. Such unpleasant thoughts are merely a waste of the precious energy you wish to devote to beautifying thoughts—to understanding, tolerance, forgiveness, sympathy, friendship, love, and appreciation. Margery Wilson in her wonderfully wise book, *The Woman You Want to Be,** offered this advice to those who wish to develop charm. "Your job is to keep yourself so saturated with beauty that you cannot help expressing it under all conditions, and continue to express it without hope of reward.

"The practice of this . . . is, in the last analysis, the sternest economy of emotion, time, and happiness. When the expression of loveliness fills you as completely as that, the reward is much greater than any return you could dare to plan or wish for."

LISTEN WITH YOUR FACE

Some of the most successful conversationalists are the best listeners. Your face can often say more than words in encouraging a speaker. Let your features and expressions respond to his words and reflect his feelings. Show that you are concentrating on what he is saying by letting your eyes follow his. Blink occasionally to avoid staring. Nod slightly when you agree with a particular point. Even without saying a word, you will seem to speak volumes with great eloquence and understanding.

MIX WITH MODERATION

Any recipe for developing facial vivaciousness should include the caution "don't overdo it." Excessive mugging, screaming enthusiasm, and clownish behavior are childish. Any facial expressions you adopt must be an outgrowth of *your* personality. The too-cute wrinkling of the nose or the affected sidelong glance can be deadly if practiced by the wrong type. In everything you do, you want to express the mature warmth and kindness of a poised, cultivated young woman.

CHECK YOUR UNCONSCIOUS EXPRESSIONS

Many people are unaware that they possess unpleasant facial expressions that give a wrong impression. Check yourself frequently for a day or two to be sure none of these bad habits have crept into your expressions.

132

* Published by J. B. Lippincott Company, Philadelphia, 1942.

- A frown while concentrating—gives the impression you're a sour apple.
- Overuse of eyebrows to add intensity to speech—looks artificial, pulls the face apart.
- Raised eyebrows—can seem superior or haughty.
- Too wide a smile—can look insincere.
- Too mild a smile—can seem halfhearted, lacking in warmth and spirit.
- Biting, pursing, or licking your lips—betrays nervousness.

Become conscious of your face and how much it can say, and use it well to project the pleasant, friendly thoughts that mean so much to your charm.

 FOLLOW-UP

1 For one whole day see how many *sincere* compliments you can pay.

2 Act out the following situations, remembering to use your eyes as well as your mouth to reveal your feelings. Talk aloud and make up the dialogue as you go along.
  a You are greeting a good friend you haven't seen in some time.
  b Someone has just surprised you with an unexpected gift.
  c You are showing a friend a little baby robin that fell from its nest.
  d You are describing something beautiful you have recently seen or heard.

3 Demonstrate different expressions by acting pleased, angry, surprised, pained, sympathetic, humorously aloof, disappointed, impressed to a "Wow!" degree, and so on. Add your own ideas to the list.

PART

THREE: YOUR WARDROBE

Who's the girl with the daisy freshness? You, we hope. In the business world you're not only under obligation to do a good, conscientious piece of work, but part of the bargain is that you look decorative while you're doing it. Companies often spend large sums of money to make their reception rooms and offices into glamorous settings, and they expect their employees to help further the effect by always appearing perfectly and tastefully groomed.

Of what worth are the potted philodendrons, the lavish drapes, and the modern furnishings if the customer is confronted with the sleepyhead who staggers in, featuring curlers and kerchief, or the gumchewer in the grimy blouse with a button missing? The customer won't be taken in by the elegant props. People, not props, produce the services and products he buys. After all, the company *is* the people who work for it. Their appearance reflects strongly on its reputation.

Not only the big brass and the board of directors are concerned about employees making a good impression, but your own particular boss is also mighty interested. Your good grooming is evidence that he knows how to pick a smart girl—that he's a pretty clever fellow. He may be only third assistant to the purchasing agent, but if he can choose an attractive and charming Girl Friday who's efficient as well, his prestige has leaped several notches. Needless to say, when he can take pride in you the benefits are sure to bounce back your way.

8

THE WELL-GROOMED LOOK

THE BOSS IS LOOKING

Priceless as the well-groomed look is, it can be had for the taking. We all know the requirements of good grooming, but most haphazardly-strung-together characters feel that they can occasionally get away with breaking the rules. "Nobody will notice that tiny rip," they tell themselves. Or, "I'm too tired to set my hair; it will just have to do." How they kid themselves! Everybody else is tired and busy, too, when it comes to an unpleasant chore, but smart girls make themselves do it. Men, particularly, have a keen eye for this type of neglect. The boss may not notice whether a girl wears the green suit with the gold scarf or the gold dress with the green scarf, but just let the hem sag or the spaghetti sauce splatter and his eagle eye focuses immediately. He sees you on rainy days and after big date nights, and this day-in–day-out exposure crystallizes into an opinion that is a mighty potent factor at promotion time.

SWEET AND CLEAN

A daily bath or shower is the first line of defense against causing offense. A bath should be a thorough scrub session, yes, but it needn't be put on a par with a chore like hosing down a truck. Treat yourself to some of the bubble bath or bath oil preparations that leave your skin soft and silky and help waft tensions and troubles away with their relaxing fragrance. Give special attention to your elbows and feet, particularly the backs of your heels. A wet pumice stone can be used to rub off any unbecoming calluses. If you wish, dab on cologne or toilet water when you're finished. Apply cologne to the pulse spots—wrists, the inside of the elbows, the back of the knees—for most effectiveness. If you're office-bound, please let this be only a discreet touch of a light fragrance. Anything too strong or too heady is inappropriate.

After a bath, ensure all-day daintiness with a deodorant-antiperspirant. Some girls mistakenly feel that it's enough to *be* clean. Unfortunately, a bath is no safeguard against future perspiration. Worst of all, the person who offends with body odor is usually completely unaware of the problem. Every girl owes it to herself to use a good deodorant *each day* throughout the year. Nervousness, hurry, tension, wearing heavy clothing indoors in winter, or the shock of cold when we go outdoors can cause perspiration troubles. Some girls find a deodorant loses its effectiveness through regular usage and that by alternating brands they have better protection. Perspiration stains on clothing can be avoided by using dress shields, which should, of course, be laundered after each wearing.

If the hair on your legs is dark enough to be seen through your nylons, take a few minutes to defuzz your legs during your bath (that is, if you don't use an electric shaver). Rub the soap cake right on your wet skin to form an easy-gliding surface for your razor. Shaggy-dog legs can spoil the appearance of the prettiest nylons.

Underarms must also be kept hair-free. Not only does underarm hair look unsightly, but it tends to hold perspiration odor. During hot, sleeveless-dress weather, underarms must be shaved every two or three days, sometimes oftener. A daisy-fresh appearance can be shattered by whiskery underarms.

While we're on this subject of cleanliness, let's not forget your teeth. Far too many people brush their teeth when they get up and neglect the toothbrush the rest of the day. Actually, the best time to brush is right after each meal, so that you brush away food particles that create mouth acids and cause cavities. You'll be able to do this if you keep a brush and small-size toothpaste in your desk at work. Brushing your teeth also helps avoid bad breath. Purse-size packages of breath-sweetening tablets are handy for any working girl. When you have a hamburger with onions for lunch, there's no need to let your breath advertise it to the rest of the staff all afternoon.

THOSE CERTAIN DAYS OF THE MONTH

During your menstrual period it is more important than ever to guard your daintiness. Despite the superstitions that are sometimes still whispered around, a daily bath does no harm during menstruation. In fact, it's more necessary than ever. Menstrual flow develops an unpleasant odor when it comes in contact with the air, and most girls also perspire more during this period. Change pads or tampons frequently, pay extra attention to cleanliness, use a deodorant powder on pads, and you can cross off any worries about embarrassing moments or wondering if you are offending anyone.

Some girls notice that a day or two before menstruation they may feel more tense, more tired, perhaps slightly depressed. This is a perfectly normal reaction—as is the fact that your breasts and abdomen seem to swell and become tender at this time. Don't let it get you down. Take your mind off yourself and try to do things you enjoy. A little more rest and a little more exercise will probably help. Incidentally, many girls ask if they can go swimming during their periods, if they should wash their hair, if they can go horseback riding, biking, skiing. The answer to all these questions is yes. By all means keep up the activities you participate in regularly. The one precaution is that you do not allow yourself to become chilled. Avoid swimming in cold water and lying around in a wet suit—not the best practices no matter what the calendar date.

If you are bothered by cramps, here are two exercises that should help alleviate them.

1 Lie flat on your back on the floor. Breathe deeply, expanding your abdomen as much as possible while you breathe in, and contracting it as you exhale.

2 While lying on your back on the floor, bring your knees up close to your chest and hold them there. This stretches the opening of the vagina and promotes relaxation.

CLOTHING CARE

A girl can be wearing a dress that's straight out of *Vogue* and recently bore a three-figure price tag; but if there's hair and dandruff on her shoulders, perspiration stains, or wrinkles, the dress might as well be the $2.98 number from the bargain basement. No outfit can look smart unless it is kept in good condition.

Dresses, separates, suits, coats · Brush them after each wearing before you put them away, and give them a quick check for any spots, rips, or loose buttons. Give special scrutiny to elbows, underarms, neckline, cuffs, and hems. While you're wearing the outfit, you often fail to notice these areas. (Plastic cuff-protectors will help keep long sleeves from becoming soiled while you work.) If a dress needs pressing, keep it at one end of your closet—away from clothes that are ready to wear—until you have a chance to press it. Incidentally, many pressing jobs can be avoided if you hang your clothes in the bathroom while you take your shower or bath and let the hot steam remove the wrinkles. This works especially well with wools and crepes, but you must be careful with rayons because hey may shrink. Never steam moiré, lamé, heavy satin, taffeta, faille, or brocade. Instead, give them a very light pressing on the wrong side, using a cloth that is just slightly moist. Cottons and washable fabrics can often be made quite presentable without ironing by patting the wrinkled areas lightly with a wet washcloth and letting them hang in the open until they are dry.

Whenever possible, give your clothes an airing after each wearing. Hang them inside out and air them outdoors, if you can. If not, hang them before an open window.

When you iron clothes, be on the lookout for any stains you may have missed. Never press over a spot; heat often sets the stain. Keep a little bottle of cleaning fluid and other cleaning essentials on hand. If you can't remove the spot yourself, take the garment to a cleaner as soon as possible. If you know what caused the stain, tell him so that he won't have to experiment needlessly.

141

WHAT YOU SHOULD KNOW ABOUT STAIN REMOVAL

GENERAL KINDS OF STAINS

Greasy
butter
grease
ink, mimeograph
   (only fresh stains)
wax

Nongreasy
alcoholic beverages
antiperspirants
blood (put a few drops of
   ammonia on stain first)
candy
catsup
cocoa
coffee, tea
deodorant
egg
fruit juice (rinse immediately)
ink, writing
mud (first dry and brush)
perfume
scorch
soft drinks (rinse immediately)

Combination
chocolate candy
coffee or tea with cream
gravy
ice cream
mayonnaise
milk

HOW TO REMOVE STAINS

Greasy Stains

WASHABLE FABRIC:
(a) Wash as usual.
(b) Work detergent into stain; rinse in warm water.
(c) Sponge thoroughly with grease solvent; dry.

NONWASHABLE:
(a) Sponge well with grease solvent; dry.
(b) Repeat.

Nongreasy Stains

WASHABLE FABRIC:
(a) Sponge with cool water, or soak in cool water.
(b) Work detergent into stain; rinse.
(c) Use bleach.

NONWASHABLE:
(a) Sponge with cool water.
(b) Work detergent into stain; rinse.

142

In these days of changing hemlines, it's important that you keep your dress length fashionable. If your legs aren't quite show-off caliber, you can probably get away with wearing your hems about an inch below current fashion. Too low a hemline looks dowdy, too high looks childish.

Underwear · One of the most important points about underwear is that it should be kept *under*. It should be completely invisible. No panty wrinkles or garter bumps allowed. At neckline, underarms, or hemline there should be no peekaboo bits of white. Slip and bra straps can be kept under control when you wear wide-necked dresses if you use a dime-store lingerie guard that pins into the shoulder seam. When the dress is on the hanger, the guard can be snapped around the hanger to prevent the dress from slipping off.

It goes without saying that lingerie must be clean and should also be neat. Nobody else may know if you haven't had a chance to mend the lace on the slip you're wearing—but *you* know and can't help feeling a bit sloppy and somewhat ill at ease because of it.

Bras and girdles should fit properly and should be of sufficiently recent vintage that they do a good job. If you wear sheer blouses or dresses, be sure your slip covers your bra and is opaque enough and long enough to avoid telltale shadows. Never wear a black bra or slip with *any* light-colored blouse—it shows through and labels you as a person who is careless about her grooming.

Odds and ends · Drooping or dirty accessories can ruin your appearance. Keep them in good order at all times.

· HATS.   They should be perky and dust-free. Every once in a while, take a good, critical look at your chapeaux. Sometimes a hat gets a little battered and bedraggled without your noticing it. Be sure all trims are crisp and neat. Is the veil perky? If it goes limp, you can give it more stiffness by ironing it between sheets of wax paper. A quick revitalizing trick for veils if you're late some morning is to run the veil over a lighted bulb. It will come out smooth and crisp.

If you have trouble keeping your hats on in windy weather, sew a small comb to the inner band at the front of the hat. Anchor the comb in your hair at the front, put a hat pin in the back, and you're ready for the strongest blow.

· SHOES.   Regular brushing and polishing is essential for a well-groomed look. Keep some shining-up equipment in your desk drawer. A soft cloth saturated with a neutral liquid

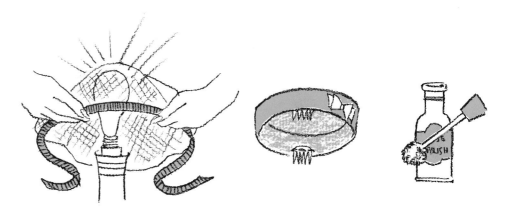

wax is very good for this purpose. Paper towels make a good emergency suede cleaner. If suede becomes scuffed, it can usually be rejuvenated with one of the special suede sprays. In general, watch for run-down heels or tips. A trip to the shoe repair shop as soon as you notice them can save you from having to buy new shoes. For the summertime problem of chafing from perspiration, put talcum in your shoes before putting them on. Air your shoes often and try to alternate pairs.

• SHOE BOOTS.   Wonderful for winter weather, they can save your shoe leather from wear and tear. They, too, need to be checked frequently for run-down heels and tips. They should be kept polished, just like shoes, as they will last longer under adverse conditions if you care for them well. It is possible to keep a pair of shoes at the office for daily wear, or you can carry them in with you each day. There are many smart shoe bags available for this purpose.

• PURSES.   Shapely and unscuffed purses are a fashion must. Leather bags can be given new life with shoe cream polish in a neutral or matching shade. Plastics respond to soap and water. Suede requires brushing (in a circular pattern) with a suede brush. Fabric purses should be dry-cleaned. Occasionally turning bags inside out and brushing the linings removes the messy tobacco shreds, powder, dust, and who-knows-what that accumulates. When not in use, bags should be stuffed with tissue (so that they will retain their shape) and stored carefully to prevent scratches. Don't hang purses by the straps, as this will weaken the handles. To save space, a small bag can be stored in a larger one.

Occasionally take an inventory of the contents of your bag to see if anything can be discarded. Although men seem to have zillions of pockets, they don't appreciate your one lone carryall if it bulges or seems to overflow.

• STOCKINGS. They should fit well without wrinkling or sagging. Seams must be straight and there should, of course, be no runs, holes, or visible mends. Ankle smudges can sometimes be rubbed off with a *soft* eraser. Mud splashes usually cling to skin more than to hose and become almost unnoticeable if the stocking is removed and the leg is washed. Many girls keep an extra pair of nylons in their desks for emergencies.

• ACCESSORIES. Your gloves, scarves, and jewelry should all be clean and neat and fresh. Store them carefully so that they are protected from dust or wrinkling. Every now and then, go over your costume jewelry with a jeweler's rouge cloth or a silver polish cloth to remove tarnish and brighten the pieces up again.

147

MORNING CAN BE BEAUTIFUL

Shortly before bus time, Barbara reluctantly drags herself out of bed, grabs some cold cereal, and downs gulps of hot coffee as she slithers into the first blouse and skirt that seem to match. If time allows, she stuffs some jewelry into her pocket to be donned during her bus ride. Then a mad dash to the bus! By the time Barbara arrives at work she may be fairly presentable, but her nerves are frazzled and her responses to the cheerful "good mornings" of the staff echo a bit hollowly. She realizes, too, that her appearance never has the carefully planned and coordinated look it could have.

When mornings become a hectic gray blur, no girl can look her best. The obvious solution is to get up a half hour earlier so that enough time is allowed for leisurely breakfasting and careful dressing—and, if necessary, for brightening drab spirits. But if this is too painful a prospect, considerable time can be saved by planning the next day's outfit the night before. Laying out jewelry, hat, gloves, and special accent accessories, as well as all inner and outer clothing, makes dressing a speedy matter. It also allows time for experimenting with different accessories so that the same yellow scarf isn't always worn with the same brown dress. Of course, getting up just a little earlier is wise insurance—there's always the possibility that there may be a downpour the day you'd planned to wear your new spring outfit!

AN EMPLOYER SPEAKS OUT

An executive in a large plastics manufacturing concern was asked for his opinions on what composed the well-groomed look for business girls. He was glad to have an opportunity to air his opinions because, as he said, far too many girls don't realize how important grooming is and how disturbing it is to employers to have shoddy-looking personnel around. "We can't go up to a girl and tell her to do something about her hair or to go get a clean dress. We just look for some way to get rid of her as conveniently as possible."

First on the executive's list came the request that clothes be neat and clean. "A sloppy girl gets on my nerves." Next he expounded on the need for tasteful and appropriate clothes. One of his pet peeves was outfits that were too dressy—necklines down to *there*, flashy fabrics, extreme styles, glittery jewelry. Another was provocative costumes—tight sweaters and skirts, form-hugging dresses, and short-short skirts. Almost as annoying were outfits that are too casual for office wear—bulky sports sweaters, flats, sporty school clothes, sunback dresses, black tights—or other inappropriate items such as jangly jewelry or bulging purses. "If a girl dresses like a business woman, she will be treated like one," he said.

"Of course, her hair and makeup should be neat and appropriate, too. No Dragon Lady eyebrows—or fingernails, either. But appropriate hairstyles are especially important," he went on. "Ask them to get rid of those dangling pony tails. They're strictly schoolgirl stuff. Other than that I'm not too fussy about how they wear their hair as long as it's not one of those weird affairs and is clean, neat, and becoming."

"One thing more," he said. "Ask them not to do their prettying up at the desk and not to spend all day at it. I don't like to have to send the St. Bernards to get them out of the ladies' room. And—a last *vital* point—if a girl stands up straight, she can do a lot to help that well-groomed look."

FIRST AID FOR BEAUTY

Every girl has a different idea of what grooming essentials she likes to keep in her desk drawer and carry in her purse cosmetic kit. The lists below are fairly typical and may give you some suggestions.

DESK DRAWER GROOMING NEEDS

Cleansing lotion	Hair spray
Foundation	Tissues
Rouge	Cleaning fluid
Eye makeup	Small clothes brush
Hand lotion	Suede brush
Nail file	Pair of stockings
Nail polish remover	Pair of clean white gloves
True red nail polish	Veil hat
Colorless nail polish (run stopper)	Collapsible rainwear
Toothbrush and paste	Umbrella
Tiny sewing kit	Shoe buffing cloth or shoeshine kit

PURSE GROOMING NEEDS

Comb or brush	Small safety pins (3–4)
Bobby pins	Collapsible rain bonnet
Compact	Package of tissues
Lipstick and brush	Breath sweetener
Nail file	Hat pin

1 Hold an inspection session for your entire wardrobe. Check carefully for any spots, split seams, loose or damaged buttons, weak straps, frayed edges, loose hems, soiled belts, dirty collars or trimming, wrinkles, and so on. Make a determined effort to see that anything wrong is fixed as soon as possible.

2 What about your closet? Can you make it more tidy and efficient by rearranging shelves, adding shoe bags or other space savers, storing some garments elsewhere, if necessary, and trying some of the suggestions in this chapter?

3 Take stock of your purse and your office beauty kit (if you are now employed) to see if there are any additional beauty or grooming aids that you might like to include.

Rich or poor, fat or skinny, tall or short, we are all faced with the same problem—how to choose the clothes that are most flattering. If you are rich and willowy, with the preferred combination of horizontals and verticals, your task is, of course, considerably easier. But many girls who lack these plus qualities possess such a highly developed sense of fashion that they can give a look of chic* and elegance to the simplest outfit.

Exquisite fashion sense is rarely inborn, but it *can* be acquired. Your taste can be sharpened by constant awareness and analysis of what *is* good fashion. Study the fashion magazines, clothing ads, the window displays of better quality shops, and the smartly dressed women you see. Scrutinize them carefully. Exposure to good fashion is an excellent teacher. Try to decide just what makes an ensemble outstanding. Is it the becoming design of the style, the beautiful coordination of color, or the clever use of accessories? Look for new features—a change in sleeve or collar, a jewelry fad, the set of the shoulders, a new shape to hats. The girl who is on the watch for fashion smartness finds many ideas she can apply to her own wardrobe.

9 KNOW YOUR LINES

YOUR FASHION FLAIR

The essence of good taste is simplicity—simplicity with a flair, yes—but always refined, uncluttered simplicity. Tasteful attire is never ostentatious, never overdone, never offensively revealing in cut or fit, always appropriate. Good taste is conservative rather than spectacular, so that you—not your clothes—are the star attraction.

The well-dressed woman considers the following essential:

Flattering lines. Certain styles will dramatize your figure. Develop a clear, unclouded awareness of your good points and your bad points. Then select only those outfits whose lines will do the most for you.

Coordinated look. This depends on beautiful and discreet use of color and on a careful combination of clothing elements for each outfit. Dress, coat, hat, jewelry, and shoes should all be equally casual or equally dressy and should all be in correct proportion to your figure and to each other. They should produce an attractive all-of-a-piece look.

* Chic—no girl has it who can't pronounce it correctly. *Chic* should sound the same as *sheik*. It's no baby rooster.

Cued for the occasion. Clothing must be appropriate—neither too casual nor too dressy. If you are in doubt about an occasion, wear an attractive go-everywhere dress rather than a party style that may seem overdone.

Expressive of her personality. What looks heavenly on one girl may be horrendous on another. Some girls (few) can wear ruffles and frills; some girls (also few) can wear high-style exotic clothes. Discover what is right for you—the type of clothes that express the real YOU, the best YOU—and don't let yourself be hypnotized into buying something that is not your type.

Fashionable timing. If you like a new fashion or new color and find it flattering, choose it at the upsurge of its popularity so that you can ride on its prestige. Be discriminating in your choice, however, and don't let fashion timeliness goad you into selecting something that isn't exactly right. The girl who throws caution to the wind and tackles an extreme or highly sophisticated fashion may find it more dramatic than she wishes. Keep pace with fashion as much as possible, always letting your own personality and physical enhancement be your first considerations.

Good fit. If it is to look smart, a dress must fit smoothly but not tightly, must set properly, and must be the proper length.

Wearing all the essentials. Looking well dressed involves wearing a hat and gloves for business and for city affairs, wearing stockings year round, wearing a well-fitting bra, and wearing a girdle under playclothes as well as dresses.

Good taste in fashion depends on equal parts of self-knowledge and self-discipline, with a dash of originality added to make it completely YOU. Improve *your* self-knowledge by learning just which styles do most for you. Perhaps you will receive inspiration here for the original touches that give your fashions individuality. Combine this with unwavering self-control when you shop, and you will find your fashion sense blossoming into exquisite personal chic.

THE SLIM AND SHAPELY LOOK

The ideal American girl look is a slim one—slim but shapely, preferably with bust and hips measuring the same and the waist ten inches smaller. In choosing clothing, you should try to maintain—or create—this balance. An imperfect figure can be given an illusion of balance if clothing lines and colors that diminish body flaws are worn. A hippy figure, for example, will seem slimmer in the hips if you broaden the shoulder line and call attention to the upper part of the body so that the eye will be drawn away from the lower portions.

The average girl finds flattery in styles that make her look taller and, therefore, more slender. She should avoid lines that cut her height and add to her girth. All but the very tall and the very very thin will find vertical lines most attractive.

FOOL THE EYE

Camouflage in clothing is, as with cosmetics, a matter of attracting the eye to the best features and distracting the eye from any figure imperfections. Here are some of the tricks that can create desirable illusions:

• The eye will always be led along a line. In clothing, a line can be formed by a row of buttons down the front of a dress, rows of tucking, a band of colored trim, the bottom of a jacket, a neckline, the yoke of a blouse, a belt, a seam, fancy stitching, pockets, pleats, gathers, stripes or other patterns in the material, a necklace, or the angle of a hat. A line can be curved or straight. A line must never emphasize a figure fault; it must draw the eye away. The girl with a full bust, for instance, must not choose a blouse with a band of bright color across the yoke or with pocket trim. The stocky girl should avoid shortening horizontal lines such as those formed by big hip pockets, a wide or contrasting belt, or a large brimmed hat.

• The eye will be attracted by the lightest or brightest color in a costume. A white collar or a bright jewelry accent will call attention to the face. A light skirt teamed with a dark blouse will draw the eye to the lower part of the body. For double-barrelled emphasis, use a lighter or brighter color to intensify a flattering line. The heavy-set girl who wears a black button-front dress will obtain a more slenderizing effect from white buttons than from dark ones.

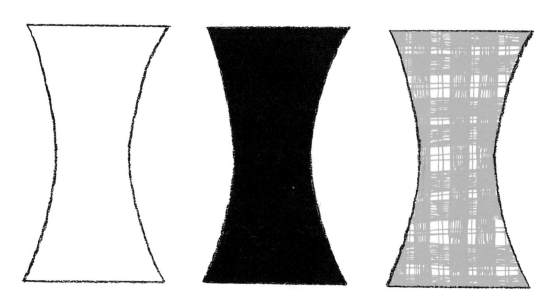

• Light or bright colors enlarge; dark colors diminish size. This is the reason a heavy woman appears slimmer in a navy dress than in a bright red dress. It is the reason a dark shoe makes the foot seem smaller than a white shoe does.

• By extending certain lines, balance can be given to a figure that is not in perfect proportion. If hips are too wide, puffy or cap sleeves will make shoulders seem broader and will have a correspondingly narrowing effect on the hips.

• The type of fabric can affect the illusion of size. A heavy-textured fabric such as a bulky tweed or a knit seems to increase size; so do shiny fabrics such as satin and glossy silks. A smooth-textured fabric is more slenderizing. A stout person will look more slender in a dull-finished fabric.

• The fabric design can affect size. Large prints or widely spaced prints, big plaids, and tablecloth checks are more enlarging than small overall prints, plaids, or checks. A stout person would do better to choose a tiny subdued print rather than a large splashy flower print. A petite girl will also look better in a small print, even though she has no need to create the illusion of slimness, because a large print may be too overwhelming.

156

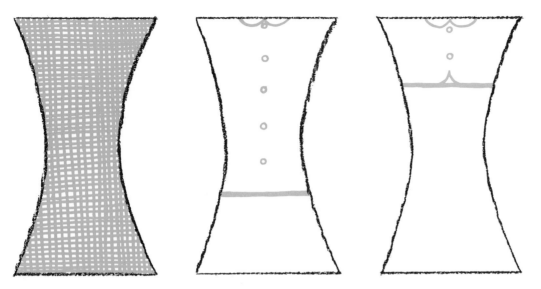

• The longer the distance between a height-bisecting horizontal line and your toes, the greater the illusion of height. A longer suit jacket will cut height more than a short jacket or bolero. A high empire line gives an effect of even greater height to a figure. The short girl will, therefore, prefer the short jacket or empire line, leaving long jackets and tunic styles to her taller sisters.

NOTES ON NECKLINES

A neckline should be chosen to flatter your face as well as your figure. If your face is not the "ideal" oval shape, the general rule is to avoid a neckline that repeats the shape of your face. A round face should avoid a round neckline, a square face should avoid a square neckline, and so on. Often a neckline that is not the most desirable shape can be changed to a flattering line by the addition of jewelry, a scarf, or a collar. A high jewel neckline is not usually the best choice for a round face, but if it is teamed with a long rope necklace, the effect can be quite pleasing.

157

Square face. A good-sized pin at the center of a collar will sometimes make the face appear more oval. Choose a V-shaped neckline, or a round one. If you can't avoid a square neckline, round it out with the addition of a necklace or scarf.

Long face. Bateau or turtle necklines, peter pan collars, mandarin collars, and jewel necklines will all give desirable fullness. V- or U-shaped necklines will make a long face—and long neck—look longer. Such a neckline can often be filled in with a multistrand necklace. Long rope necklaces should be avoided because of their lengthening effect.

Round face. Instead of high necklines or round necklines, choose V-shapes and scoop styles. Pointed collars are better than rounded types; narrow lapels are better than wide coachman styles.

Short neck. Most attractive are the deeper cut U's and V's and the scoop necklines that allow the full length of the neck to show. Be sure that the neckline sits low in the back of the neck as well as in front. Necklaces should always be fairly long.

158

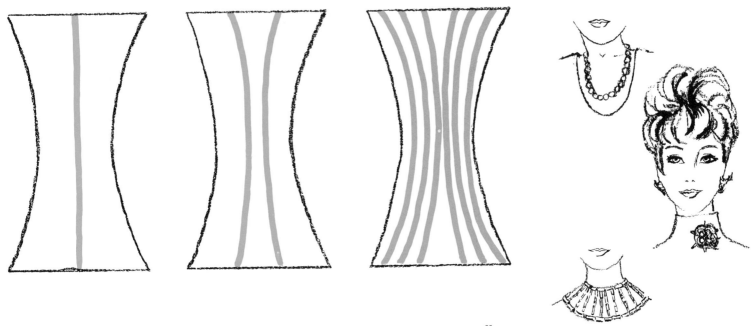

Long neck. Keep necklines high and look for stand-up collar styles. Scarves are excellent for this type neck. Chokers and large, important-looking pins at the collar are flattering touches.

Bony shoulders. Steer clear of open, revealing necklines. Décolleté evening styles can be made more attractive if they are filled in with filmy stoles or bib necklaces.

WHICH LINES FOR YOU?

The vertical line · A single vertical line is very slenderizing. It adds to height and whittles width, whether. it is created by seaming, buttons, color or trim—a flattering line for all but the very tall and very thin.

   Not all vertical lines are slenderizing. Compare the shapes shown above and note how much slimmer the shape with the single line looks. Multiple pleats and multiple vertical stripes, especially broad, vivid stripes can make a figure look heavier.

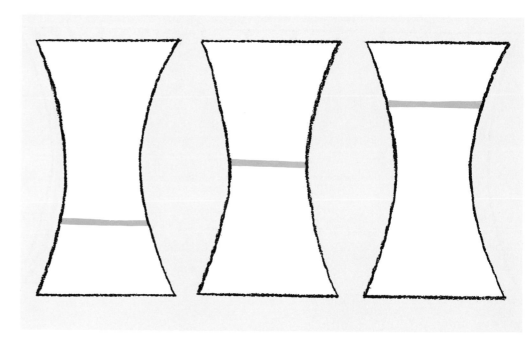

The horizontal line · A horizontal line, whether achieved by the lines of a jacket, by a seam, or by color, affects the illusion of height. A long suit jacket or overblouse shortens the figure considerably by keeping the horizontal line low.

A waist-length jacket, a distinctive belt, or other line cutting the figure at the waist has less of a shortening effect. A high horizontal line, made by an empire line, a bolero jacket, or yoke trimming makes the figure look taller. Basically, the larger the unbroken area on the bottom half of the figure, the taller the figure will look.

The sheath · A sheath dress is sophisticated and adds height, but is the hardest to wear of these three styles. It demands a perfect figure because of its stark outlines. Every so often, fashion imposes a Year of the Sheath, a lean year for all but lean females. Fuller figures should then look for peg-top skirts and gathers to give a little more ease to the silhouette. Narrow, straight skirts are not flattering to heavy or hippy figures; choose one with just a bit of fullness.

The gentle flare · This easy silhouette is more feminine because of its soft, gently rounded lines. It is generally flattering to most figures. While it does not add as much height as the sheath style, its lines are subdued enough so that it still maintains a vertical look that does not diminish height.

The full flare · Notice the shortening effect of this silhouette. Its soft flaring lines are excellent for the tall or very thin figure. A short or round figure will look better in a more subdued flare.

161

SPECIFICS FOR YOUR FIGURE TYPE

Short (under 5'4")? - - - - Please wear

• Clothes and accessories that are in perfect proportion to your petite size.

• Vertical lines that are not cut by belts and trim. Belts should be narrow and preferably of the same fabric or at least of the same color as the rest of the outfit. The fitted, unbelted princess line and empire line are good for you.

• Skirts that are straight or gently flared. Too wide a flare is overpowering.

• One-color outfits.

• Waist-length jackets, boleros, short suit jackets.

• Short toppers, full-length coats (preferably fitted or boxy).

• Dainty accessories and shoes, gay small-brimmed hats that are scaled to your tiny size.

• Small collars and cuffs.

• Eye-catching details at neckline and shoulder area to draw interest to the upper part of your figure.

162

• Smallish prints and fabric designs.

Don't wear

- Anything that is not small-scaled, that cuts your height, or appears to drag you down.
- Outfits with definite horizontal lines—bands of contrasting color, yokes, contrasting belts.
- Long suit jackets, tunic styles.
- Three-quarter coats, very flared coats.
- Big skirt pockets, overly flared skirts, tiered skirts.
- Large collars, big sleeves.
- Wide belts and those with large buckles or heavy trim.
- Large purses, chunky jewelry, bib necklaces, big rings.
- Large bulky hats and wide-brimmed styles that produce a toadstool effect.
- Shoes with wide straps, wedge heels, or heavy design. Heels that are too high may be too much of a good thing; medium-high heels prevent a walking-on-stilts look.

Tall (5'9" and over)? - - - - Please wear

- Horizontal lines—yoke treatments, wide belts, inserts of contrasting color, dropped shoulder lines. Especially good are outfits with low horizontal lines—long jackets, large skirt pockets, tiered skirts or those with horizontal trim, and tunic effects.
- Separates of different colors.
- Boxy jackets with slim skirts to break the line.
- Flared skirts.
- Belted toppers, especially three-quarter length ones, flaring coats.
- Fairly short hems.
- Large purses, good-sized jewelry and accessories.
- Large flamboyant collars, big cuffs, interesting sleeves.
- Shoes with medium heels.
- Hats with low crowns and wide brims.

• Bold prints and plaids.

Don't wear

• Prominent vertical lines such as narrow sheath styles or dresses with a beltless waistline.

• Waistlines too short; hemlines too short or too long.

• Deep V necklines.

• Little-girl styles—you can carry the more sophisticated fashions.

• Severely man-tailored styles.

• Too many accessories—simplicity is striking for you.

• Fussy details and trimmings that are too cute.

• Either very high heels or flats.

• Peaked hats or high crowned styles.

• Vertically striped fabrics.

Full-figured? - - - - Please wear

- A good foundation, preferably an all-in-one.

- Vertical or diagonal slenderizing lines. Especially flattering is a vertical line that cuts you in a one-third, two-thirds ratio.

- Skirts that are not too straight. Gores or fullness at the side front will produce a more graceful effect. Modified peg-top styles are also good.

- Full-length coats that fit loosely, perhaps with modified back fullness.

- Hems an inch or so longer than current style.

- V or U necklines, collarless or with small lapels.

- Simple accessories. Long necklaces that keep a V-line.

- Self-belts or color-matching belts that are not too wide.

- Medium heels; high heels *only* if legs are slender.

- Pretty, colorful hats with an upward tilt or with medium brims.

- Dark or subdued colors in shadowy patterns.

166

Don't wear

- Horizontal lines in styling or fabric.
- Color contrasts that cut height. No two-tone suits or ensembles. Better yet, no suits.
- Clothes that fit too tightly.
- Straight skirts or very full skirts.
- Bateau or round necklines or any high-collar styles.
- Belted coats or short flared jackets.
- Too much jewelry; one important piece is best.
- Novelty belts, large buckles, wide belts.
- Ornate shoes.
- Hats that are too small.
- Sleeveless, cap, or tight-sleeve styles unless arms are slender.
- Fabrics that cling to your figure (knits, jersey, chiffon), transparent fabrics, or stiff or bulky materials.

167

Too thin? - - - - Please wear

- Lines that are softly bloused or flaring.
- Skirts that are either gathered or pleated all around. Wide, flaring skirts—if legs are not too thin.
- Suits that have a break in line, either a boxy jacket or a belted blousey style.
- Blouses and jackets with horizontal lines (stripes, yoke treatments, pockets, trims).
- Loose-fitting blouses that have tucking, gathers, or ruffled fronts.
- Coats that have fullness, or fitted styles with flared skirts.
- Wide contrasting belts to show off your slender waist.
- High necklines, turtlenecks, interesting collars, bow ties.
- Bracelets, wrist-length or longer gloves, multistrand necklaces, scarves.
- Light-colored stockings, preferably seamless.
- Delicate shoes.

- Bright and light colors; prints are better than plain fabrics.
- Bulky fabrics (tweed, corduroy, loop knits or bulky knits), crisp fabrics (faille, starched cottons, taffeta), and shiny fabrics.

Don't wear
- Vertical lines or stripes.
- Severe hair styles or angular hats; you want soft, feminine curving lines.
- Fitted styles that require more curves than you have to offer.
- V-necks, scoop necks, or off-the-shoulder styles.
- Severe styles or mannish outfits.
- Overly large earrings if face is delicately boned.
- Sleeveless styles or shortie gloves if arms are extremely thin.
- Clinging fabrics, tight sweaters.

CAMOUFLAGING FIGURE FLAWS

Narrow shoulders • Look for horizontal attraction at the shoulders—yokes, wide necklines, wide lapels, cap sleeves, puffed sleeves, wide collars, cape treatments, and short sleeves with big cuffs. Avoid halters, raglan sleeves, and sloping shoulder lines. Consider hats with brims to give more balanced proportions.

Wide shoulders • Select styles with vertical trim at the center front of the bodice and avoid all shoulder emphasis. Look for unmounted sleeves, raglan sleeves, sleeves without shoulder fullness, halter styles, V-necklines, narrow lapels. If shoulders happen to be padded, experiment with removing the padding.

Full bust · Play down a large bust by keeping the area from shoulder to waist as simple as possible and drawing attention to your face (interesting hairdos, hats) and to your skirt. You can do this by combining dark tops with light or patterned skirts and choosing a dull-finish fabric for blouses and bodices. Pass up transparent fabrics or clinging materials (sweaters, jerseys, knits). Bodices should not be tight. Look for vertical lines at the center front of the bodice, and for V or scoop necklines. Please do not wear bows or flowers or large pins low on the bosom. Slightly flaring skirts with pockets or other details will help balance your silhouette. Boxy jackets and coats are flattering for this kind of figure.

Flat chest · Choose clothes that have bodice fullness of their own and avoid any that fit tightly through the bust. Look for yoke treatments, bib effects, pockets, full armholes, gathers, rows of ruffles, tucking, neckline bows, empire styles. Crisp fabrics will provide shape; clinging fabrics only emphasize your problem. Select slips with gathers at the bust. Keep accessory accents near your face or high on your shoulder. To help clothes gain a better line, consider a conservatively padded bra. After all, it is no more deceptive to provide a little more curve where Nature fell short than it is to girdle in bulges where figures are too generous.

Full stomach · Wear clothes that have some sort of fullness at the stomach area—skirts with front gathers, covering jackets, peplums, tunics. Rather than figure-revealing silhouettes, choose clothes that are slightly bloused above the waist and have easy skirts. Draw attention away from the waistline by using high accessory accents, lapels, and interesting necklines. Needless to say, a good girdle is the underlying factor here.

Large hips · Aim for styles that have simple skirts and keep the accent high. Anything that broadens your shoulder line will make your hips seem in better proportion. Look for attractive blouses, interesting shoulder treatments, accents near your face. Try skirts that are darker than blouses and that have some flare. Certain tunic and long-jacket styles can be flattering.

Heavy legs · Choose eased skirts rather than straight skirts. Look for fabrics that have no shine. Slightly darker shades of hosiery will be most flattering. Try wearing skirts just an inch or so longer than current fashion and stick to long shorts and slacks that are not too tapered. Bathing suits with skirts are best.

Thin legs · Straight or slightly flared skirts are usually more attractive than billowing styles. Slightly lighter shades of seamless hosiery give the illusion of fullness. Stick to shoes that are light in character.

Large feet · Keep shoes simple without too much ornamentation. Horizontal details in styling will shorten a long foot. Vertical or diagonal stitching and trim will flatter a wide foot. In order to keep feet as inconspicuous as possible, stick to dark basic colors, choosing dull finishes such as calf or suede rather than patent leather.

 FOLLOW-UP

1 Examine your wardrobe, keeping in mind what you have learned about flattering lines for your figure. If any outfits possess undesirable lines, perhaps they can be altered in some way. If this is not practical, experiment with jewelry, separate collars, scarves or other accessories to see if the unsuitable lines can be counteracted or hidden.

2 Go to a place that is frequented by the most smartly dressed women (an expensive store, a popular restaurant, a theater, and so on). Observe the women you see there and try to decide what makes them so attractive.

3 Study fashion advertisements and articles to see which versions of the new styles contain the lines you need.

A flair for color—a look of beautiful coordination—does more than money for your appearance. Chalk it up as the surest way to catch the eye of a man—and as foolproof allure that evokes compliments from all sides.

You've already learned to be an expert in using colors to create optical illusions that make your figure more perfect. Now learn how to combine colors and to select shades that will do most for your beauty: your eyes, skin, and hair. The ability to use color with flair is worth a goodly stack of dollars in the clothing budget. Color, a no-cost item in itself, can, when cleverly used, give a priceless look of chic to an inexpensive outfit.

10

USE COLOR WITH FLAIR

LEARN TO SEE COLOR

The prerequisite for using color dramatically is developing a good eye for color. To put color to work for you, you must know it well. The girl whose color schemes win acclaim has learned to see a color for what it is—to see the various nuances of shading a particular hue can have. To her, blue is no longer just blue. She carefully notes that it is a teal blue with tones of green, a periwinkle blue with tones of violet, or slate blue or sky blue or turquoise. When you have learned to *see* color, you are able to select the precise shade that is most becoming and can combine colors with skill and artistry.

WHICH COLORS FOR YOU?

Your skin · Your skin and facial coloring are the most important considerations in choosing attractive wardrobe colors. The basic rule is to select colors that repeat the most desirable undertones of your skin and to avoid colors that repeat any undesirable undertones. For example, a girl with golden or olive coloring will usually look her best in shades that have a yellow cast to them (coral and orange-reds, yellow-greens, browns, greenish-blues).

Pink-and-white complexions usually look best in shades that have a bit of red to them, and in general are flattered by colors that have blue undertones rather than yellow (pink rather than orange, and blue-green rather than yellow-green).

If skin coloring is pale, the pastels and grayed-down shades (slate blue, forest green, dusty rose) will be more flattering than the vivid shades (royal blue, kelly green, red). Intense shades tend to drain color from the face. While this makes them a poor choice for **175**

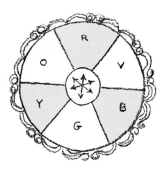

sallow skins, it does make them quite desirable for girls with florid complexions. Beige, chartreuse, and mauve are other shades that can be unkind to a pale complexion. If skin is blemished or there are dark circles beneath the eyes or lines in the face, violet and purplish grays near the face should be avoided. These shades repeat the colors of natural lines and shadows and, therefore, emphasize them all the more.

As you can see, healthy vibrant skin is a great asset. If your skin is clear and has no unattractive tints, almost any color can be worn successfully.

Your eyes · The color of your eyes will usually be enhanced if you wear a shade that matches, or is slightly darker than, your eye coloring. If your eyes are quite pale, experiment with wearing a softer shade of your eye color near the face and a more intense shade farther away, so that your eyes will not be overpowered.

· BLUE EYES (ALSO GRAY-BLUE, GREENISH-BLUE). Wear the same color, if possible, or one that accents the most desirable tones of your eye coloring. Since blue-green eyes tend to pick up green or blue in apparel, you can play up whichever tone is most flattering to you by your choice of clothing.

· GREEN EYES. Wearing green, particularly dark shades, will deepen and dramatize green eyes. If they have a slightly bluish cast, this can be played up by wearing brown or blue-green colors. Grays are good for contrast; and reds, particularly yellow-reds, will emphasize your eyes.

· BROWN EYES. Accent your eyes by wearing orange tones, perhaps those that pick up any golden glints in your eyes. Beige with brown touches should be flattering. Blue and blue-green will intensify eye coloring.

· HAZEL EYES. Since most hazel eyes contain several colors, it is usually advisable to highlight the strongest color. Green, brown, blue, coral, and gold should all be flattering.

Your hair · To flatter your hair, you can choose complementary colors, those that fall opposite on a color wheel. These will intensify your hair color. Or you can select harmonizing shades. When using a harmonizing shade, however, you will want to avoid too vivid a hue, which might steal the show. Golden blonde locks, for instance, look lovely with pale yellow or soft gold; but team them up with vivid buttercup yellow and they seem washed out.

- BLONDE. Emphasize its beauty with blues, greens, and turquoise. Yellow in a paler shade is an excellent backdrop. Also good are navy, rust, browns, black. If your hair color is drab, wear grayed tones and pastels to brighten the hair by contrast.

- BRUNETTE. If your hair has gold or red highlights, you can play them up by repeating this color in clothing. Blues, greens, reds, yellows should all be flattering. If your hair color is a rather drab brown, do not use a richer brown close to the face; use it in a skirt or some other area at a distance from the hair.

- REDHEAD. Greens are wonderful for you—dark greens, light greens, blue-greens, yellow-greens (olives); also peach and yellow. Dark chocolate browns and black should be excellent for basics. Avoid blue-red tones.

COLOR AND YOUR PERSONALITY

Color can have a strong psychological effect on us. Red and yellow are warm, cheerful colors. They are exciting, inspiring, and make us feel more energetic—happy colors to wear on a drab, rainy day. The blues, greens, and violets are restful colors. They are more calm, more cool-looking—good psychology for busy, hectic days. Black is considered dramatic, navy blue genteel and ladylike, purple regal, and so on. But the effect a color has on *you* is most important.

Above all, the colors you wear should feel *right*. They should make you happy, let you feel at ease, be an outer expression of your inner feelings. Bright red may disturb some more retiring girls because of its eye-attracting brilliance; others find the much-touted "little black dress" far too drab to be the wardrobe mainstay they want. Perhaps you can't abide one of your recommended colors. Then skip it for now, but try to make a study of this color. Perhaps in time you will find an off-shade of it that will appeal to you.

When a favorite color isn't flattering, you needn't forsake it entirely. Save it for small accents—perhaps a scarf looped in your belt, a purse, or gloves—or use it for skirts so that a more flattering color can be near your face. The girl who loves colorful clothes but realizes bright shades make her look too heavy can compromise on the duller shades of her favorite colors—maroon instead of bright red, forest green instead of kelly green.

Don't be afraid to experiment with color. Possibly, now that you are more experienced with makeup, you will find that colors you had formerly ignored are quite flattering. In summer, when your skin tans and your hair brightens, you may be able to consider more brilliant shades. Widen your color horizon and you'll find a pot full of compliments at the end of your rainbow.

On the job · One day an attractive young girl was trying on a beautiful white topper from a clearance rack in a store. The coats were all reduced to the point where they were marvelous bargains. The white coat was very becoming and she seemed quite pleased with it. Suddenly she unbuttoned the coat hurriedly and put it back on the rack. "I don't know who I think I am to consider that coat," she declared emphatically to her friend. "It's certainly glamorous, but I'd need to have it in the cleaner's every week!" Cleaning bills can quickly erase such a bargain for the girl who commutes by train or bus or who works in the city. An impractical white coat or a light-colored nonwashable garment can soon become a white elephant.

In business almost any tasteful color combination is acceptable. Loud plaids and shock shades are best avoided, but most employers no longer demand the dark dress as an on-the-job uniform. Just the same, it's a good idea to discover whether your boss has any color incompatibilities. Your colors shouldn't conflict with his personality either. You don't want to sashay into the office in your lovely new lavender dress only to find that lavender is his pet aversion. If he's irritated by a color you wear, chances are your day will be far less pleasant.

HOW TO COMBINE COLORS

The trick in combining colors is to play one color against the other so that both will be enhanced. Put a bright kelly green with a brilliant tangerine and you have something fit only for a circus poster. Neither color stands out; the effect is loud and garish. Just change the shades slightly, however. Suppose you put pale green with tawny tan or use shrimp with dark forest green—both colors look much better. Good taste is never loud. Combined colors should whisper compliments, never shout their rivalry.

Your colors will blend handsomely if you:

- Accent dark colors with a light or bright color.
- Accent light colors with a dark color.
- Accent bright colors with a neutral or dark color.

For instance, a dark outfit is dramatized and brightened when it is teamed with a brilliant color (black dress, hot-pink hat). Pair black with navy and the effect is dismal. Basic dark colors (black, brown, and navy) should never be combined or used to accessorize each other. The girl who has brown shoes but not navy ones shouldn't consider buying a navy dress until she can afford suitable accessories.

Bright colors will look more vivid if teamed with a dark color than with neutrals like beige or gray. A red blouse with a black skirt has intense brilliance; switch to a light gray skirt and the red assumes a softer cast—an idea worth trying if you wish to subdue a shade.

If two pastels, such as pale pink and blue, are put together, the effect is weak and rather candy-sweet. Teamed with a dark shade, each would come into its own.

Very striking results can be achieved by using just one color, particularly one of the neutrals. Many a top fashion personality has wowed the feminine population with an all-beige ensemble. Gray is also very sophisticated for a one-color-tone outfit, and sometimes blue can be handled effectively in this manner. With other colors, a more dramatic treatment is to use shades of the color varying from light to dark. The success of this look depends on a keen eye for color, because each shade must have the same undertones to avoid a clash.

The rules that have been given here are general rules. Follow them and your color success is assured. But occasionally they can be broken with stunning results. Every few years some fashion potentate seems to wax enthusiastic about pink with orange—a rule breaker if ever there was one! Bright reds and blues are often teamed in summer wear and bright turquoise with buttercup yellow accents and light blue with avocado are particularly attractive warm-weather combinations. An occasional variance of this sort can be handled successfully by the girl who is thoroughly grounded in fashion lore and who is experienced at judging just how appreciative her personal public will be.

HOW MANY? HOW MUCH?

How many colors should be used in a costume? Three at most, and two are sometimes better than three. A russet-brown suit with a yellow and orange scarf, orange hat and brown accessories would be a smart combination using three colors. Suppose green shoes and a green blouse were added—the smartness of the color combination would be diluted. The result would be more of an autumn garden effect—lovely for gardens but too hodgepodge for fashion chic. Perhaps an even more attractive outfit could be created by using only two of the colors, such as russet and yellow.

In using three colors, the trick is to use one color in large doses, your second color in a moderate amount, and just an accent dash of the third color. As with the russet-orange-yellow combination just mentioned, one color (or shade of a color) must predominate. The dominant color (russet) is used for the large areas; the second color (orange) is kept to accessories (hat and scarf). Another use of the second color might have been orange blouse and gloves and a russet hat brightened by orange and yellow trim. Your third color is usually a single smaller spot, such as a handsome pin, the trimming on a hat, or a handkerchief tucked in a pocket. Often it is merely blended in jewelry or in a print. Balance of this sort gives unity to a costume. If nearly equal amounts of each color are used, there is no uniting color and the effect is choppy.

How many accents of your auxiliary color or colors should be used? Again, the fashion-wise number is three. Three places are usually sufficient for accents, two often better. A navy blue suit teamed with red hat, red earrings, red-and-white necklace, red belt, red purse, white gloves, and red shoes is at least three reds too many. The effect is blotchy. An all-navy costume sparked with red hat, red-and-white necklace, and white gloves would be far more attractive. Your auxiliary color should be used for accent and

WRONG ▶

◀ RIGHT

should not fight for first place. Color touches should emphasize your best features and not confuse your beholders with too many focal points.

Dramatic effects can be created by keeping an entire costume in one hue with the exception of a single use of a second color. In this case, the color accent should be important—a beautiful hat or a striking piece of jewelry or even elbow-length gloves. Too insignificant a spot of color is lost. A small blue pin may not be noticed on a dark dress. Show your good taste and color awareness by repeating this color in a second more prominent accessory (such as a blue hat or belt), so that both items will enhance each other.

When a costume is primarily a print or a plaid, a charming effect can be created by picking out the most becoming color of the print and keying accessories to this. Prints are, of course, combined only with solids. Stripes, plaids, polka dots, checks, tweeds, or other designs are *never* used together.

1 Conduct a color clinic for yourself to see which colors and which color combinations will do most for your particular coloring. You've learned the colors that should be most flattering; now you will want to test them to find the precise shades that are best. Check each color carefully to judge its effect on your skin tone, hair, and eyes.

2 Go over your own wardrobe to see if you have collected any really unflattering colors. Eliminate them—either by having a swap session with your friends (what's poison for you may be perfect for them), or by dyeing them.

A well-coordinated, attractive wardrobe is a boon to any girl's charm. What's better for self-confidence than the assurance that you always have something marvelous to wear—something to give you a look of smartness and competence by day, something spectacular to make a substantial splash for evenings? You're ready for any change of plans, any big fun. And knowing you look your very best brings that priceless elation that allows you to forget clothes and to concentrate completely on being your most charming self.

Such a well-coordinated wardrobe is the result of clever planning and clearheaded shopping. The girl who plans her wardrobe well knows the wisdom of buying a few basic changeabout fashions that can lend themselves to many occasions and thereby save her enough money for the special splurges that make her appearance a standout. She shrewdly shops by color schemes, insists on good fit and practical fabrics. She knows where she should invest her money most heavily and where she can get by with unnoticeable skimping. She's always well dressed because she leans less on dollars and more on sense.

11 PLANNING YOUR WARDROBE

LIFE EXPECTANCY OF A FASHION

The little fashion and how it grew is an interesting study. Basic trends in styling, such as the skirt length, the shoulder line, the figure-fitted look versus the loose cut, come on us rather gradually and stay with us, with slight variations, usually from five to eight years. When the pendulum begins to swing in the opposite direction, fashion-wise women take notice. A new trend of this basic sort will be with us for some time, and wardrobe plans should be geared accordingly. These trends are factors that date a wardrobe—considerations you can't escape.

More changeable fashion features—the meanderings of the waistline, the shape of the sleeve, the flare of the skirt—have a shorter life-span, usually about three years. Pick up your cues when the fashion first shows its refreshing lines. Take a style to heart when it's past its prime and you're stuck with the old dog that can't do new tricks for your wardrobe. This type of fashion is one you can usually ignore if it isn't flattering. When the skirt length changes, yours must, too; but a three-year fashion usually isn't so pervasive that you can't find flattering exceptions.

The other type of fashion is the one-year fad. Here you tread lightly and invest as little as possible. This fad can be a color craze or it can be an extreme version of a three-

1920   1930   1945

year trend. Remember the chemise or sack dress? Sometimes it's a jewelry fad, a hat style, a new shape scarf. These are the fashion touches that can make you look in-the-know. Smart girls buy less expensive versions and play them hard while they are stylish.

WHAT IS A GOOD BUY?

A good buy must meet several qualifications:

�$ It must do something for you. If it doesn't, pass it up—no matter how great a saving it offers. Almost every girl has had in her closet a wrong-type dress or a drab dress that she bought because she couldn't see past the marked-down price—a bargain, perhaps, but a drag on the ego every time she dutifully wore it.

1947   1954   1959

🌼 Any clothing item you purchase must also do something for your wardrobe. The most gorgeous hat might as well belong to someone else if it only goes with one outfit and can only be worn on rare occasions. Ask yourself, "Will this blend with my color scheme? How many things will it go with? Will I get my money's worth out of it?"

🌼 Fashion life should be considered. Before you shatter your paycheck, you want to be sure you're investing in lasting style. This is particularly important with coats and other large purchases. You can afford to indulge in a fad only if you can afford to donate it to a rummage sale in two years or less. Blouses, inexpensive hats, and other relatively low-cost items are best to use for the timely touch because there is less loss when they become outmoded.

❦ Look for good fit. The difference between a so-so $60 suit and a spectacular $60 suit may be merely a matter of fit. Shoulders should be big enough but not sloppy, and there should be enough room through the bodice and back for easy movement. Long sleeves should stop at the break of the wrist and not flop down over the hand. If a skirt is tight, you're in for lap creases and a baggy seat. It's a good idea to try on a straight skirt over a blouse to see that there won't be a ridge where the blouse ends. Is it roomy enough through the thighs? (No garter bumps, please.) The waistline of a dress or fitted jacket should hit your waist exactly all around. The right hemline also makes a big difference.

If you are planning to alter a garment, make sure you're not tackling too big a job. Skirt alterations are usually not too hard, but jacket or bodice alterations are often extremely difficult to do successfully. In any alteration job, it's always easier and safer to take in than to let out. If you plan to let out a seam, check before you buy to see if it is wide enough. You'll want to be sure the seam isn't notched too deeply. Certain fabrics, such as satins, failles, moires, taffetas, and some cottons, hold stitch marks; and any let-out areas will show no matter how much you press them.

❦ Insist on good workmanship. Shoddy seams and unauthorized puckers can spoil the effect of the smartest style. Check to see that the seams are straight and the sleeves and zipper are set in smoothly. Are the points of the collar even? Are the lapels cut correctly and reinforced? Is the waistband of a skirt stitched carefully and backed with a sturdier fabric to keep it from wrinkling? If its fabric is a loose weave, a slim skirt should be lined. Are the buttonholes finished properly? In buying a suit or coat, check also to see that there is enough fullness in the lining. Well-made garments usually have a pleat or extra fullness down the length of the back to allow leeway for easy movement, so that the lining will not be strained. Check, too, that any stripes or linear patterns in the fabric are straight where they should be and match evenly at the seams.

❦ Good materials pay off. Put your money in materials that will be easy to care for and will hold up well. Look for labels that guarantee against fading, shrinking, wrinkling, spotting, sagging, and all the other undesirables. If a garment must be dry-cleaned, you should consider upkeep expenses as well as the purchase price. For good wear, look for flat weaves rather than nubby or fleecy fabrics and for tightly woven materials rather than loosely woven ones.

Is it a good value? There are high-priced bargains and low-priced booby traps. The smart shopper learns to tell when a bargain really is a bargain. You don't need to spend a fortune on clothes, but the garment that is too cheap usually gives itself away. Some of the telltale signs of a cheap dress: poor fabric, harsh bright color, wavy seams, gimmicky trim. Sometimes it's wiser to splurge on one good dress than to buy two low-priced ones.

The girl who shops at sale time° gets most value for her dollars. In many areas there are traditional big sale days. Election Day and Veterans Day are often special coat sale days, for instance. Look for early-in-the-season sales of manufacturers' samples if you want the newsiest selection. Look for end-of-season clearances for the really big savings. When you buy at the end of the season, you may not have a wide choice; but often you can pick up the better quality clothes, which you could merely admire before, at marked-down prices you can now afford. Look for classics of good material and cut at end of season clearances rather than for something that might become dated.

Where you shop often has a lot to do with the price tag. In most cities there are the elegant stores and the bargain stores. It's fun to go to the prestige shops, and you can usually be sure of getting topflight merchandise; but if you don't mind walking on uncarpeted floors and trying clothes on in less glamorous fitting rooms, you can often find the same dress for several dollars less in a bargain house. It takes a good eye for value (and a bit more stamina) to shop successfully in a bargain store. You must be able to sort out the real buys from what may actually *be* cheap, and you must inspect carefully for good workmanship; but the shrewd shopper can usually make some significant savings that warrant any extra effort involved.

Will I get my money's worth out of it? Practicality should also raise its righteous little head when it comes to evaluating price tags. The girl on a budget remembers that a $5 nylon slip will do as good a job as a $10 one, but a $3 one will wear out much too fast for real economy. She asks herself if she really needs to spend $40 for a New Year's Eve dress. How often will she wear it? If her social life is filled with less formal affairs, she may settle on an inexpensive polished cotton cocktail dress and save the rest of the

°For a list of clothing sale times, see p. 380.

treasury for clothing items that will get more frequent wear. Or perhaps the dress is so super-stupendous that it is worth twice $40 because of the wonderful things it does for her—and to him. Maybe her social calendar is dotted with many gala occasions when she can use the dress. Maybe this dress is the type she can vary so that it won't look the same each time. Or maybe it has a cover-up jacket that lets it do double duty for less formal occasions as well. Put your money where it will give you the *most* satisfaction if you want to be sure of getting your money's worth.

 Is a less expensive version worth considering? Certain accessories are so simple in design that they could be any price. In these items a medium- or even low-priced version may be as satisfactory as a high-priced version. This is often true in hats, patent-leather-type plastic belts and purses, and simple accessories such as scarves, gloves, and summer jewelry. In a year when everybody is wearing a beret or a pillbox or what-have-you, a simple velvet or wool jersey version may be just as smart as an expensive felt. And white

eads are white beads, whether they come from the five-and-ten or the fanciest specialty
op.

The first step in building a wardrobe plan for yourself is to see just what you have
o work with. Go through your closet and bureau and make a list of every speck of cloth-
ng you own. As you come to each garment, examine it carefully to see how much life is
ft in it—how soon it will need to be replaced. And as you read through the following
ections, note any items you would need to buy to provide yourself with a well-balanced,
ell-coordinated wardrobe.

BE A SUCCESSFUL COLOR SCHEMER

Any girl, unless she can afford as extensive a wardrobe as her little heart desires, is
ise to develop a color plan. A color-planned wardrobe far outstretches a hodgepodge
f solo items and assures a cleverly coordinated look at all times.

A wardrobe color scheme should begin with the choice of a basic color (usually
lack, brown, or navy). A girl on a limited budget can do splendidly with even one basic
olor. This becomes her choice for shoes, purse, and everyday gloves; and the rest of her
lothing selections are keyed to go with them. Quite possibly her coat will be in the basic
olor, also. Girls who work in the city or who travel on trains and buses find that dark
olors are most practical for outer wear.

Of the basic colors, black is most popular. It is the easiest to use if you are limited
o one basic color, because it allows the greatest variety. There seem to be more prints
ith black in the design and more dresses trimmed with black buttons and belts than
ere are in either navy or brown. Black is usually very flattering to girls with vivid
oloring, dark brunettes, and redheads. It may tend to be a bit severe for young girls or
ose with paler coloring.

Navy is a softer background color than black. It is generally very flattering and
akes possible some lovely color combinations.

Brown, too, lends itself to marvelous color harmony and is generally flattering. It is
bit more difficult to work with because fewer ready-made outfits are patterned or

191

trimmed in brown. The prints and plaids that are available are usually quite interestin. however, and many combinations, such as the black and brown prints, can be ve. sophisticated. Brown tends to be slightly more sporty than the other basic colors (mir coats to the contrary). If brown is selected for the basic color, a rust or beige co. that could also be teamed with accessories other than brown would be more adaptab. than a dark brown coat.

Once you have selected your basic color, you can build on this, choosing clothir and accessories that are interrelated. Each clothing purchase you decide on should be : a color that is not only flattering to you but is keyed to the other items in your wardrob. Because a coat must blend with everything in your wardrobe, you can save yourself muc. trouble by choosing it in a neutral color or your basic color.

In making your plan, you'll want to correlate your winter wardrobe with your sur mer wardrobe. During the in-between days of spring and fall you'll be mixing wint coat with spring hat or spring topper with winter dress, and all should blend attractivel.

FALL-WINTER

 SPRING-SUMMER

SAMPLE

COLOR-COORDINATED WARDROBE PLANS

Basic color: black

Coat—charcoal gray
Hats—black, blue
Suit—slate blue
Dressy dress—black
Tailored dresses and skirts—royal blue, gold,
    green and blue print, blue and purple tweed

Coat—dark royal blue
Hat—natural straw
Dressy dress—gold
Tailored dresses—light blue,
    pale green, rose

Color accents—blue, gold   Shoes and purse—black

Basic color: navy

Coat—bright navy
Hats—navy, red
Suit—dark navy
Dressy dress—blue
Tailored dresses and skirts—gold,
    bright green, red and navy pincheck

Coat—light gray
Hat—white straw
Dressy dress—light blue
Tailored dresses—navy,
    violet, aqua

Color accents—red, yellow   Shoes and purse—navy

Basic color: brown

Coat—rust
Hats—rust, brown
Suit—brown and rust check
Dressy dress—green
Tailored dresses and skirts—light blue,
    gold, brown print, brown

Coat—gold
Hat—yellow straw
Dressy dress—royal blue
Tailored dress—dark green,
    tangerine, pale yellow

Color accents—yellow, rust   Shoes and purse—brown

BUILDING ON BASICS

The wardrobe that stretches furthest and always looks best is one that has a backbone of a few ever-dependable basics. A basic is a simple fashion with superb lines that can be dressed up or down to suit a variety of occasions. It's not in the show-off category that immediately reminds everyone that this is the same dress you wore Tuesday, nor need it have the kind of plain look that gives it a why-bother ordinariness. It's the kind of ungimmicked good fashion that looks more attractive each way you wear it and doesn't shoot off all its steam in one quick pouf.

A basic can be any color that harmonizes with your wardrobe. Perhaps it is blue or green, maybe a neutral or a dark color, possibly even a red. (Red, because of its brightness, has a look-at-me quality that usually makes it a less versatile choice.)

A basic coat · In cool weather many people see you only with your coat on. They must judge you by the coat you wear rather than the lovely dress it covers. Your coat makes the first impression. It is an important investment and should be the best you can afford in style and quality.

To be more flexible, your coat should be so basic that it can look as right with a cocktail dress as with a sweater and slacks. It should have no dressy trims, such as fur or velvet, and should be in a solid color rather than a tweed or plaid that dubs it as strictly sporty. Contrasting color in buttons, collar, and the like will make it less adaptable. A dark or neutral color is likely to be easiest to coordinate; but if your wardrobe consists mainly of dark colors, a bright coat can be a snappy contrast.

If your coat is to take a lot of hard commuting, a smooth, tightly woven fabric, such as wool broadcloth or flannel, will be most serviceable. Cashmere, high-pile fleeces, and nubby or loosely woven fabrics succumb too quickly to hard wear. (Chinchilla cloth, despite its nubby texture, is such a hard-finished fabric that it gives excellent wear.) You might consider one of the imitation fur coats in a simple style.

Before making a choice, it is wise to consider your height and what you will wear your coat with. Girls who live in the city will need more highly styled coats than those who are living in the country.

* SHORT COATS AND JACKETS.   Jackets, car coats, and shortie coats are popular for casual wear, but they are difficult to pair attractively with dresses. A flared or boxy jacket look

well only with a slim skirt; *never* wear it with a full skirt. A much better silhouette is created if the full skirt is combined with a Spencer or Eisenhower jacket or other close-fitting bolero or waist-length style. These are the only styles that look well with both full and sheath skirts. Some girls, especially if they are city dwellers, find that a bulky-knit cardigan sweater is a more satisfactory—and generally more basic—jacket choice.

Short girls, you remember, look best in the shorter length jackets that hover near the waistline. Tall girls can cut their height if they wear longer jackets and three-quarter length coats.

A basic dress · A basic dress is the dearly beloved mainstay of your wardrobe; it can go from desk to date with equal aplomb, and even if the date turns out to be two-on-the-aisle at the theater instead of top bleacher seats at a nighttime football game, you'll be well dressed. It plays up perfection of line rather than gadgetry and seems more stunning each way you wear it. To allow you the greatest fashion mobility, it should have no contrasting trim that is not easily detachable. The neckline should be simple so that you can bedeck it with jewels for festive occasions and alter it with scarves for daytime wear. The dress can be in any flattering color that coordinates with your wardrobe.

If your coat is not a solid color, your dresses should be. This will avoid pattern conflict. Wool and wool blends are the most versatile fabrics for cold weather. Silks, failles, crepes, nylons, and the miracle-fiber jerseys are good for milder days, with cottons, rayons, and polyesters among the summer favorites.

Some girls are such masters of changeabout tricks that they multiply a few basic dresses to amazing proportions. A clever receptionist in an advertising agency is famous for her quick-change devices. She once knit a turtleneck dicky for last year's sheath. She made big puffy sleeves to snap into a summer sleeveless dress. Her wool jumper is worn to work with a blouse but goes to dinner later with pearls replacing the blouse. She has also made a filmy overskirt that she adds to simply styled dresses for festive affairs.

A basic date dress • Here's where you want drama—whether your personal prescription calls for grand entrance effects, subtle sophistication, or beguiling femininity. To do the trick, look for a beautiful color in a simple style or, just the reverse, a glamorous cut in a dark color. The most usable style is a beautifully cut dress in a fabric that spans seasons easily (no velvet or organdy, for instance). A dress with a jacket, as mentioned before, lets your date dress double for many occasions when without the jacket it might seem too formal.

A basic suit • A suit provides a look of efficiency and style that makes it rate high with business girls. Suits are available in so many forms that they can fill a large number of social requirements as well. The most basic style is the softly fitted suit with the slim skirt. This style weathers the whims of fashion, while pleats and flared skirts come and go. Look for good lines and good fit. The most adaptable suit is one in an all-season solid color or perhaps a muted tweed. Two-tone effects and contrasting trim limit its flexibility. The neckline should look well with a variety of blouses and also be able to do nicely without a blouse if necessary. To allow the most freedom in accessorizing, there should be no large jeweled buttons, no fur collar (unless detachable), or other restricting decorative trims.

Your non-basics · No wardrobe needs to consist entirely of basics (although many of the best ones do). Every now and then you find a dress that looks so perfect you wouldn't dream of changing it, or a blouse that makes such a beautiful ensemble when worn with one suit that you don't mind if it doesn't go with any other skirt in the closet. But, being a woman, you probably will want change—and only a wardrobe with a good supply of basics allows this flexibility. A dress with fussy details or "cute" trim is eye-catching at first but may soon become boring because it allows no change and remains the same forever and ever and ever. Scan the photos of the women who are rated best-dressed. Nine times out of ten these women, despite their wealth, are wearing basics—superb simplicity at its best.

A basic wardrobe, then, presents a good takeoff point for any flights of fancy. When you have acquired the essentials, then you can go for the extras. And basic styles save you money because they can be transformed so easily that you need less clothes. Once you've acquired your minimum quota of good basics, you'll have saved enough to indulge in the new car coat, the dressy hat, and some of the other non-basics you might not otherwise have been able to afford.

MULTIPLICATION TRICKS WITH SEPARATES

By mixing and matching separate blouses, skirts, and jackets, many business girls provide themselves with a wardrobe that, even if small, allows a great deal of variety. As with shortie coats, care must be taken to create a well-balanced silhouette.

The most successful combinations are generally a detailed blouse with a simple skirt, or a plain blouse with a more decorative skirt. Both items should be neither too plain nor too fussy. The best effects are achieved when only one element seeks the spotlight.

In teaming separates, care must be taken that the same degree of formality prevails between them. No one would wear sneakers with an evening dress; yet occasionally we see a very dressy blouse with a sporty skirt, or a combination of satin with tweed. Such pairing up is completely incongruous.

A print blouse with a plain skirt creates a smart twosome, but the styling, color, and texture must all be carefully cued to one another. It is best to avoid fabrics that are difficult to coordinate, such as gabardines, slub textures, or bold weaves.

197

FOUNDATION FOR GOOD FASHION

How well a fashion looks is often a matter of the elastic and nylon miracles produced by a good girdle and bra. What's underneath can be more important to the appearance of a dress or suit than its cut or fabric. And, when properly fitted, a good bra and girdle are not only a boon to good looks but do much for posture and morale as well.

Bras · Some girls, when they purchase a bra, ask for a certain size and let it go at that. But unless you are familiar with the particular style and brand, it is best to be measured because of the variations in each manufacturer's product.

When you try on a bra, put your arms through the straps and lean forward so that your breasts slip into the cups. Then straighten up and fasten the band. The shoulder straps will probably need adjusting. If a bra fits correctly, there will be firm uplift from the underside of the cup and the top side will not put any strain on the breasts. This is especially important with strapless bras. Wires or boning should be fitted to the rib cage and shouldn't put pressure on the breasts. Your breasts should fill the cups but should not be crowded together or toward the sides. Bras with elasticized undercups are good for in-between figures—that is, between A and B, or B and C cups. If you're quite small, you may want to consider a padded bra to help your dresses to fit better.

A bra that fits well should not only give you a lovely contour; it should be comfortable. It shouldn't interfere with deep breathing or ride up when you lift your arms and should not cause bulges under the arms or across the back. You should be able to run your finger easily under the band of the bra; otherwise it is too tight.

A bandeau of cotton, nylon, or other miracle fabric is probably sufficient for the young figure with high and well-separated breasts. Mature, more developed bosoms should have a bra with a band under the cups for extra uplift, perhaps even a style that fits to the waistline if the diaphragm needs control. Full figures require built-up reinforced cups, wide straps, and possibly underbust wiring. A long-line bra is best if your midriff is fleshy. If shoulder straps dig into your shoulders, you may find help in the broad pads that are worn under straps.

Investigate a wide variety of bra styles so that you have types to fit your wardrobe needs. There are bras with wide-apart straps for scoop necklines, halter bras for halter necklines, strapless bras, brasalettes for princess-line outfits, and bras with more rounded cups for wear under sweaters. Overly pointed styles are *always* in poor taste.

Girdles · Whether a girl struggles into a size 40 dress or slithers into size 10, a girdle is necessary for a smooth look. Even the slimmest models wear girdles because they realize that even their lean figure needs the light controlling touch that refines curves and presents an attractively molded silhouette.

The type of girdle you choose depends on your figure. Your girdle *size* is based on your waist measurement, but if you require anything more elaborate than a simple two-way stretch, you will need to know which style and length is best. Garments with no-stretch or vertical-stretch panels must be fitted carefully. The *style* you need is determined by the fullness of your hips and the length that best suits your frame. The difference between hip and waist measurements is about 8 to 10 inches for the average figure. Full-hipped figures may measure 11 or more inches larger and require a girdle that is designed for full hips. Slimmer figures (with a less than 8-inch difference between waist and hips) can wear a straight-hip style. Proper length can make the difference between a sleek line and border bulges. The measurement is taken at the side, from the waist to the thigh, and is sized as follows:

14 inches or less—short ❧ 15 to 16 inches—medium ❧ 17 inches or more—long

If your stockings feel strained, the difficulty may be either that your girdle is too short or that hosiery is not long enough.

For accurate—and comfortable—fit always consult an experienced corsetiere. She knows the special features of each brand and style and which will do most for your figure. Tell her whether you intend to use the garment for play or for business and dress wear. A lightweight girdle is excellent for sportswear but may not give you the firm control you want for other clothes.

A slim, willowy figure needs the least amount of control and can usually get by with a simple all-elastic, roll-on style. A fuller figure will need panels that give more control. Longer lengths and long-legged panty girdles help heavy thighs. High-rising styles control spare tires at the midriff. For heavier figures the corsetiere may suggest an all-in-one (a corselet) to give you a smoother, more defined line. Corselets, however, are sized for figures in which the bust and hips are in proportion. If yours vary from the norm, consider a long-line bra to team with a high-top girdle.

Before making any final decision, try on the girdle, fasten your hose, and then sit down. Does it dig at the waist, produce a spare tire, or pull on stockings? If so, it doesn't fit properly. Try the bend-over test also. Does the girdle ride up or poke your middle? It shouldn't. Here are some other points to check. The garment must either be rejected or altered if it does not pass with a perfect score.

- Does it fit snugly at the waist without gapping or squeezing?
- Does it prevent a spare tire? (This can be caused by a girdle that is too tight or one that is not built up high enough.)
- Are the boned sections comfortable?
- Do garters feel comfortable, without strain on hosiery?
- Can you walk forward and backward and move comfortably without constriction or without the garment riding up?

An all-in-one should be checked to see that the bust cups fit comfortably. If there is any downward pull over the bust, the corselet is probably short. Are the shoulder straps comfortable? Too much strain on straps can rub your shoulders raw. An all-in-one foundation should fit properly so that no roll is caused at the top edges, particularly across the back. Check to see that it fits smoothly through the waist and hips and is long enough to allow you to sit comfortably.

Do you know how to put on a girdle? Often more damage is done by the strain and struggle of getting into a girdle than by weeks of wear. The simplest and safest method is to pull the girdle partway up over your hips and then grasp the lower edges and flip the girdle inside out as you pull the entire garment up above your waist. (A bit of swivel at this stage makes the job easier.) Then smooth the waist section into position and, grasping the bottom edges of the girdle, slide them down again (right side out) over your hips. By pulling the girdle down from above your waist, you are working with Nature instead of against her, and your flesh is smoothed into proper position, not all squeezed up to overflow in a roll at the top.

Be sure that your girdle is centered on your figure—that the center panel is really in the center. With so many of the lightweight elastic pull-ons, it's easy to don the girdle off-center. Unless it's on correctly, you'll be uncomfortable and won't get maximum support. If your garment has a zipper, don't try to close the zipper before you've fastened all the hooks beneath it. Fasten from the bottom up—never from the top down.

Panty girdles can't be put on in this flip-the-bottom-up manner, obviously. Instead, first fold the garment down, top to bottom. Step in and smooth the folded girdle up over your hips to the right position. Then roll the top up to your waist. This makes the tugging much easier.

Some girls mistakenly believe that the longer their foundations go without washing, the longer they will last. On the contrary, dirt, oils, and perspiration cause elastic to deteriorate and discolor. Suntan lotion, for instance, is especially destructive; it's a good idea to wash off all traces from your legs before putting on your girdle. In laundering your garment, gentleness is the rule. The villains are hot water, harsh soaps, irons, radiators, and rough handling. Do be sure zippers are zipped. Soak in mild lukewarm suds for about seven minutes, rinse thoroughly, and roll in a towel so that excess moisture is absorbed. To dry your girdle, close the garters over a hanger and hang it away from heat or direct sunlight. Fabric sections can be ironed, although this may not be necessary.

Never iron the nylon or elastic. If you wish to use a washing machine, put your girdle in a cheesecloth or nylon bag for protection and be sure the water is not too hot.

The average girl needs at least three girdles—one to wear, one to wash, one for play. Alternating foundations helps them last longer, for it gives the elastic time to rest and regain its shape between wearings.

When you take off a girdle, inspect it for rips or loose garters. It's most disconcerting to anyone's poise to have a garter pop at an inopportune moment. Small rips should be repaired before another wearing. Try to let your girdle air for a while before putting it away.

LINGERIE

Your slips, panties, pajamas, housecoats, and such need not be expensive, but for the sake of your morale they should be attractive and neat. Perhaps nobody but your family sees them—and they love you—but you *feel* best in pretty underthings.

Look for good fit and serviceability rather than frills. Consider that pleated or ruffled fabric hems of slips are opaque, whereas fragile lace hems may be too peekaboo (and must be laundered with special care to prevent the lace from becoming ragged). Slips with lined cover-bra tops and shadow panels are a must for wear beneath sheer dresses or blouses. Dark slips give extra inky depth to dark outfits; and if you wear a dark bra as well, you will be completely coordinated.

HOSIERY

Stocking bills can eat a sizeable chunk out of a working girl's budget. *Pfft* goes a run and *pfft* go your plans to buy the new hat you'd been saving for! In order to get most wear for your hosiery dollar, it's important to choose the proper weight and style for each occasion and to obtain the type and size that fits best.

The weight of stockings can seem confusing, but it all boils down to this. The sheerness—and strength—of your nylons depends on two things: denier (the thickness of the nylon yarn with which the stockings are knit) and gauge (the number of stitches in the fabric). *With both denier and gauge, the higher the number the stronger, more snagresistant the stocking.* Low numbers equal sheerer stockings.

Many girls consistently wear the 51-gauge, 15-denier hose for all occasions. This is pretty fragile stuff, not intended for the hard abuse of career or classes. Because nylon is a plastic and is transparent, even a 20- or 30-denier stocking still looks sheer on the leg. Hosiery manufacturers advise that for greater longevity we select for daytime wear the 20 or 30 deniers in the 51 or 60 gauges. Gossamer sheerness for dates and glamour occasions can be had with the 12 and 15 deniers in 51, 60, or 66 gauges. If you prefer the very sheer 15 and 20 deniers for daily wear, you'll have better luck with the 60 and 66 gauges.

For better wear you might also investigate the mesh stockings. When these are snagged, a hole may develop—but they will not run. A tiny hole in a hidden spot can be dabbed with colorless nail polish and forgotten, whereas in regular stockings it would mean a run. Large holes, however, look just as bad as a run does.

Many hosiery troubles arise from poor fit. Your stocking should be long enough so that when it is on the foot it can be pulled out about a half inch at the toe, heel, or instep.

A stocking that fits too snugly may cause a burning sensation on the sole of the foot, and it is prone to runs that start from the toe.

Correct length and proportion also affect comfort and wear. If stockings are too short, there is uncomfortable strain, and breaks at the knee soon develop. If stockings are too long, they will wrinkle and wear excessively at unreinforced points. Even though two girls may be the same height, one may have fuller legs and will require a longer stocking than the other, whose legs are slim. Several manufacturers now offer proportioned nylons so that very slender and very heavy legs can have a smooth, comfortable fit. Stretch hosiery also helps solve this problem.

A girl with thin legs will be helped by seamless styles in slightly lighter shades. Heavier legs look best in slightly darker shades. Unless you have perfectly molded legs, forgo the fancy heels and clock designs. They are not for business wear in any case.

Whenever you purchase stockings, always get three or more pairs alike. This allows you to wear them in rotation and to match up any leftovers when one in a pair gets a run.

Handle with care · The tender care you give your nylons keeps them pretty and snag-free longer.

· Handle nylons with caution. Wash nightly in mild suds; don't rub. If your fingers or nails are the least bit rough, wear gloves whenever you handle stockings.

· Brand-new nylons should be rinsed before wearing.

· When putting stockings on, turn your rings in so that they won't catch. Then roll stockings down to the foot and unroll upwards slowly, keeping the foot and leg seams straight as you do.

· Fasten garters properly—do front and side garters while seated, back garters while standing. Be sure garters are fastened in the welt (top reinforced hem) of the stocking but not on the seam.

· Protect nylons from damage by storing them in transparent plastic bags—one for daytime hose, one for dress hose.

• Be careful that you don't rub your legs against chairs and furniture that might be rough. If you are a working girl confronted with a splintery desk edge or chair, either sandpaper the rough spot or cover it with tape.

SHOES

Every girl on the job must be a girl on her toes, not only in regard to her work but in regard to her shoes as well. High heels have been decreed a good grooming essential. They make feet look smaller, calves and ankles look prettier; they are required to set off dresses, coats, and suits properly; they give a sophistication no flat can offer; they are preferred by men; they are berated by medical specialists; and corn plaster manufacturers grow rich because of them. Good or bad, we wear them. If high heels torture your feet, look for a shoe with a medium heel (you really needn't wear *high* heels, you know), or a graceful lower heel. Flats are never appropriate for office wear except in the most informal of circumstances, where a girl must be on her feet all day. Even then, the girl who wears heels stands out as better groomed, more mature, and more businesslike than her flat-heeled co-workers.

The most versatile shoe is a simple opera pump. Fashion trends come and go, but this unadorned closed design is always stylish and always appropriate for every costume. Calf or kid are best for tailored wear, suede for dress. Sandals and similar fancy cutout shoes should be reserved for dressy occasions. They are not appropriate for business.

Your height, weight, and the size of your foot are all factors to consider when choosing a flattering shoe style. Tiny girls and those with full figures do best in a medium heel. Too high a spike makes them look off balance. A long foot will seem shorter if there is less shoe (wide and low-cut vamps, open toes, sling backs) or if there is contrasting color or a bow to break the length. A broad foot will seem slimmer in a shoe with an unbroken vertical line, such as a plain pump or one with vertical details. High vamps, ankle straps, needle heels, and ornate styling are not for the broad foot. Thin legs with straight contours will seem more attractive in simple delicate shoes with fairly high, slender heels. Brightly colored styles that attract the eye should, of course, be avoided by anyone with large feet.

Fit first · Good fit is essential to comfort. No matter how attractive a shoe, don't buy it unless it feels right. In the shoe store make a point to walk off the thick carpet to a spot where you can give your shoes the hard-floor test. Be sure there is no pressure and that there is wiggle room through the toes but a snug fit at the heel. The ball of your foot should come exactly at the widest part of the sole, and your instep should be well supported. If your foot rides forward, the salesman can put in a metatarsal pad or a foam rubber sole cushion, which often helps a low-arched foot.

For surest fitting, it is best not to buy shoes early in the morning. As the day progresses and we walk around more, our feet swell; this is particularly true in warm weather. What may seem a perfect fit at ten may be causing you agony by six. Never never buy cheap shoes for daily wear. Shoes that are poorly made give out fast and result in aching feet, a short temper, and an anguished expression that is detrimental to any girl's charm. Foot specialists advise that we have at least two pairs of daytime shoes so that we can alternate them. This adds to foot comfort by giving your feet a change, and adds to shoe life by giving the leather a chance to rest and to air out.

Keeping your shoes in good condition is very important for business grooming. Scuffed shoes, run-down heels or tips, and smudgy suede can spoil a smart appearance. For emergency cleanups try facial tissue to restore a shine or paper towels to brush suede.

 FOLLOW-UP

1 Try to become acquainted with the characteristics of good quality clothes. Examine the clothes in the windows or on display in better stores. See what factors you can observe that warrant the expensive price. The girl who is familiar with the look of quality will be a better shopper even though she buys in a lower-priced department. She will be able to appreciate a true bargain and to recognize shoddy merchandise.

2 Work out your own color-coordinated wardrobe plan based on the clothing you have on hand. Note any new items that may be required for proper balance and coordination.

The accessories you select and what you do with them reveals your personality—particularly your cleverness and your good fashion sense. Some girls can give a gilt-edged look to the simplest outfit by the way they use accessories. The difference between one girl's shirtdress and another's may hinge on a marvelous belt. Perhaps a handsome bag sets off the whole effect. Or maybe it's the scarf tucked in at the neckline or her unusual color combination. Smart accessories are a wise investment. They aren't limited to one costume but can be used to spark several different outfits, paying their way in compliments for years to come.

In using your accessories, keep in mind these points:

- The total effect must be one of perfect harmony—accessories and dress must agree with each other in degree of formality.

- They must also blend into a happy oneness. Too many eye-catchers splinter attention.

- The more elaborate the outfit, the simpler the accessories—and vice versa. A detailed or frilly dress requires only the simplest accessories; a plain dress can use more lively accents.

- Use dramatic accessories to play up your best features. A girl with big hips cleverly avoids tricky purses, saving her fireworks for hats and face-flattering jewelry.

12 ACCESSORIES MAKE THE DIFFERENCE

RULE OF FOURTEEN FOR ACCESSORIZING

Back in January, 1849, a famous Parisian couturier pronounced in *Godey's Lady's Book* that no lady should appear in a street costume that was comprised of more than fourteen eye-arresting elements. This rule of fourteen has been used by fashion experts ever since, and is used today in checking the costumes of movie stars to be sure that they are not overdressed.

According to this rule, you should be able to count no more than fourteen items that are visible to the eye. A coat and everything that might be seen if the coat were removed is included. If you are not wearing a coat, your outfit should total less than fourteen points. Check yourself according to the following scale:

Dress, one piece (one color) 1		Coat 1	
–plus 1 for each additional color		Buttons, self-fabric, simple matching. . 0	
Suit or two-piece dress (one color) . . . 2		–other . . . . 1 for each	
–plus 1 for each additional color		Belts, self-fabric 0	
Blouse 1		–leather, plastic, etc. 1	
Hat, plain 1		Scarf 1	
Hat trimming . . . . 1 for each color		Necklace . . . . 1 or 2	
Hat, flowered or feathered . . . . . 2 or 3		Earrings, small 1	
Hose 1		–large . . . . 2 or 3	
–with clock or design 2		Pin 1	
Shoes, plain 1		Bracelet 1	
–high style or decorated 2		Ring with stone 1	
Purse, small 1		Wristwatch 1	
–large 2–3		Glasses, plain 1	
Gloves 1		–with trim 2	

YOUR HATS

Although American women seem to go hatless more and more, the girl who wishes to make a good impression wears some kind of hat—even if it is a mere wisp of veiling—in summer as well as winter. This extra touch adds a flattering finished look that sets her off as someone who cares just that much more about her appearance. Job seekers should know that wearing a hat is one of the things many personnel managers look for when seeking desirable applicants. A hat also gives a big assist to beauty. It can improve a figure and highlight your best features while camouflaging your worst ones.

210

round   long   square

◄ RIGHT

◄ WRONG

Hat lines • A new bonnet that "does something" for you must be chosen carefully—the old camouflage techniques again. You do not want lines that repeat undesirable body or facial flaws but, rather, lines that counteract them. The most dazzling hat must meet your personal qualifications or its loveliness is lost.

ROUND FACE. Add length to your face by choosing a hat with height (either in crown or trim) and with enough width to balance your facial contours. Look for styles that cut the circular effect: uptilted, irregular brims; diagonal brims; draped crowns. Avoid round, head-hugging crowns, flat pancake styles, very small brims, and drooping mushroom brims.

LONG FACE. Add width by choosing low, level hats; round crowns; wide, turned-down brims. Avoid hats with vertical lines, tall crowns, high trimmings, those with little or no brims.

SQUARE OR RECTANGULAR FACE. Wear styles that counteract the square corners of your face—softly rounded or rippled brim lines, tilted lines, large brims. Avoid square crowns, small-brimmed sailors, pillboxes.

211

RIGHT ▶

pear   heart   diamond

WRONG ▶

- PEAR-SHAPED FACE. Hats that concentrate their interest above eye level will widen your brow and diminish your chin—tilted hats, oval sailors with brims slightly wider than the chin, hats with lines that slant upward and outward. Avoid pointed crowns, small-brimmed sailors that are worn straight, and hats with low brims in back that add width at jawline level.

- HEART-SHAPED FACE. To add fullness at the chinline, select hats with low back brims or trims or veiling that spreads out in back. Off-the-face picture hats and styles with uneven brims are good. Avoid high crowns and level, wide brims that accentuate brow width.

- DIAMOND-SHAPED FACE. Choose hats that add fullness at the temples (bretons, sailors, level brims, picture hats). Avoid styles that add width at the cheekbone, berets and profile hats that repeat the diagonal contours of your face, and close-fitting hats or turbans with center trim.

212

prominent nose   receding chin   ◄ RIGHT   pretty eyes

◄ WRONG   glasses

● NOSE TROUBLES. Minimize a *prominent nose* with a hat brim that extends beyond it. For a *long nose* choose a brim that slants upward and out. For a *pug nose* wear narrow brims that slant downward. A *crooked nose* needs irregular or slanting brims, not a style that has equal width or trim on both sides.

● CHIN TROUBLES. Build up a *receding chin* with hat lines that are shallow at sides and curve up off the face; avoid wide brims. Play down a *protruding chin* with brims that reveal most of the forehead in front but are wide enough in back to balance the chin in profile.

Your hat should emphasize your best features as well as camouflage poorer ones. Make the most of a double opportunity.

● PRETTY EYES. Wear off-the-face hats and styles with trim at the temples. Small, filmy brow veils stopping just above the eyebrows are also good. If you wear *glasses*, choose small off-the-face hats rather than low, shadowing brims that tend to crowd the face.

213

- LOVELY LIPS.   Accent them by choosing a pink or red hat or hat trimming and matching your lipstick to it. Wear nose-length veils.

- BEAUTIFUL COMPLEXION.   Show it off with a colored hat and colored veiling. Particularly flattering are the pink and red veilings. Pale beige is flattering to cream or tan complexions; dark shades and light blue are lovely for fair pink-and-white complexions.

Your hat wardrobe · How many hats you feel you need is a personal matter, but the minimum you should plan on is probably three: one go-everywhere winter hat in your basic color; a winter hat in a more lively color, perhaps with slightly more dressy styling, and a spring-summer model. Your basic hat should be fairly simple so that it will be neither too dressy nor too tailored to go with most of your outfits. Some girls produce stunning effects with a simple hat by making several snap-on hatbands or other detachable trims in colors that coordinate attractively with their wardrobes. Often a basic style can be made to double for dressy occasions by the addition of a simple small rhinestone or pearl pin. A spring hat (which, incidentally, takes on special attraction if worn very early in the season) should be a gay fillip. If it is to serve for summer, too, you might look for a style that depends on line and color for its appeal. The posy-covered bonnets that catch the eye at Easter may seem tired and too much in July.

How to buy a hat · If you are shopping for a hat that is not a standard color, try to wear the outfit it must blend with or have a bit of the fabric along to guide you. In many cities, health department regulations forbid the return of hats, so you will want to be certain any new chapeau is a good match before you buy it.

When trying on a new hat in a store, note how the salesgirl adjusts it. She knows what the latest fashion quirks are and how each design is intended to be worn. But don't stop there. You know your face and the lines that will flatter it. Sometimes, if a hat doesn't look right, just a bit more tilt here or a twist there is all that is needed. Be sure the hat you choose is the correct head size. If it is too small, it may not sit down as far as intended or may be snug enough to become uncomfortable after you have been wearing it for a while.

Before you decide on a hat, check it from all angles. How does it look in profile? Your face is different on both sides, you know. Your best side can be emphasized by a design that concentrates trim on that side.

tall

sloping shoulders

short

How is the full-length view? Never buy a hat until you can see yourself while standing. The correct hat must be in proper proportion to balance your figure. A short girl seems taller in a hat that is the same color as her outfit and is small in size but has uplifted lines with perhaps an upflung feather, stand-up flower, or bow to give an illusion of height without overpowering bulk. Tall girls can cut their height with hats of contrasting color and with good-sized brims. If shoulders are thin or sloping, avoid droopy brims; upturned brims provide better lines. Upslanting brims are also good for hippy figures if there is enough width at the sides, and for bosomy figures if brims extend forward enough to balance the bust. Full figures are flattered by a hat that has enough bulk to be in keeping with their proportions, especially if it is in a flattering color that draws the eye upward to the face. While you are standing, use a hand mirror to check your view from all sides. This is the way your public sees you.

Office storage · Pamper the prettiness of your new chapeau by keeping it well brushed and free from smudges. Many hats are carefully guarded in hat boxes at home but at work are flipped into the bottom of the typewriter storage section (along with dust cloths and rubbers) or else left on top of the desk at the mercy of the mail boy and flyaway carbons. Smart girls keep a large plastic bag in their desks to encase their hats and protect them from office wear and tear.

PURSES

A handsome purse is an eyecatcher, fashionable as well as serviceable. The most basic type of purse is, of course, a one-tone leather bag in your basic color. In summer a tailored white or patent leather purse, a casual basket, or a neutral plastic bag is a pleasant change to blend with any color scheme. Prints, stripes, and multicolor effects are fun but are often difficult to coordinate unless you have several solid-color outfits in shades that will match.

Quality is an important factor in the life of a purse. Fairly inexpensive leathers are available, but a better quality leather is a wiser choice. Cheap leathers scrape off and scratch too easily. If your budget is limited, a good quality leather-look plastic or fabric bag will give better wear. Check the frame—is it sturdy? does the catch close tightly?

A daytime purse should be large enough to hold all your totables without bulging and yet be in proportion to your size. Larger purses may get the fashion nod, but small girls are wise to keep to ones of fairly moderate size. A bag that can look quite smart on a tall girl will seem like a suitcase when hauled by a short person.

In addition to your basic purse, you will probably need a small bag for dressy evening occasions. Faille, satin, silk and other dressy fabrics in a dark color are most usable but a gay little clutch in a hot pink, tangerine, bright blue, or other vivid color adds zip to a dark outfit, especially when teamed with one other accent in the same shade. Needless to say, since our gala occasions are not too frequent, the major investment should be in a daytime purse rather than a dressy one.

If you have any figure flaw, don't call attention to it by carrying your purse at that spot. For instance, a girl with a large bust shouldn't tuck her purse under her arm; a girl with a large waist won't choose a shoulder-strap bag; a hippy figure looks more so if a purse dangles at the side.

216

Here's a tip for carrying strap or handle styles. When you put your hand through the strap, go from the outside toward your body—don't aim out away from your body. When you aim in and then keep your arm against your waist, your purse can be held securely and won't bob back and forth as you walk. Ever had your hat knocked askew by somebody's purse when you were seated in a bus? If you carry your purse properly, you'll never be guilty of causing such mishaps.

GLOVES

Every girl needs a pair of simple, not-too-tailored, not-too-dressy gloves in her basic color and about three pairs of white ones. But for fashionable fun you may want a couple of extra pairs in gay accent colors. A black outfit with a daisy-trimmed white hat takes on extra sparkle when yellow gloves are added to pick up the yellow of the daisy centers. Beige or gray can be spiced with turquoise or rust, and so on.

Fabric gloves are now made in such attractive and smooth-fitting styles that they go everywhere, and they are often better choices for budget watchers than leather gloves. If you buy leather ones, look for the washable label; otherwise they must be dry-cleaned— a sure way to limit their circulation. Most leathers are dressy, but pigskin and similar textured skins are reserved for tailored wear. Insewn seams also are more dressy than outsewn styles and are more flattering for large hands. Broad hands look best in styles with vertical designs. Be sure you purchase the correct size; too tight a glove will constrict your fingers uncomfortably and will actually make your hands feel much colder in the winter.

Wearing gloves has long been considered one of the essentials of ladylike grooming. Gloves should be worn to business, on downtown city streets, and to all dress-up occasions such as luncheons, banquets, teas, receptions, weddings, dances, and similar more formal affairs.

Incidentally, in regard to glove etiquette, it's perfectly permissible to shake hands with your gloves on; it's considered poor taste (and rather precarious) to smoke, eat, or drink while wearing gloves. If you are wearing long gloves at a formal affair, you can unbutton them to the wrist so that you can slip your hands out; then tuck the fingers back into the wrist to keep them out of your way. At a public banquet or a dinner in a friend's home you would remove them completely.

217

SCARF TRICKS

Whenever a dark dress looks too dark or a basic seems too basic, it's time to dig out a scarf and twist up something special. A girl with a long slender neck will look marvelous with a gay ascot tucked inside her collar or twined around her throat. Watch the fashion magazines and the scarf counters at department stores for new ways to wear scarfs. Instead of letting the ends dangle, experiment with new tricks yourself. Try looping the ends into a bow or making a pouf by tucking each end back through the tied section and pulling out a little puff of the material.

Neckline scarfs should be anchored in some way so that they don't twist out of place. A scarf that goes inside a collar will stay put when the ends are tucked under your bra straps. If you are wearing a dress or jacket that buttons in front, you can tuck the scarf ends in at the collar and let them peek out between the buttons. A necklace is also good for holding a scarf in place. A small scarf can be twined in and out of pearls. A larger one can be slipped under a two- or three-strand necklace or a long chain.

One ingenious scarf addict snipped enough fabric from the hem of a dark dress to make a loop about an inch and a half long and an inch wide. This she sewed vertically just below the center of the jewel neckline of the dress. This loop is an excellent spot to adorn with a pin and provides attractive anchorage when she wears a scarf. She loops scarf ends back and forth through this loop to make a variety of attractive bows, poufs, and ties, and uses a pin atop the loop to keep them from slipping.

This loop trick can be tried by girls with shorter necks, too. To give a lengthening V-line, the loop should be sewn (or pinned so that it would be detachable) a little lower on the chest.

A girl with a really short neck will look too bundled up in a neckline scarf. She should save scarf accents for other areas—perhaps looping one around her waist as a cummerbund (if she is tiny), pinning it in a skirt pocket to let the ends flare out as a colorful note, or fastening it to a belt.

JEWELRY

Well-chosen jewelry is like the bow on the gaily wrapped birthday present. Many a dress looks unfinished until the proper piece of jewelry is added.

Today so many attractive designs are available that inexpensive pieces can look many times their value. If your budget is small, choose one metal color for all your jewelry—either gold or silver—and stick to it. The two are not to be mixed in one costume. Gold has the advantage of being generally more dressy, but in inexpensive plated jewelry it is more subject to discoloration. (A light coating of colorless nail polish can be used to help prevent tarnish.) Sterling silver jewelry gives you quality at often very moderate prices. Although silver will tarnish, it can easily be cleaned with a silver polish cloth and will always keep its beauty.

No girl should be without a pearl necklace, earrings, and bracelet. Pearls are always in good taste, and their soft glowing luster is flattering to every complexion. Also, it is a fact that men love pearls.

Costume jewelry with stones or fake pearls should be chosen with care. Very inexpensive pieces give themselves away by large glassy stones and poorly finished settings. In the low-priced group, it is usually advisable to stick to small stones, with your best buy being pearls. When you wish to purchase a pin or earrings with rhinestones or colored stones, you'll get much better value and more realistic appearance if you pay more. Some of the better manufacturers even guarantee stones against falling out. Rhinestone jewelry is, of course, strictly nighttime glitter.

As with all your accessories, proportion is again important here. Chunky jewelry overpowers the small-boned face and weighs down the diminutive figure. Tiny pieces look inappropriately doll-like on a tall or full figure.

Necklaces · Remember the effect of a necklace line on facial contours? A quick review:

- The thin face and long neck profit by the illusion of width created by a choker length.

- Multistrand necklaces are excellent for filling in a bony neckline.

- If you aim to slenderize your face, choose a length that comes below the base of the throat. Long ropes also have a slimming effect, the only exception being with the bosomy figure; a rope swinging in space below a large bust merely emphasizes its size.

- Even the shape of the bead can affect your appearance. The larger the bead and the rounder it is, the more it gives an illusion of width. Round or oval beads soften angular features; irregularly shaped beads are recommended for full faces.

Earrings · Your earrings should match or blend with your necklace or pin. They need not be exactly the same; they need have only the same general feeling—plain tailored style worn with heraldic emblem on a chain, more decorative design with a dressier stone-studded pin.

The most generally flattering earring is the upslanting wing shape that follows the curve of the ear. If earlobes are large, a bigger earring is preferred. Girls with small lobes need dainty styles and should look for screw-backs or magnetic-type backs if they have trouble keeping earrings on.

If a clip-type earring seems too tight, don't resign yourself to letting it just sit in your jewelry box. Many styles can be adjusted by bending down the arm that joins the

220

clip to the back so that the clip won't snap so tightly. Your jeweler can probably fix it for you very easily, but if you try it yourself, use small pliers (or tweezers) and bend the arm just *slightly*. Strong-arm methods can do damage.

The earring style you choose should also balance the lines of your face. As you have probably figured out by this time, there should be no round earrings for round faces, no bulky styles for small features, no dangle designs for short necks. Drop earrings are the most difficult to wear. Although they lengthen a face, they can swallow up any but a long, swanlike throat. Dangle earrings should be reserved for dress-up occasions; tailored button styles are a more suitable choice for business. Always suit the style of your earrings to the style of your dress.

Pins · Perhaps a pin is *the* most versatile bit of jewelry. You need not always wear a pin on your lapel or collar. Show it off on a hip pocket; let it adorn your hat, cuff, or belt; or loop it through a chain to make a pendant. When you want to make a simple pin more dramatic, you can back it up with a cockade of ribbon or display it badge-fashion atop striped grosgrain.

In choosing a place for your pin, remember that it is an attention-getting accent. Use it to direct all eyes to your best features. Wear it on your best side, or near a tiny waistline, for example. To create width for your face, perch a pin high on your shoulder. To give length, center it, preferably two or three inches below the base of your neck. If your bust is large, don't plunk a pin at the base of a low V-neckline.

Some large pins are too heavy for jerseys and certain other soft fabrics. You can often keep a pin from pulling by fastening it through your slip or through a strap as well as through the blouse.

Bracelets · These are excellent for long, thin arms—the best being slim styles, charm bracelets, and more delicate links. A heavy arm with a short hand needs a wider type of bracelet, one that give the effect of being solid without creating too much bulk, such as larger link bracelets and openwork designs.

During office hours avoid wearing jangly bracelets. Your watch on one wrist and one wide or two or three narrow bracelets on the other are maximum. Never wear a bracelet with your watch.

Ankle bracelets? They are considered poor taste.

Gems on display • It's easy to fall in love with jewelry. Occasionally a female with a kindergarten sense of fashion tries to display too much glitter at once. Incorrect adornment would be a three-strand necklace with matching earrings, a shoulder pin, a watch, bracelets, rings. (What, no nose ring!) Ornate or jeweled buttons should also be considered when tallying your jewelry quota. A necklace and pin are usually not worn together unless the necklace is merely a single strand of small pearls and is not an obvious accent. Colored jewelry tends to be more overpowering than plain metal pieces and should be used more sparingly. Sometimes just a single piece of jewelry, such as dramatic earrings with a formal, is all that is required.

GLAMOUR WITH GLASSES

Today, eyeglasses are so attractive and come in such a variety of shapes (to flatter all faces) that they have become a charming beauty accessory instead of a beauty hazard. No longer need a girl take off her glasses when the man of her life draws nigh. The right type of glasses enhance her good looks—and who isn't prettier when she doesn't squint, and more graceful when she can see clearly where she's going?

Since your glasses are so much a part of your costume and your general appearance, it is not extravagant to build up a wardrobe of frames that suit you and the life you lead. One of the most practical extensions of your glasses wardrobe is a pair of prescription sunglasses. They are useful all year round.

If you wear glasses, make the frames a definite accessory and you will not be tempted to keep whipping them off. Whether you are choosing sunglasses or reading glasses or all-the-time glasses, you want to be sure that the frames compliment your features. The frame color should blend with your skin and hair, and the size of the frames must be compatible with the size of your face. If they are overpowering, they give you a beetle-like appearance. Lenses, however, should be large enough to show off the whole eye, including the lashes at the outer corners. If you have only one pair of glasses, choose a simple frame that does not have too much decoration. Not only is this best for office wear, but it is less likely to conflict with jewelry and other accessories. Colored frames must, of course, be coordinated with the outfit you wear.

222

The shape of the frame should be governed by the shape of your face.

Oval face. No problems here; almost any shape will be flattering.

Round face. Counteract the roundness with frames that have sharp angles or squared-off bottoms, and ones that sweep up at the sides.

Square face. Avoid frames with squared-off lines. Choose a style that has a gently curving upsweep.

Oblong face. Give width by choosing glasses that extend beyond broadest part of your face. They should be softly curved without too much upslant.

Heart-shaped face. Choose oval lines at top and bottom. Avoid harlequin styles.

Diamond-shaped face. Select a style that adds breadth to your forehead. Frames should be wider at the top than at the bottom and should have a definite upsweep.

Pear-shaped face. A frame with a heavier top piece that slants slightly upward is flattering. The bottom should be oval and should not be as wide as the top.

Long or short nose. A long nose can be visually shortened by wearing frames with a low bridge. A short nose seems longer if you choose a frame with a high bridge.

short nose   long nose

CONTACT LENSES

Although contact lenses are unnoticeable and eliminate a few problems, they can create many more. Before you consider buying contacts, be sure to give the matter careful investigation. You'll find that they are very expensive (in this area a "bargain" definitely is not good sense) and must be fitted by an expert. Then comes a lengthy series of visits for checkups and lessons in insertion, removal, use, and care. There are many dangers in contact lenses and many cases of severe eye damage caused by incorrect use. One of the difficulties arises because they can be worn for only relatively short periods. Not everyone can wear them comfortably, and if you have ever seen a girl who is having trouble with her lenses, you know how very unflattering they can be. Constant blinking, tearing, and irritation are the least of the problems. Before you take the big expensive step, have your eyes thoroughly checked and ask yourself if you have the patience and fortitude to learn to wear contact lenses.

SAYING IT WITH FLOWERS

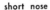

Fresh or fake, a pretty flower gives a lift to any outfit. In both cases it must be crisp and perky. A frazzled or droopy artificial flower is no asset to appearance and should be considered no more suitable than a wilted garden flower.

224

Show your individuality in the way you wear your posies. They will always look pretty perched on a shoulder or collar, but somehow they seem a little more special when pinned to a purse or tucked into a belt or pocket.

When pinning on artificial flowers or a corsage of fresh blooms, keep the heads of the flowers upward, the way they grow. A spray corsage, when worn on the shoulder, should be placed as far out as possible and then angled so that it slants diagonally across your chest in a slimming line. If worn at the waist, a spray can be fastened horizontally at one side of your belt to show off a tiny waistline; otherwise let it hang vertically.

When your beau asks for corsage suggestions in advance, you might consider something a little different—perhaps a single flower attached to a ribbon to wear as a bracelet or a choker necklace. Flowers for your hair can be lovely, provided they are small or flat, so that they are in proportion to your coiffure. The florist may not have you or your hairdo in mind when he chooses.

 FOLLOW-UP

1 Pay particular attention to the way fashionwise women use accessories. See how many attractive new ideas you can find.

2 Experiment with your own accessory collection. Don a basic dress and conduct a mirror study session. Can you find four different places to put a pin? What different styles of necklaces could be worn? How could you dress your outfit up or down with belts? What scarf ideas would be flattering? Have you any separate collars or ties you could add? Don't overlook the possibilities of pairing up a matching jacket or knit cardigan to create an ensemble.

3 How successful a wardrobe planner are you? Based on your clothing inventory and your list of needed items, make yourself a three-year purchase plan that will provide a balanced, well-coordinated wardrobe. Note which items should be purchased each year for the next three years.

Consider that the life expectancy for each coat, suit, dress, blouse, or skirt is three years. Shoes, hats, purses, and other accessories can usually be counted on for about one year's wear. Plan to purchase a winter coat every three years, and apportion your expenses so that a suit or other major expense comes in an alternate year.

PART FOUR:

YOUR SOUND EFFECTS

A warm and pleasing speaking voice is an asset anyone can have—and it is truly a great asset for charm. The only requirement is learning how best to tune up your voice, and then putting good habits to work to drive out any bad ones. By concentrating on achieving a melodious, happy voice, you make yourself a lovelier person. Almost any voice can be improved. There's probably no other area of charm that is so neglected, yet offers such rich rewards.

Voice is the result of the vibration of the vocal cords in your larynx, or Adam's apple. Your feminine voice results from the fact that your vocal cords are shorter and thinner than a man's. These cords can be shortened and tensed to produce a high note, or lengthened and relaxed to produce a low note. Your emotional state, therefore, directly affects your voice. Joy or anger will be revealed by your tone, regardless of the words you use.

The force that provides the vibration is the expelled air from the lungs. This is why good breathing habits—something few of us have—are so important to good speech.

Sound produced when the expelled air of our lungs vibrates the vocal cords would sound rather flat if it weren't for our built-in resonators. Musical instruments all have resonators of some kind. If someone ever claims you have holes in your head, just say "Thank goodness." These holes—the throat, mouth, nasal, and sinus cavities—are the resonators that give your voice tone and quality.

13 TUNING UP YOUR VOICE

DO YOU KNOW HOW TO BREATHE?

The first and most important step toward good speech is proper breathing. Unfortunately, most people never breathe correctly except when they're sleeping. Even when conscious of their breathing, they don't know how to go about inhaling air—they pull in their stomach, raise their chest and shoulders, and try to gulp in as much air as possible. This is not only wrong but unnatural. We are generally ignorant about this important subject and, worse yet, most of us ignore it, although proper breathing habits are essential to good speech—not to mention good health.

The muscle that controls breathing is the diaphragm. To locate it, place your hand just above your stomach, right between your lower ribs. Then cough slightly, moving your hand until you feel the spot where the diaphragm muscle pulls in when you cough.

Make this muscle do the work of breathing. It should push your abdomen down and out to allow room for the lungs to expand as they take in air. Then, to expel the air, the diaphragm pushes up and the abdomen is pulled in. This is called *diaphragmatic breathing*. To feel diaphragmatic breathing in action, lie flat on your back for a few minutes and let your mind wander to any subject except breathing. Then note the way you breathe—this is the natural and correct way.

Women, especially, tend to be upper-chest breathers. Breathing from the upper chest cannot produce the steady flow of air needed to control the strength and steadiness of tone and resonance. It also causes tensions that interfere with good voice control.

To establish good voice control, you do not need to inhale great gulps of air. Neither should your chest rise and fall with each breath. Your diaphragm should do all the noticeable work. Help it along by lifting your chest high (which you should be doing, of course, as part of your good posture).

Try this exercise to develop good diaphragmatic breathing habits and to increase the airstream that will produce good, clear speech. Sit tall and breathe slowly from the diaphragm. Check your posture—chest up, hips against back of chair. Get comfortable, not rigid. Try to remain completely relaxed. Inhale slowly and deeply from your diaphragm. Hold your breath a few seconds; then count aloud slowly and evenly as you exhale. Continue to count as long as possible. If you can only get to fifteen, you should practice frequently until you can do better, perhaps twice as well.

Good breathing habits make a world of difference in both health and speech. Practice diaphragmatic breathing every time you think of it during the day. If you find yourself forgetting, provide little reminders for yourself. Leave yourself notes or wear a certain piece of jewelry as a reminder. If possible, get good, fresh air in the process and your energy and spirits will improve, too. Soon deep, diaphragmatic breathing will be a welcome new habit.

THE MELLOW TONES

Your resonance chambers—those holes in your head—are what give your voice a full, rich quality. If they are not functioning properly, the voice becomes flat or distorted. When you have a cold and your nasal passages become blocked, you are aware of how peculiar your voice sounds. But resonance is also under your control—at least partially. If, for instance, your mouth is not open wide enough for the vowel sound *oh*, you lose resonance and the resulting sound is dull and flat.

You also have control of the soft palate at the rear of your mouth—you use this for the nasal sounds *m, n,* and *ng.* Too much nasal resonance produces a twang; too much throat resonance, a guttural sound. Helped by the lips and tongue, your mouth becomes a resonating chamber of infinite variety. So many possibilities exist that no two human voices are exactly alike. You will want to do all you can to improve your resonance so that you develop your voice potential and get all the mellow, rich tones possible.

Try humming to help improve resonance. Can you feel the vibration in your nose? You should be able to. Also practice saying the nasal sounds *m, n, ng.* Add a vowel to them and make up words such as *pong, bong, dong, kong,* holding the sound long enough to hear full resonance. Using the same consonants, vary the vowel sound to include the other vowels; for example, *pang, peng, ping, pong, pung.* Keep practicing until you can get rich resonance with all the possible combinations.

Too much resonance will produce harsh, nasal tones. Avoid this by being sure the throat is open wide, not constricted and tense. A good exercise to eliminate nasal harshness is to practice the type of exaggerated singing that imitates the open tones of an opera singer. Of course, this is strictly for your private moments, but let yourself go and have fun—all in the cause of a charming voice.

LISTENING IN ON YOU

Have you ever listened to your own voice? The usual reaction is a shocked "Do I sound like that?" Through the magic of the mind we are able to concentrate on *what* we are saying while ignoring the *way* we say it.

The best way to find out how you sound to others is to tape or record your voice. Does your school have a tape recorder for this purpose or can you borrow one from a friend? When recording your voice, be sure to converse normally—forget about the recording and let your natural, unconscious voice speak. Only after listening carefully to the recording several times should you begin analyzing your voice.

If you are unable to record your voice mechanically—or even if you are able to—listen to your voice the next time you are in a lively conversation. This takes enormous concentration but can be done. Listen critically not only to your own speech but to the way others speak. Sometimes you can spot flaws in others and then realize you do the same thing. Listening to the way words are spoken will make you aware of both good and poor speech habits.

Here is what to listen for:

Pitch. This means the position of your voice on the musical scale—how high or how low it is. Your voice operates within a pitch range; you raise or lower pitch to suit your mood or to emphasize meaning. If you feel light and gay, you will use a higher pitch; when serious or sad, you lower the pitch of your voice.

Listen to whether your voice sounds warm and mellow. If it is pitched too high, it may sound shrill or squeaky; too low, and it becomes unfeminine. Your ideal pitch range should be about one-fourth of the way up from your lowest possible note. You can find your vocal range—your highest and lowest possible notes—on the piano. About a quarter of the way up from your lowest note is the point where your pitch should center. If in doubt, it is usually best to *lower* the pitch of your voice. When you speak softly and tenderly, your voice naturally has a lower pitch. Just be sure you don't make it so low that it becomes unfeminine.

Enunciation. Do you speak clearly? Or are you a mumbler and an ending-dropper? If people have to ask you to repeat what you say, faulty enunciation is apt to be the cause. This will be discussed fully in the next chapter.

Pronunciation. Do you mispronounce words? Often we pronounce words incorrectly without realizing it. Whenever you are uncertain about a word, take a moment to check its pronunciation in the dictionary. You spotlight your ignorance—and your charm rating takes a quick dip—when you say words incorrectly.

Emphasis. Do you give proper or sufficient emphasis to words? Individual words or groups of words within a sentence take on different meanings according to the emphasis they receive. Try saying the sentence "Give me my book," four times, each time emphasizing a different word. Did you get four different meanings?

Correct emphasis gives richer meaning to speech; but care should be taken not to use too much emphasis, because this slips into exaggeration and loses its effectiveness.

Inflection. We use a rising inflection to signify a question or an incomplete thought. A positive assertion is generally accompanied by a falling inflection—a signal indicating completeness or finality. Most of us could use more varied inflection in our speech to liven it up; nothing is more boring than a lifeless monotone. On the other hand, overuse of inflection will, of course, produce an unpleasant effect.

Rate. How fast do you speak? Too rapid speech tends to become shrill, and the meaning is apt to be lost or garbled. Speech that is too slow bores us. About 150 words per minute is a good normal rate for ordinary conversation.

Although you have a normal or usual rate of speech, you also vary your rate to suit your mood or type of speech. If you are tired and morose, or contemplative, you naturally slow down. With friends at an exciting basketball game, you'd speak much faster. In intimate get-togethers, rapid conversation may be easily understood. In addressing a large audience, or when an electronic voice reproducer such as a telephone or public address system is used, it is necessary to slow down.

Variety is the spice of speech, and changes of pace in speaking can effectively stimulate your audience, large or small. Try consciously to pace your words to the mood you are trying to express.

Projection. Do you have to cup your hands and shout to make your voice project? A good actor can make a whisper heard far back in the balcony seats. The secret is combining proper pitch, rate, and enunciation. But most important is diaphragmatic breathing. Clear unmuffled tones must come from the diaphragm.

Volume. No doubt you have wished for the ability to adjust someone's volume control—either up or down. Loud voices are irritating and grate on the nerves. The too-soft voice is wildly frustrating. Neither does anything for charm. Try at all times to keep your volume at an appropriate setting. The girl at the next table who talks too loudly is probably completely unaware of how she sounds. Charm requires consideration and control at all times.

As you listen to your voice, be on the alert for any traits you dislike. Does it sound whiny, singsongy, timidly apologetic, harsh, brusque, or does it have some other undesirable quality? Would you be attracted to that voice? Most voice flaws are easy to correct and when we detect any in ourselves, we should make every effort to abolish them as soon as possible.

MELLIFLUOUS DESPITE PRESSURE

Your voice is so important that it should always sound its best and never betray your emotions. Next time you are upset, try these hints to keep your voice lovely while you struggle to smooth out your emotions. If you are irritated, take a deep breath before you speak. This helps relax your vocal apparatus—as well as your nerves. Another good suggestion is to yawn—a big, wide yawn—and your voice will come out sounding more like the sweet natural self you want it to express. If you are tense, a yawn will help, or you might try humming (softly to yourself if you are in an office or any place where you might disturb others, but as loudly as possible if you are alone). Humming improves your voice and also provides immediate release for tense feelings.

Let your voice represent your best self. Next to appearance it is the most important factor in creating a good impression and deserves much conscious thought. Like facial expressions, voices reflect inner harmony or discord. Keep your thoughts happy, kind, and charming, and they cannot help but be projected in a lovely voice.

 FOLLOW-UP

1 Perhaps you've heard of the technique used by Demosthenes in the days of ancient Greece to improve his voice so that he could become a great orator. Demosthenes would stand at the ocean's edge, put pebbles in his mouth, and with great vigor and gusto make rousing speeches to the thundering waves. With such practice he soon developed a powerful voice and became one of Athen's most stirring orators. Skip the pebbles, but take a note from Demosthenes and hold practice sessions in which you speak as loudly as possible. Go off alone somewhere and start talking in normal tones. Gradually increase your volume until you are speaking in full, loud, robust tones. Breathe deeply and watch your pitch so that your voice does not become shrill. If you can practice against the noise of ocean waves (or a household facsimile such as the racket of a vacuum cleaner, washing machine, dishwasher, or power lawn mower), you will be spurred to even greater vocal accomplishments.

2 Make a conscious effort for the next two days to listen to your speech. If you discover any flaws, start an immediate campaign to correct them.

3 Concentrate right now on breathing from your diaphragm. Breathe deeply and slowly for at least two or three minutes. Then find someone to talk to—or talk aloud to yourself. As you speak, make a determined effort to continue to breathe properly.

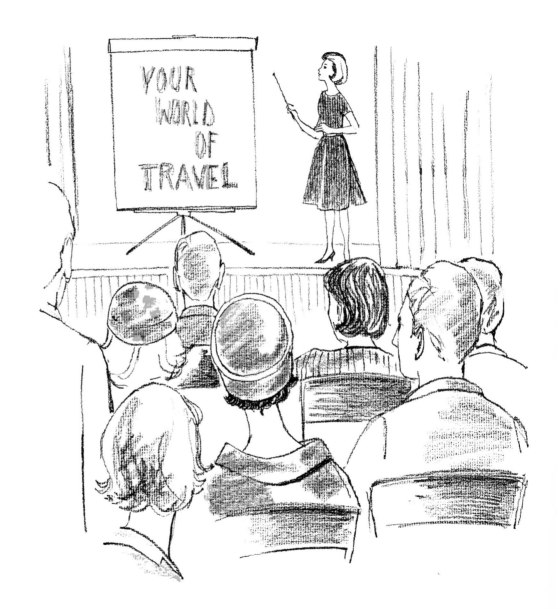

"Harya doin'?" "Kay. D'jeet?" "Nah. Nothin' enny good." "Yeah? Glad ya tolme. S'long."—

Such is the jibberish that passes for English every day. Some parakeets do better! It's all too easy to let speech become sloppy—and sloppy speech has the same effect on charm that sloppy dress does. You just can't afford to let little slips in enunciation or correct usage mar the effectiveness of your speech.

Environment is a strong influence in causing good or bad speech habits. From the time we're able to toddle over to the adult who says "Ka-mere," we are exposed to poor speech habits—they surround us like cold germs and are about as catching. Even as adults, we tend to imitate the talk we hear. A memorable example of how easy it is to pick up another's speech mannerisms occurred a few years ago when a distinguished Senator, who is an excellent speaker, was investigating gamblers and racketeers. Parts of the proceedings were televised and, try as he would, even the well-educated Senator found himself slipping into the colorful but decidedly mishmash vernacular of the witnesses.

EXPOSE YOURSELF TO GOOD SPEECH

While we can't avoid contact with persons who use poor English, we can avoid exposing ourselves unnecessarily to the slaughtered speech used on some of the TV whodunits, Westerns, and similar shows. Just a little twist of the knob is all it takes. Topnotch programs *are* usually available. True, you may have to search for them, but they are there. And when you can find a good one, the speech style alone is often stimulating and rewarding. Listen for a colorful choice of words, and notice the pleasant tone and good diction of the actors. Aside from the entertainment value and mental inspiration good programs offer, you're bound to be influenced for the better in speech habits.

PRACTICE FOR "PEAR-SHAPED" TONES

You can also improve your speech through watchfulness, practice, and exercise. Most poor speech comes from carelessness and just plain lazy habits. Often we fail to make full use of our lips, tongue, and teeth in pronouncing sounds. Speech can deteriorate into mumbling and incoherent jabber simply because the speaker doesn't open his mouth sufficiently and make the effort to speak distinctly.

Below is a list of vowel sounds and pronunciation instructions recommended by the New York Telephone Company. Stand before a mirror and carefully check your mouth action as you say each vowel clearly, firmly, and exactly as described. Repeat each sound several times until you are sure you are saying it accurately and distinctly.

Vowel	Sounds like	As in	Position of mouth
A	ah	father	Open
A	ay	ate	Half open
A	aw	call	Open, lips slightly rounded
A	a	hat	Half open
E	ee	he	Almost closed
E	e	met	Slightly open
I	eye	kite	Open, then closing
I	i	it	Slightly open
O	o	hot	Open
O	oh	old	Open, lips rounded
U	oo	flute	Almost closed, lips slightly rounded
U	uh	hut	Half open
OI	aw-i	oil	Open, lips slightly rounded, then opening wide
OU	ah-oo	south	Open, then closing

Consonants require more movement of the tongue and lips, and they are more easily mistaken or not heard at all. Special care should be taken to give them sufficient emphasis so they will be heard distinctly.

EXERCISES FOR GOOD ENUNCIATION

If your diction needs a little improvement, practice the following exercises recommended by the New York Telephone Company. They will help improve your speech by limbering up any lazy lip, tongue, and jaw muscles.

ips

Extend your lips forward in open circular form; relax and return to normal position. Repeat.

Starting with lips closed, puff them apart with the breath (as sound of "p" in the word part") and repeat rapidly.

Repeat, adding vowel sounds in the order given in the vowel pronunciation list—pah," "pay," etc.

Once again, using "b," sound the vowels—"bah," "bay," etc.

239

Tongue

1 With your mouth well open, curve the top of your tongue upward to touch the gum just behind the front teeth. Return to normal position. Repeat several times, gradually speeding up.

2 Repeat, sounding "lah" each time tongue is lowered.

3 Try it again, using the sounds "tah," "nah," "dah."

Jaw

1 Drop your jaw, with muscles relaxed, far enough to permit inserting your thumb sideways between teeth. Return to closed position, and repeat several times.

2 Repeat, saying "mah" each time jaw is dropped.

3 Try again, using the sounds "mah" and "moh." Avoid forcing or stiffening your jaw. It should drop loosely.

Saying tongue twisters is also good practice for making speech more distinct. Try "A big black bug bit a big black bear." You probably know many more you can also try. Announcers and others who must enunciate clearly find that tongue twisters are an excellent exercise.

PERFECT PRONUNCIATION, PLEASE

Often we are completely unaware that we are saying English poorly. Take the word "English" itself. Is it pronounced *Eng-lish* or *Eng-glish?* The second pronunciation with the double *g* sound is correct. Perfect pronunciation is required for good speech. Check yourself on the following frequently mispronounced words. Many of them are an important part of your cultural know-how and reveal your sophistication—or lack of it. How many do you say correctly?

Word	Pronunciation	Word	Pronunciation
amateur	am'-a-ter	culinary	kewl'-eh-ner-y
gauche	gosh (*o* as in go)	cuisine	kwee-zeen'
subtle	sut'-el	menu	men'-you
lingerie	lahn'-jeh-ray'	au gratin	oh-graht'-en
chassis	shass'-y	canape	can'-a-pee
abdomen	ab'-do-men	hors d'oeuvre	or-derv'
coiffure	kwah-fewr'	table d'hote	tahb-el-dote'
preferable	pref'-er-a-bul	a la carte	ah la cart'
connoisseur	con-eh-sir'	demitasse	dem'-e-tahs
vehement	vee'-a-ment	petit four	pet-ty four
chaise longue	shaaz lawn	concerto	con-chairt'-o
data	day'-ta	Wagner (the composer)	Vahg'-ner
suite	sweet	Verdi	Vaird'-y
savoir faire	sav-wahr' fair'	Mozart	Moht'-sart
repartee	rep-ar-tee'		

Whenever you have the tiniest wavering doubt about pronunciation, save yourself possible embarrassment by avoiding the word for the moment and then looking it up at the first opportunity. In the dictionary, correct pronunciation is shown in parentheses after the word. The key to pronunciation is usually found along the bottom of the page, and also in the front of the book.

KNOW YOUR GRAMMAR

Poor grammar is certainly a drag on anyone's charm. The person who slips into "he don't," "I don't want none," and similar bad constructions, not only gives a poor impression of her intelligence but also crosses herself out for consideration for interesting meet-the-public jobs or any other work that involves letter writing or telephoning. Anyone who is shaky in grammar should take a good business English course or study a book until she is sure of the rules.

Listening closely and being guided by those you know use the King's English properly will also be helpful. Grammatical errors can be easily corrected if you are aware of the problem and concentrate on improvement.

Good practice for tuning your ear to proper grammar as well as to a rich choice of words is reading good literature aloud. (Read to a child, to an elderly person, or to some one who is ill and you get double benefit from your practice.) As you read, try to notice the construction of the sentences and the clear, logical order used to express an idea. Association with the best in both the written and spoken word can do a great deal to help develop the good speech that is essential to charm. And it can aid pronunciation and enunciation, too.

 FOLLOW-UP

1 Listen to the speech of those around you and to your own talk. See how often you notice slips in enunciation, pronunciation, or grammar.

2 Read aloud, either to yourself or others, using your best enunciation and expression. Practice good breath control, pausing for breath (if possible) only where the punctuation indicates a period, comma, or other pause. As you speak, listen to the words. Note the various constructions used by the author and how skillfully the words flow together.

3 In all your reading—aloud or silent—note any words whose pronunciation you aren't sure of and look them up.

Since the widespread adoption of Alexander Graham Bell's little black gizmo, a definite premium has been put on a business girl's voice quality. As far as a telephone caller is concerned, when you pick up the receiver, you *are* the company. He can't see the efficient staff, the modern equipment, or even your big, baby blue eyes—everything depends on your voice. The telephone has become so important in the business world that a pleasant voice, good speech habits, and correct telephone etiquette are essentials for good office performance.

Although your listener can't see your expressions or gestures, you can put a smile in your voice. How? Simply by smiling when you speak. Prove it to yourself. Smile and try to sound unpleasant—pretty hard to do, isn't it? A smile was considered so important to telephone technique by one large department store that a mirror was put in front of each girl in the telephone order department. When she saw her expression sagging, she knew her voice was not at its best and was reminded to brighten her countenance so that her voice would again smile a welcome to customers.

Being pleasant is usually easy the first time you pick up the phone in the morning. But it's that ninety-ninth call just one minute before quitting time that determines your caliber. The words you use may be the same, but even "May I help you?" can sound like "What on earth do you have to bother me about!" Just the tone of your voice is most important. A pleasant voice has been known to take the wind out of the sails of an irate customer and to diminish many a potential problem.

15

TELEPHONE TACT AND TACTICS

HANDLING THE BOSS'S CALLS

Whether you are a secretary or a worker in the department, you should be skilled at taking calls for an executive. Few things elicit more praises or complaints from employers than the way their telephone calls are handled. To put yourself in the praiseworthy category, begin by answering his phone promptly and properly. "Mr. Perkins' office, Miss Wilson speaking" or merely "Mr. Perkins' office" will let your caller know he has reached the proper party. A plain "Hello," no matter how dulcet the tones, is useless in business. It gives no clue as to whether you're the cleaning woman or the secretary of the chairman of the board.

When someone asks to speak to your employer, you will want to find out immediately who the caller is. Perhaps Mr. Perkins will want to be "out" to this particular individual.

A tactful way to find out the person's name is to ask, "May I tell Mr. Perkins who is calling?" If he mumbles or if you are uncertain, don't be afraid to ask him to spell his name. Then spell it back to him and pronounce it, saying, "Is that correct?" If the name is not familiar and the caller doesn't offer any other identification, you can add, "Thank you, Mr. Soandso. And what is the name of your organization, please?" No matter how bombastic a caller may seem, you want to have the right information to relay to your boss. You'd feel pretty foolish if Mr. Perkins answered the phone expecting to talk to Mr. Brandt, a top customer, only to find it to be Mr. Grant, a persistent and unwelcome salesman.

Once you know a caller's name, use it when you address him. Nothing is sweeter to his ears at this point than his own name and the knowledge that he has made sufficient impression to be recognized as an individual.

You will say, "Hold on just a moment, please, Mr. Quinn," as you check with your boss: "Mr. Perkins, Mr. Quinn of the Apex Company is calling." If your boss takes the call, your duties are over. If Mr. Perkins does not wish to talk to him, you will tell the caller in sympathetic tones, "I'm sorry, Mr. Quinn, but Mr. Perkins cannot be reached now." Then you will offer to take a message.

This form of evasion is a polite way of saving face for both parties. If you said that Mr. Perkins could not be disturbed at that time, the caller might feel offended. Saying he wasn't at his desk is perfectly reasonable, and gives Mr. Perkins a chance to decide what he will say before he calls back.

A good rule for your boss's phone calls: *Reveal as little as possible about your employer*. You must be careful to give no clue as to whether or not he is in until you know he wants to take the call. If your boss is out of town, you must still be discreet. Play safe and merely tell callers that Mr. Perkins isn't in. Such an innocent remark as "Mr. Perkins is in Detroit on a business trip," might be a solid gold tip for a rival company.

If your employer is busy on another line when a call comes in, ask the caller if he wishes to hold on or if he would rather leave a message. If he decides to hold on, check back with him frequently. This assures him that you haven't forgotten him and left for lunch (which has happened!) and gives him an opportunity to give you a message or ask you to return the call should the wait be too long. You will also want to be alert to see that your boss takes the call as soon as he is free.

You'll win friends for yourself and your boss if you maintain a natural and sympathetic attitude. Some girls annoy callers by their officious manner and artificial or stuffy phraseology. The caller is made to feel that so unworthy a one as he is indeed fortunate to be put through to Mr. Big-Big. This is extremely poor public relations. Let your charming manner make even the lowliest caller feel that he is being treated with special consideration.

TAKING A MESSAGE

What's complicated about taking a phone message? Not much, yet an amazing number of mangled messages agitate the blood pressure of bosses every day. Probably one of the most important things to remember is to *write down the message*, preferably reserving a distinctive note pad for telephone messages. If your office doesn't provide a specially designed telephone message pad, keep a separate pad—perhaps one with colored paper—beside your phone. Never trust a phone message to a stray scrap of paper or the back of an old envelope. Too many harrowing tales have been told about the message that got away—usually because it was thrown by mistake into somebody's wastebasket.

Particularly disturbing can be a too-brief note such as "Call Mr. Harris," especially when the boss can recall no Mr. Harris. "Who's he with? What's his phone number? What does he want?" are disturbing questions that quickly switch any boss's mind from thoughts of how much you deserve a raise.

Your message report should include the following information:

* The name of the caller.
* His firm (or other identifying information).
* His phone number (if your boss should need to call back).
* A brief report of what the caller wanted, anything you might have done to help him, and anything that might still need to be done.
* The date and time of the call—so that in case your boss mistakenly shuffles your message in with other papers, he won't need to worry about when the call came.
* Your name or initials—so that he can check with you if he has any questions.

PLEASING YOUR PARTY

Your telephone will win friends for you and your company if you observe the following suggestions:

🌸 If your job requires that you answer telephone calls yourself rather than relay them to your boss, always identify yourself when you pick up the receiver by saying,

"Advertising Department, Miss Smith." Even though a good many of the calls you receive may be of the informal, interoffice variety, you will still want to continue with a business-like identification. Just the time Susie Smith is expecting Laura Mae in the filing department to call right back and answers with a breezy "Hi!" it is sure to be her boss's boss.

🌹 Make a special effort to speak distinctly. Background noises and other interferences may make it difficult for you to be heard. Hold the mouthpiece so that it is about a half inch away from your lips. Many people are hard to understand because they don't hold the mouthpiece close enough.

🌹 Be sure that you explain as fully and carefully as possible. When everything depends on your voice, misunderstandings can easily arise and an innocent remark can take on quite a different meaning from what was intended.

🌹 Be helpful. Take the extra moment it may require to give the caller complete information or assistance. It is wiser to spend a few minutes keeping a customer than months regaining him. If the caller is upset, don't argue with him. Attempt to soothe his ruffled feathers, and calmly express regret for any misunderstanding in as face-saving a manner as possible.

🌹 Whenever more than a few moments will be required to get the information the caller requests, offer to phone back. If he decides to hold on, use your hold button if you have one. Otherwise you must be particularly careful of what you say while the receiver is lying on your desk. Idle chatter often comes in loud and clear. When you return to the phone, say "Thank you for waiting."

🌹 If you must transfer a call, be as tactful as possible and explain to the caller the reason for doing so. Calls to big corporations sometimes bounce from one department to another like tennis balls, especially if the problem doesn't fit neatly in any one person's particular domain. "Pass it to somebody else" is the all-too-prevalent psychology. After the caller has explained his story even a couple of times, he doesn't relish hearing the familiar "Hold on, please—I'll transfer you." Try to ascertain first whether the department you are transferring him to can actually help him. If necessary, offer to check further and call him back.

🌻 Keep alert. The antics of the office clown or other nearby distractions may be far more interesting than the caller's problem. Courtesy demands that you be attentive and listen carefully—even though you think you know what the person is about to say. Considerable confusion—and irritation—can be caused when someone wrongly anticipates what will be said.

🌻 Include a happy ending. "Thank you for calling. Goodbye" closes a conversation with a feeling of friendship. The person who ends with an abrupt "Okay" or who merely lets his voice fall and then hangs up often leaves the caller talking to himself, much to his embarrassment and resentment. He may think twice before calling again.

🌻 Before you make a call about an involved matter, make a few notes of what you want to say. This helps you get complete information and avoids delays, omissions, or embarrassing call-backs.

1 Whenever you make a telephone call, practice putting a smile in your voice. Notice how much more cooperative the person on the other end of the line becomes.

2 Check your telephone technique. Do you make a special effort to talk clearly and distinctly on the phone? Do you hold the mouthpiece close enough? Do you explain carefully and completely, so that others understand you fully?

3 Whenever someone is rude to you on the telephone because of something that is not your fault (perhaps he is annoyed at your boss, your firm, or his own inability to get the information he wants), keep in mind that you personally are not the real target of his anger. Remind yourself that he is mad at something else—not you—and endeavor to train yourself to overlook such rudeness so that you can maintain your composure and can reply calmly and courteously.

If you've passed your third birthday, you can probably talk well enough to make yourself understood. Most of us learn to speak at an early stage, but a surprising number never learn to be the interesting talkers they could be. They plod along using the same dull, worn-out words in the same dull way. When they meet someone whose speech is a brilliant fast-paced flow of sparkling phrases, they attribute it to a gift for gab that somehow wasn't in their genes.

Anyone can learn to develop more vivid speech. Just stir up your imagination and mix with a wide variety of words. Sound easy? It is! The reason most of us go on using the same old humdrum expressions is that we're lazy, we don't bother to seek out new words, and we stay in the same old rut using the same old familiar phrases.

Some girls collect stuffed animals; some collect diamonds. Far more negotiable in charm benefits are collections of good words.

Be on the lookout for catchy words, colorful words, expressive words, and new words whose meaning you may not be sure of. As you listen to people talk or hear radio or television programs, notice the words used. When you hear a good one, give it an extra check in your brain and try to use it in several different conversations so that it will become fixed in your vocabulary. When you have used a new word three times it is yours, the saying goes.

16 SAY IT WITH SPARKLE

KEEP GOOD COMPANY

Good speech, like poor speech, is extremely infectious. When you listen to a stimulating speaker, you will find all sorts of colorful phrases popping into your own thoughts. Read a good writer and you are likely to catch a case of good-word-itis without even trying. In fact, many writers warm up by reading something clever that will start their own thoughts perking. Humorous writers such as James Thurber and Cornelia Otis Skinner are good stimulants, and there are many best-selling authors and newspaper columnists whose styles are marvelously incisive and expressive. Reading poetry, whether it be Ogden Nash's or Shakespeare's is a particularly good way to enrich your vocabulary. Poetry, which deals largely with feelings and descriptions, is restricted by rhyme and meter so that only the richest words can be used.

In all your reading, notice how the author expresses himself, the words he uses, how he evokes feeling or emotion, how he gets an idea across. Read slowly so that you can get the full appreciation of the style and language. Jot down the words that seem particularly good so that you can practice using them. They needn't be new words or extravagant words. Most of them will probably be simple expressions that are quite familiar to you but that somehow are not part of your active vocabulary. Many times our talk seems trite, not because we don't know the meanings of a wide variety of words, but merely because they don't occur to us at the proper time. We can "say it with sparkle" only when the sparkling phrases are on the tips of our tongues. A little awareness and a little practice will put them there.

When you come across a new word that you don't know the meaning of, take a moment to look it up. There is still no substitute for consulting the dictionary. Particularly note prefixes and suffixes, and learn how they affect meanings. You may meet the same word root in many forms and will have a clue to its meaning from your knowledge of prefixes and suffixes. While you are looking up a new word, check its pronunciation so that you can say it properly as well as use it properly.

Word collecting can be extremely satisfying. Develop a love for words and you won't settle for the rags and bones of talk. You'll soon know the pleasure of having on hand the exact word to express your precise shade of meaning. Words will come easily. Your speech will be vivid and lively. Often the difference between a meager vocabulary and an excellent one is only a few hundred words. With so many words available from all sources, any vocabulary can be flourishing in a very short time.

OPEN FOR IMPRESSIONS

Sparkling speech depends on emotions as well as words. Often a speaker develops a sense of kinship in his listeners because he makes them share his feelings as well as his thoughts. Alert your subconscious to the details of life surging around you; be aware of how you and others react to what is going on. A story about your trials and tribulations on a lunch-hour shopping jaunt comes alive when you include such details as the suffocating perfume of the customer ahead of you, the interminable time the salesgirl took to sharpen her pencil, or how in order to get the right size box you had to go back to some dusty, dingy corner of the store to a man who looked as though he dealt only with customers whose accounts were long overdue. While too much detail can hamper a story, a few choice impressions—told briefly—help your listeners share your emotions with you.

An awareness of the surrounding sights, sounds, and smells, hopes and joys, fears and frustrations, lets you live life fully and helps you express it better to others. Picturesque words are required to portray these feelings, and you will find your own imagination kindled by the circumstances.

STRETCHING YOUR IMAGINATION

Your imagination quickly responds to exercise. The more you use it, the more flexible it becomes. Put it to work often and you will find that it will provide you with the apt and lively words you want.

255

a laborer—stocky and ruddy . . . . . . a poodle—frisky and fun-loving . . . . . . a day—brilliant with sunshine

Good exercise can be gained by practicing describing what you see. Some people look at nothing but the advertising posters every time they ride in a bus or subway. Instead, examine the people and scenes around you. Describe them to yourself in a few brief terms, as in the illustration. This sort of quick labeling improves your powers of observation and your ability to describe rapidly, so that you will acquire a ready use of words. Make your descriptions succinct so that they paint the scene in a few bold strokes. Appearance, motion, setting, and emotion should be noted. By such enforced brevity you will also learn to highlight the important points quickly and protect yourself from the effusiveness that is a bad habit of tiresome talkers.

WEED OUT THE HUMDRUM

Any vocabulary improvement program should begin with a check to see if there are certain phrases that we habitually use over and over again. Probably you know the girl who describes everything as "terrific" or "cute" or who throws "you know" into every other sentence. Even the most divine expression when used by the most divine people is not the least bit divine when it is overdone! Other people make pets of such words as "really" or "very," which are usually just as well omitted—or tag on meaningless endings like "yet" and "already."

Tiresome, too, are those who cram their talk with hackneyed clichés. There's the character who will tell you you look like a doll, are good as gold, hit the nail on the head when you said it was easy as falling off a log to look cool as a cucumber, etc., etc. Most of these clichés were probably considered pretty clever way back when the first individual thought them up. Since then they have been mouthed so often that they have lost their luster. When you stop to think, it's actually quite easy to come up with better and more stimulating language. If, in a pinch, you can't find anything better, try speaking in a simple straightforward manner rather than repeating the same old ho-hum expression. Saying just plain "You look so cool" sounds much better than piping "You look cool as a cucumber."

SLANGUAGE

There's a certain type of slang that shows you are "in." It's the latest colorful phrase that capsules an idea—the slang used by smart and sophisticated people. You'll hear your boss use a bit of it; you may even have noticed your teachers using a bit of it. The important point is that *they use only a bit*. Slang is like garlic: a little adds savor, but too much—no, thanks!

The type of slang used is also extremely important. The juvenile slang that sounds so smart around school is likely to be frowned on in the adult world. The wisest course for any business girl is to feel her way cautiously and to stick to the language she knows is genuinely acceptable until she is sure of what is right. You can never go wrong in the office if you restrict your use of slang words; and you may find that using "regular" words gives your speech much more punch.

257

LEARN IT—BURY IT

So far in this section on voice improvement you've been advised to watch your pitch, your volume, your breathing, your grammar, your enunciation and pronunciation, and your choice of words. These all require your attention, but they should be stashed away in your subconscious during conversation. When you are talking to someone, you don't want to be so conscious of how you are expressing yourself that your speech sounds studied or artificial. If we are overcareful, our speech is robbed of its spontaneity, which is in essence the warmth and charm of conversation. If you learn to love words and practice using them correctly, they will come readily when you need them. Direct, simple talk is far more desirable than stilted speech, no matter how splendid the words and how elegant the diction may be.

1 Select a good book to read. Choose one that has a lively writing style and read it analytically for style and word choice as well as for meaning and enjoyment.

2 Read a little poetry every day for a week. Let it be humorous or light verse one day, more serious poetry the next. Look for the beautiful image-creating words and the lovely sounds formed by various word combinations.

3 Examine your speech carefully for an entire day to see if you overwork any words or expressions.

Charm is made effective to a large degree by what we say. The girl who is easy to talk to is always popular. Her friendly manner attracts and delights. Her conversation relaxes her listeners and inspires them, bringing out their best. As a result, friends flock to her and respond to her as to catchy lilting music.

The secret of many a girl's charm is that she is literally easy to talk to. *She makes it fun for others to talk to her.* She is a good listener; she has the ability to suggest interesting conversational subjects and to inspire others to contribute their best. And she willingly lets others have the stage and do the major share of the talking. When necessary, she can add the proper remarks that keep the ball rolling and can guide conversation to pleasant subjects; and she has a storehouse of interesting anecdotes and observations that enable her to contribute something interesting and vital.

The reason she is so easy to talk to is that she has trained herself to be YOU-minded. She is always thinking of the other person. She is considered excellent company because she thinks of what *you* would like to talk about, what would make *you* happy. And she allows the other person to do as much of the talking as he pleases without extraneous interruptions or stories of her own which sidetrack the conversation. Her own talk is usually of an impersonal nature that draws others in and encourages them to share their feelings and experiences.

The benefits of such an approach are many. It provides the surest cure for any charm-stifling self-consciousness, because you are forced to get your mind off yourself. When you set for yourself the goal of making *others* happy, you must become so completely involved with YOU-thoughts that there is no opportunity for ME-thoughts and for haunting self-appraisal. And as your guest warms and responds to your charm, you cannot help but gain confidence and express the best of yourself.

Another side benefit is that through encouraging good conversation and playing the straight man more often than the star, you can learn many things. After all, you already know the anecdotes and experiences that you can relate. Give the other person the opportunity to talk, and you will get ideas for topics for other conversations.

17 TALENTED TALK

GRAND OPENING

The opening remarks that start off a conversation can dispel any awkwardness or strangeness if they lead quickly to a pleasant discussion. But what shall the topic be? **261**

Find the solution by asking yourself what the other person has been doing that he would like to talk about. Perhaps he's just returned from vacation, has an interesting job, is a bug on photography or sports. What was he doing when you last spoke to him?

A compliment is always a gracious beginning. Is there something you can admire about a person's appearance, about his recent accomplishments or activities, or about his home if you are a guest? Needless to say, sincerity is all-important. It gives warmth and feeling to compliments and also protects you from any tendency to overdo.

Another technique is to ask someone for information or advice. Anyone who is even a small authority on some subject is usually delighted to share his knowledge. There's always the girl who can tell you about the newest books, the artist who can suggest the proper paints for some project you might be undertaking, the bargain specialist, the girl who sews or knits well. Almost everybody has some field they've investigated a bit more than the average person—and how it does their hearts good to have a chance to expound to an interested listener! When you can direct the conversation to a person's favorite topic or specialty, you can be sure the conversation will have plenty of momentum for quite a while.

But suppose you are confronted with the problem of making conversation with a complete stranger, someone whose interests and activities are unknown? A compliment is a good beginning, or perhaps a favorable comment about your surroundings. When you are in someone's home, a remark such as "Lynn has such a wonderful record collection" can give you many convenient handles for conversation. You can talk about Lynn and her musical interests, new records, favorite musicians or singers, the best places to buy records, lyrics of certain songs, and so on. The good conversationalist can usually find several directions a subject can be turned so that it will strike a responsive feeling.

Here are some specific subjects that usually help to break the ice:

The weather. Don't be afraid to talk about the weather. The cavemen probably discussed it, and long after we're gone it will still be a topic of interest and concern. Very often it can serve as a convenient opening wedge to lead into other subjects. For example, a beautiful day may remind you of those lovely billboard ads of people driving through the countryside. From there you can go on to discussing ads, ban-the-billboards legislation, cars, beautiful places, and so on.

Food. The way to a man's heart may be through his stomach, but talk about food usually interests both sexes. Good restaurants, favorite foods, foreign dishes, memories connected with different foods, recipes, new products on the market, food advertising—all are good for spirited talk.

Animals (perhaps pets) or children. If discussing a younger brother or sister, please include only the kindly comments, however.

A recent news item. If something such as the political situation or the status of world affairs seems too heavy for the occasion, you might well find a lighter feature of more interest. Perhaps you might discuss a personality in the headlines or some recent occurrence, such as an accident, fire, act of heroism, a new scientific development, or some startling idea, such as a Russian scientist's claim to be able to make two hours' sleep give the benefits of eight.

Local history. An outsider might be interested to know that during the Revolution a local parson once tore up the hymnals and used the paper as wadding for the muskets used to hold off the redcoats. Or perhaps some famous person once lived in your area or an interesting event took place in the vicinity.

Something of common experience. A feeling of kinship can be aroused when we share sentiments about a familiar subject. It might be merely the problems of commuting, but more fascinating topics are travel and the places you have visited. Strange supernatural occurrences (ghosts, mental telepathy, palm readings come true) and fears are also engrossing subjects.

The best subjects—and the safest ones—are impersonal topics. Unless you have lived an extraordinarily rich and full life, talk about yourself usually is bound to be rather unexciting. And perhaps you've noticed that even the people who have led the most interesting lives often avoid overemphasis on the personal, preferring to tell about things and places they have seen rather than about their own accomplishments. Occasionally we come across the individual who can't seem to get away from "I." No matter how vast the topic, at the first opportunity she will narrow it down to some trivia in her own experience. While there are many occasions when our own feelings and reactions are pertinent, often a story would be more interesting if unencumbered by "I" references.

EXPANDING YOUR REPERTOIRE

The more things you know and the more things you are interested in, the more versatile you will be as a conversationalist. The person with a broad background can easily find common ground for conversation with others, for she has a rich and varied supply of material to draw on. A broad background doesn't require a European tour and a Phi Beta Kappa key. It can be acquired by listening closely to what is said and by observing and absorbing what is going on in the world. Conversational ability comes easily to the person who reads a good newspaper daily, listens to some informative TV and radio programs, reads good books, keeps up on new movies and plays, and who is alert to what's going on around her.

Fascinating material can be gleaned from many sources if you are on the lookout for it. Some people can get more interesting material from a short bus ride than others gather from a coast-to-coast trip. Next time you walk down a busy street, see if you can't observe at least five little human dramas. With a bit of practice you will probably find even more.

Salespeople are sometimes a gold mine of information. If, for instance, you encourage a perfume salesgirl to talk, she might be able to tell you stories about ambergris (a substance secreted by whales and used in perfumes), its rarity and the fabulous price it commands. You might be surprised at how much interesting information you can gain from service people such as dry cleaners and repairmen. Rich sources are all around us.

Conversation ideas often elude us because of our woefully weak memories, but you *can* remember anecdotes if you really try. As soon as you have a quiet moment, think about what you've seen or learned during the day. Perhaps you can tell it to yourself as you would tell it to a friend. This helps fix the information in your mental file drawer. Write down the various ideas you've discovered, if you have to. Some brilliant conversationalists actually keep little notebooks in which they jot down notes about interesting happenings so that they can quickly refresh their memories if they find themselves forgetting an important aspect of a good story.

If you know something about art, literature, music, and the world's history—the makings of culture—you will not only have a richer background upon which to draw but you'll also have good protection against self-consciousness. You needn't be an authority on these subjects. Even a slight acquaintance with them gives you added polish and enables you to hold your own or at least understand what others are talking about so that you won't be bothered by inferiority feelings.

Improving your cultural background can be inspiring and thrilling. A slight taste usually makes us want more. The paintings, books, and music that are classics have withstood the test of time—they have been favorites down through the years. They have entertained, amused, and exhilarated all kinds of people. If you haven't already done so, you owe it to yourself to discover their magnificence.

When you listen to good music or study a great painting, approach it with an open mind to discover what it can tell you. Look for the beauty that others have found in it and let this beauty play on your emotions. Try to imagine what the artist was attempting to say. Look for the rhythmic sweep of lines and interesting perspective in a picture, the ingenious blending of harmonies in music, the splendid choice of words in literature. Your life will be fuller and richer for the new joys you will discover.

One of the most delightful ways to learn about earlier times is to read historical novels and biographies of famous persons. They give us a deeper understanding of the past and are fascinating reading.

When you bring into a conversation any information that may be unfamiliar to your listeners, you will want to avoid a patronizing air. Some such prefacing statement as "As you know . . ." will be helpful in making them feel "in."

Incidental intelligence: the good worker with a rich background and observing mind rates Highly Desirable on any employer's list. There's always the day when some tidbit she learned will be mighty helpful to her boss or her work. And what girl isn't considered more valuable when she can hold an intelligent and interesting conversation with an important visitor!

Prime yourself · Before a party we devote a good deal of time to perfecting our appearance. A little time spent in polishing up our conversation is also good preparation for poise. Are there subjects you might brush up on so that you can discuss them or at least ask intelligent questions? You may want to investigate your date's favorite hobby, the developing political situation, or the afternoon's major sports event. The object is not to become an expert yourself so that you can show off your knowledge, but rather to become familiar enough with the topics so that you can direct conversation to them.

Check over the conversational subjects you've gathered to see what might be most appropriate. You might also want to run over the names and interests of people you expect to meet if you haven't seen them for some time.

If you're plagued with any inferiority feelings—and most of us are occasionally—stamp them out quickly. They do nothing but cause trouble. By now you have progressed far enough in this course to take pride in your lovely new appearance. Your posture is improving, you are becoming more graceful, developing a better figure, and you know how to dress and use cosmetics to bring out your best. Forget yourself; you can take pride in your accomplishments and needn't let your charm leak out in wasteful worry. It's time to stop wondering what others think of you. Realize that others have had—or still have—the same self-consciousness that bothers you and have overcome their fears so that they seem assured and poised. This should prove to you that you can do the same.

You won't, however, want to go to the opposite extreme where you seem too cocksure. The least little slip such a person makes becomes a loud kerboom. Instead, concentrate on helping others have a good time and you will surely have one, too.

At the party · As you arrive at the door, pause a moment to take a deep breath. This allows you to collect yourself, perks up your circulation just a bit, and gets you off to a clearheaded start. Then go first to greet your hostess. She will introduce you to someone if you are a stranger to the group and may say something like, "Ann Murray, this is Jim Brown. Jim's home from Purdue for the weekend. He just finished his exams." This gives you an opportunity for conversation so you can be off to a good start.

When you are attending a meeting or other large gathering alone, don't slink into the nearest vacant chair. You will show more poise if you walk calmly well inside to select a seat. Then instead of sinking into yourself, look around you and smile. If you

267

can't get into the conversation of those immediately around you, perhaps you can spot someone else who seems alone. Here is your opportunity to make a friend, and one friend quickly leads to another.

Men · Back to Jim Brown—and men in general. When you have met a man at a party don't cling. Men are a wary breed, always expecting a girl to try to put her clamps on them. You will be considered far more poised if you can invite others into your conversation or if, after you have talked with him for a while, you can leave to help your hostess pass refreshments or to talk to another friend. You can always come back later, you know. And you will be far more welcome than if you had overstayed. Some clever girls manage to depart so that a conversation is left unfinished—the perfect excuse for returning to resume it.

The girls that men marry are not usually the girls who flirt the most. A man values the girl who lets him do the pursuing. Of course, you will want to show him that he's interesting and important (but not the only or the biggest interest in your life). Play it subtly. Your happy manner, your kindness to everyone, and your manner of gently boosting his ego by being an encouraging and responsive audience will charm him. Of course, you will enter into the conversation frequently, too. But the greatest success is usually attained by keeping his mind on subjects that allow him to display his knowledge.

Pest control · Occasionally at a gathering you may find that you are stuck with someone who is definitely a pest or a bore. You, as a lady, will not want to be rude to anyone. Your charm rating will continue to be high if you can involve other people in the conversation and then exit inconspicuously. Treat even the most undesirable individual kindly. You can't go wrong by being kind. The rough diamonds of the world aren't noted for their high social gloss, but for other more exciting qualities. Take the matter lightly, maintain your friendly manner, and you are likely to discover that he is not quite as dreadful as predicted.

Taking your leave · When it's time to go home, announce your intention, seek out your hostess to thank her for a pleasant time, and then go. The person who prolongs his leavetaking is a burden to the hostess and a drag on the party. If you become intrigued by something and change your mind, say that you intend to stay a while longer, so that the party can get back to normal.

When you want to see someone again, Jim Brown, for instance, you might subtly suggest a possible further meeting by some such parting remark as "Let me know how your (history paper, tennis match) turned out." Then it is up to him.

SMOOTH TALKING

Here are some suggestions that will help keep the conversation running smoothly. They're as applicable to a day on the job as to a night on the town.

🌼 Keep your voice up at the end of a sentence. This adds a note of continuity that invites the listener to go on with the subject. It's as if you said "Don't you agree?" If your voice drops, the effect is one of finality, as if you said "Well, that's finished and nothing more can be said about it."

🌼 Keep strong opinions to yourself. Ben Franklin's advice against seeming too opinionated is still excellent psychology. On the whole, it is best not to air your firm convictions socially, especially not with a tone of inflexibility. How much more congenial it sounds to hear someone say, "Have you heard what the President (the editor of Time, the mayor, the scientist at Oak Ridge) has to say on _____?" Or put your idea in the form of a question, such as "Do you think _____ is good for the town?" This way of phrasing a statement invites discussion, but a flatly stated opinion quickly puts the damper on talk.

🌸 Avoid saying unpleasant things about anyone or anything. Brutal frankness, sarcasm, prejudice, and intolerance boomerang and, more often than not, damage others' respect for the speaker. If the conversation drifts to gossip or tearing down an acquaintance, rise above the situation. Don't join in or show approval. Instead, try to change the subject. How much more pleasant is the person who discusses his likes, rather than his dislikes. If you can't say something favorable, keep your thoughts to yourself. Better yet, try to weed out those critical thoughts; they can't help but dull your charm.

🌸 Watch your timing. When you are speaking, say what you intend to say and stop. Don't drag it on past the finish line. Overrunning causes some speakers to give up in midsentence—as if the idea weren't worth continuing (which it usually isn't). Others nervously drag on and on, talking long past the point where the listener was stirred to add something to the conversation. They seem afraid of allowing a pause. This type of speaker takes the words out of his partner's mouth, then wonders why his partner is so silent.

🌸 Include everyone in your conversation. If someone makes a school or office joke in a group with outsiders who might not understand, courtesy demands that you offer a brief explanation. Don't let the conversation dwell overlong on "inside" talk, but switch the subject to something that will be of interest to all.

🌸 Don't try to seem important. The other person's prime concern is his own importance. Your charm rating rises in proportion to your ability to lift *his* feelings of importance. Give him a good opinion of your heart and he'll automatically have a high opinion of your mind.

🌸 Don't belittle yourself. This tends to sound phony, especially if your listeners feel called upon to come to your defense. In some cases you might even point out flaws that otherwise would go unobserved.

🌸 Accept compliments graciously. A warm thank-you and a friendly smile are all that are necessary. Don't protest that you don't deserve the compliment or, worst of all, expound on your virtues. You will always appear self-possessed and charming if your reply reflects the speaker's kindness and generosity or the value of his opinion rather than your qualifications. You can say something such as, "Thank you, I'm so glad you enjoyed it; that makes me feel very glad!" or "It's good of you to say so; you're very kind." If the compliment is a gay extravagant one, your answer should be in keeping: "Oh, how good you make me feel! Now I can simply float through the rest of the day!" After acknowledging a compliment, casually change the subject to switch the conversation away from yourself.

🌺 Guard against the temptation to overemphasize or to exaggerate, by either tone or word. Give a word credit for its full value. Don't say *marvelous* if you mean *good*, or *horrible* if you mean *fair* or *poor*. Such overstatement undermines listeners' confidence and leads them to underrate what is said.

🌺 Be enthusiastic whenever possible. Enthusiasm has a magnetic quality that draws others to us. They somehow want to share in our pleasure. Overenthusiasm, however, leads to a tendency to gush. You need never fear letting your enthusiasm get out-of-bounds if you do not let it go beyond the point where you are sincere.

🌺 Encourage your listener to talk about himself. Give him such tag lines as "Did anything similar ever happen to you?" or "Perhaps you've felt like that, too, sometimes?"

🌺 Help your friends feel clever and important by repeating their amusing remarks to others and always giving proper credit. If someone has just told you a good story and others join you, ask him to repeat the story for everyone.

🌺 Keep personal matters personal. While you have more leeway with your close friends, it is never good to air the family wash in public. This is particularly true at the office. The girl who discusses her love life, the shortcomings of her father, or other personal matters embarrasses her listeners and loses respect because of her lack of discretion. By the same token, you will, of course, want to avoid asking others any questions that sound prying and might possibly offend.

EVERYBODY LOVES A LISTENER

From the boss to your beau, you will be highly appreciated if you can be an attentive listener. A good listener often performs a valuable function—she inspires the speaker and helps him clarify his ideas. Numerous executives have come up with brilliant solutions to vexing problems while talking it out with their Girl Fridays. And you know how often a problem seems to shrink in proportions when you can talk freely to an understanding friend.

The main reason we fall short as listeners is that we're too busy thinking ahead to what we will say next. Once you have directed the conversation to the other person and set him going, then you must perform one of the most difficult of conversation tactics— keeping quiet. Ninety percent of being a good conversationalist is being a good listener. Many people, women particularly, have wonderful reputations as charming conversationalists and yet actually say very little—they listen. There seems to be an almost universal need to talk, and since we are all essentially egotistical, we love to talk about ourselves.

Being a good listener is not easy. It requires complete attention, some prodding now and then with some good questions, and the ability to direct a conversation well. Comments like "Isn't that interesting!" encourage the conversation. Give it your best tonal quality and be sure to sound sincere. How do you sound sincere? By being sincere. By making an attempt to be as alert as possible and by following closely what is said.

Other keep-the-show-going comments might be: "How did you happen to learn about that?" "That's the first time I ever heard about such an idea." "Where were you when you ran across that?" "How did you happen to be there?"

You also convey your interest by your physical reaction—perhaps by leaning slightly forward in your seat or by shifting your hand slightly in response to what is said—by the expression on your face, and by looking directly into the eyes of the speaker. If you are genuinely sincere, you won't overdo.

Great intestinal fortitude is sometimes required to refrain from telling one of your favorite stories, which might divert the conversation to you. There are times when this is necessary and quite desirable, but remember that to your listener the best anecdote you can tell is only half as good as the one he tells. If the speaker is talking enthusiastically, let him enjoy telling his experiences—and you enjoy your reputation for charm.

HOW TO TELL A STORY

Some storytellers can make an ordinary experience sizzle with excitement, while others kill even the best tale. Sizzle or fizzle—it depends on the skill of the speaker. While there are some raconteurs who seem to be naturally gifted, more often good storytellers are made, not born. They've studied the techniques and practiced until they have achieved a polished style. Here are some points that help make a story a success.

• Make it easy to get the picture by stating the subject near the beginning of the story.

• Don't digress. Tell your tale in a clear, straightforward manner without bringing in extraneous details or haggling over whether it happened Wednesday at two or Tuesday at three.

• Use explicit terms. The person who says "it" or "thing" or "this fellow" is likely to lose his listener. The experts learn to be as exact as possible and to substitute a specific term for a general one whenever possible. How much more colorful a picture is created by saying "the smell of roast beef and apple pie" instead of "the smells of dinner."

• Keep it brief. Most stories are strung out too long.

• Once you have told your punch line, stop. Some people enjoy their own stories so much that they like to repeat the ending so that they can laugh all over again. Maybe they can, but chances are their listeners can't.

The most successful stories are told with a light touch. Some girls with reputations for humor have developed such a sense of fun that they can find something entertaining in what others would consider pretty tame stuff. They regard the world as a very amusing place, and since they look for fun they can usually find it and can project it to others.

The best way to improve your storytelling technique is to practice. Try jokes and funny stories at first. These must be kept going at a fast pace and are good discipline. Try them on your family and friends. To get a laugh, you must put a joke across well.

A good way to improve your ability to tell a serious experience is to select a brief newspaper story. After you have read it carefully, put the paper aside and write your own version. When your words are put down in writing, you can judge them more easily. Compare your version with the original to see where you are weak, where you may have digressed, or where you could have used more forceful or colorful words.

Practice telling stories aloud to yourself. Then practice telling them to your friends. The more you keep at it, the smoother your delivery will become. Make yourself tell at least three different stories to friends each day. Soon you'll be able to shine with the best of them.

 FOLLOW-UP

1 In all of your conversations for an entire day, practice directing the conversation away from yourself. Aim for the other person's interests and activities. See how long you can keep others talking about themselves or about impersonal subjects—not you.

2 On another day choose five topics that you would like to discuss with someone. In your conversations throughout the day see how subtly you can lead the talk from first one of these topics to the other. This is excellent practice in directing the conversation and will stand you in good stead when you wish to divert the talk from unpleasant topics.

3 Take a fifteen-minute walk and see how many conversational ideas you can discover. You should be able to find at least eight.

PART FIVE: THE

ICETIES OF NINE-TO-FIVE

How well you have learned and applied your lessons in charm is put to a crucial test when you apply for a job. Here first impressions are all-important. You must do a good selling job on the first try, because you seldom get a second chance.

If you are using the help-wanted ads to obtain job leads, you will probably find that some of the most desirable positions request that you write out information about yourself and mail it in. This is done not only to help the busy employer sort out those he considers unqualified but also to provide him with a sample of your work. You will therefore want to make your answer as complete yet as concise as possible, and as beautiful a specimen of your typewriting talent as you can create.

18

THE JOB INTERVIEW

THE LETTER OF APPLICATION

The most generally approved technique involves a brief covering letter plus a detailed résumé in outline form. Your letter should contain the following information:

1 The title of the position for which you are applying.

2 Why you are interested in this particular position—you want a job that lets you meet people, you are intrigued by the firm's products, and so on.

3 A reason why you feel you could contribute something to the business. For example, you've been told you have a knack for dealing well with people. Or, if the ad indicates that transcribing or letter writing is part of the work, you might mention that you have a sound background in English grammar or have won awards for your shorthand or typing skill. If the ad lists "good at figures" as one of the requirements, emphasize your mathematical ability. Ask yourself, "What is this employer looking for? What abilities would be helpful to someone in his business or profession? What qualities do I have that he would value?"

4 A mention of your résumé.

5 A closing sentence concerning your availability for an interview.

An example of what a good application letter might say is shown in the margin on page 282.

THE RÉSUMÉ

Your résumé should be typed—never use a carbon or duplicated copy of any sort— and should fit on one page if possible. It should be arranged in neat, easy-to-read outline form and should provide the following information:

1 Your name, address, and phone number.

2 The position for which you are applying.

3 Your education (high school, business school and/or college). List your most recent schooling first, mentioning the years you attended. Indicate the type of course or major.

   a Subjects studied. List the subjects that might relate to this job. Include your typing and shorthand speeds, any language courses, and any subjects that might specifically pertain to the work (science courses for a drug firm, economics and mathematical courses for a bank).

   b Awards and activities. Show off your good grades by indicating your class rank, such as "in the upper fourth of class." If your grades were low, better say nothing. You will also want to include any awards you have won or special honors you received. In addition to those for specific business subjects, you should also include citizenship or language awards. What activities did you participate in at school? Were you an officer of any organization? Any such information helps the employer sift you out from the rest of the beginners. It shows him that you possess leadership ability, have varied interests, and were well liked by your schoolmates. Your résumé is your personal advertisement and should include any information about yourself that proves you are an intelligent, responsible person with the initiative and ability to do a good job.

4 Experience. Include any previous employment, *beginning* with the most recent. Give the dates of employment as well as a brief description of the type of concern and your duties.

If you have never worked in a business office before, don't sell yourself short and classify yourself as having no business experience. Did you work on your school newspaper or yearbook? Were you secretary or treasurer of your class or of some other large organization? Did you ever relieve the switchboard operator, help with the mimeographing jobs, or do filing or clerical work in the school office? Perhaps you helped in your father's office or a local store on Saturdays and holidays. Work as a camp counselor, hospital volunteer, or baby sitter should also be mentioned because they show your ability to get along with people.

5 Personal information. Include your age, height, weight, general health condition, marital status, hobbies or interests, and any other pertinent personal information that will help the employer get a better insight into your talents and abilities. You can put your vital statistics at the beginning, your hobbies with other school activities.

6 References. Include names of three or four adults who know you well and will speak favorably of you—perhaps a teacher, your minister, and a professional or business man. Give the complete addresses and phone numbers of references. You will, of course, obtain permission in advance from these people before using their names.

When your letter and résumé have been completed, rush them to the mailbox. Good jobs always go fast—and those first in line are sure to receive most attention.

The Crestview Courier
Box 421
Crestview, Illinois 60625

Gentlemen:

Your notice, advertising a secretarial position
in a pharmaceutical laboratory, sounded very
interesting to me.

Science has always been my favorite subject,
and I received the Thomas J. Palmer Science
Award at high school. I attend Mercer Business
College, where I take many courses, including
business arithmetic and typewriting.

Enclosed is a complete resume of my background
and qualifications. If they are what you have
in mind, may I speak to you about the position?

My telephone number is 421-8767. I would be
happy to come to your office whenever it is
convenient for you.

Sincerely yours,

Joanne Burnell

Joanne Burnell

RÉSUMÉ
of
Joanne Burnell
7 Hamilton Terrace
Crestview, Illinois
Telephone: 421-8767

- **POSITION SOUGHT:** Secretarial

- **VITAL STATISTICS:**
  Date of Birth: January 25, 1944   Height: 5 feet, 8 inches
  Marital Status: Single   Weight: 135 pounds
  Social Security: 021-27-0672   Health: Excellent

- **EDUCATION:**
  Mercer Business College, Crestview, Illinois
  Year of Graduation: 196-
  Specialization: Executive Secretarial
  Significant Courses:

Secretarial
  1. Typewriting—65 net words a minute
  2. Shorthand—120 words a minute
  3. Secretarial Procedures—filing, correspondence, financial records, mail, telephone usage, etc.
  4. Office Machines—10-key adding, calculator, mimeograph, transcribers

General Business
  1. Business Arithmetic
  2. Accounting
  3. Economics
  4. Business Law

Liberal Arts
  1. English Composition
  2. Psychology—Fundamentals
  3. History—Constitutional Government
  4. Art—Drawing and Painting

Crestview High School, Crestview, Illinois, 1958–1962
Year of Graduation: June, 1962
College Preparatory Course
Significant Courses:
1. Chemistry
2. Biology
3. Spanish—four semesters

College: Treasurer, Student Government Council
             Assistant Business Manager, college newspaper
             Member, Red Cross Council
             Graduated in upper tenth of class

High School: Member, Honor Society
              Spanish Club
              Thomas J. Palmer Science Award

Hobbies: Outdoor sports, art, international relations

EXPERIENCE:

Brooks and Co., 109 Main St., Crestview, Illinois—421-7000
September, 1963, to present. Part-time salesgirl. I have consistently had one of the highest sales tallies in the departments in which I've worked (costume jewelry, toys).

Dr. Howard Dean, 42 Tall Oaks Drive, Plainfield, Illinois—421-0303
June–September, 1963. Receptionist in office of dermatologist.
Through greeting patients and answering telephone I learned to deal with many types of people. I also was responsible for sending out bills, for keeping office accounts, and for filing patients' records.

REFERENCES:

Mrs. Hannah Rowe, Dean of Instruction, The Mercer Business College, 90 Superior Boulevard, Crestview, Illinois—421-8240.

The Reverend William Schwartz, 1 Trinity Place, Crestview, Illinois—421-0972

Mr. Robert Holmes, 109 Briant Street, Crestview, Illinois—421-8926

Whether or not you are applying for a position by mail, you will be wise to compile a résumé. Many of the top-quality jobs, for which the competition is stiff (and which bring higher salaries), require a résumé. Even if none is requested, the fact that you showed the foresight and the initiative to prepare one raises you above the other applicants right from the start. One young graduate who was applying for a low-paying position—a starting position—presented such an impressive résumé that the personnel director suggested her for a much better job, and she was hired. A good résumé can bring you to the attention of other executives and might open doors that would ordinarily be available only to those with more experience.

YOUR INTERVIEW OUTFIT

The girl who knows the importance of a smooth start on job-hunting day makes complete preparations the night before. She plans her outfit carefully and completely down to the earrings and nail enamel she will wear. She checks each item to see that it is sparkling clean, fresh, polished, pressed, and that no loose buttons or weak straps will cause last-minute emergencies.

She chooses a well-cut suit or a smartly tailored dress to impart the businesslike air of efficiency so dear to the heart of employers. She realizes that her outfit must be fashionable but that it should not be too high style or too exotic. Prospective bosses scare all too easily. Color? A quiet, subdued shade bespeaks her business know-how. Although almost every hue of the rainbow is seen in the apparel of business girls today, the darker or muted shades are still favored and should be chosen for job-hunting outfits. Accessories can be more gay and bright, of course, and should be carefully coordinated to show good taste.

The clever job applicant most certainly wears a hat—one that is fairly small and not too extreme in style. Although a hat is becoming less essential these days, particularly in warm weather, many personnel directors look to see if a prospective employee has the good business sense to wear one. The girl with a hat is sure to be rated a good notch above a hatless competitor, because she has made the extra effort to finish off her costume.

The same reasoning applies to hosiery. Although many fashionable women go bare legged in summer once they've acquired a good tan, many employers consider bare legs an affront to business formality.

If the job seeker is lucky enough to own a fur coat or fur hat or fur jacket, she wisely leaves it in her closet. A simple cloth coat does more to further the idea that she needs a job, wants to work—and isn't just looking for some amusement to wile away her idle hours.

Her makeup and grooming are the epitome of perfection. Her gloves (a must in summer as well as winter) are clean and fresh. Perhaps she carries an extra pair in her purse in case her first pair becomes soiled. She's also sure her purse is in good condition with no unsightly bulges to ruin its trim lines. Shoes are simple and suitable, passing the test for even heels, unscuffed tips, and a high polish.

Appearance is such an important gauge of personality that you should be sure every detail is in order and that you look your best. Then you will feel confident and can devote complete attention to the interview.

BE PREPARED

Like a good Girl Scout, you owe it to your job future to be fully prepared for an emergency. Because the pens in personnel offices are usually a haphazard lot, you'll d well to take along a good pen of your own, plus two well-sharpened pencils, an erase and an eraser shield—all of which may be valuable in filling out applications neatly or i taking tests. Remember, too, to include your social security card and perhaps a sma notebook for jotting down addresses, directions, and other information.

When an employer is interviewing an applicant, he has so little to go on that he ma attach undue importance to minor slipups. He might be quite willing to give a secon application form if the first is spoiled or to lend a pen if the applicant's gives out durin a dictation test, but this may make him wonder about her thoroughness and efficiency

EXTRAS THAT IMPRESS

What can you do to make you stand out above the others trying for the job?

Offer a copy of your résumé · Even though you may have sent a copy of your résum along with your answer to the ad, it's a good idea to bring another copy to the interviev When an applicant is being considered for a job, her résumé may be passed throug several hands and may not have been returned in time or, worse yet, may have been lo in the shuffle.

Obtain a letter of recommendation · If possible, get one from a previous employer c from someone for whom you did volunteer office work. Glowing praise from a pa employer can strongly influence a prospective one.

Learn all you can about the firm · This most impressive extra depends on whether yo know the name of the firm in advance. If you have obtained your job lead through a employment agency, you will most likely be sent directly from the agency to the compar with no time for checking. If, however, you have time to do a little investigation befor the interview, by all means do so. Try to bone up on the firm's services or products s that you are aware of its needs and know what qualities the employer is looking for i his personnel. Your local Chamber of Commerce should be able to help you. Perhai your library has material about the industry that you could skim. Ask your father an teachers for information about the concern. A knowledge of the firm's reputation, expansion plans, and new products will all be good background information. Another advantage of such investigation is that you will probably also discover anything undesirable about the company that might make you hesitate to accept the job.

PASSING THE PRELIMINARIES

You're there. You've found your way to the office of this marvelous-sounding firm. As you step off the elevator a few minutes before the appointed time, you may suffer a few butterflies in the tummy—it's natural! Now's the time to quickly bolster your poise by reminding yourself of your perfect grooming, your careful planning, and your success in winning an interview in the first place.

A self-assured manner is a most important sales technique. If you don't feel as brave as you wish you did, call forth the actress in you to make yourself appear assured and at ease. Not only will this little pretense help you to relax and actually develop the confidence you are portraying, but it will pay off in its impression on others. A self-confident manner shows that you have faith in your ability and consider yourself worth hiring—a recommendation from the one who should know best!

Smile as you explain your mission to the receptionist. She will probably ask you to be seated for a few minutes. Don't be impatient or feel put out if the "few minutes" grow longer and longer. Perhaps your prospective boss is tied up with *his* boss. After all, businessmen *are* busy and their time is worth money to the firm that they represent. As yet, yours is not.

You'll want to maintain your best ladylike demeanor while you wait. Even now, you may be under inspection. Smoking and gum chewing are, of course, taboo. Some girls find that it helps them feel more relaxed to bring a newspaper or book to read. Make sure, however, that your choice is of a high caliber because an employer will certainly notice it and will weigh it as a clue to your interests. You may also find it helpful to look and listen to what is going on about you. Try to get the feel of the company and its personnel.

TOP FORM FOR APPLICATIONS

Even though you may have sent in a résumé, you will probably be asked to fill out an application form. Most firms like to have employment records on their own forms so that they can more easily spot the information they want. Read all the instructions carefully before you write anything. If the instructions tell you to print, be sure to print. The ability to provide all information correctly, completely, and neatly will give a good impression of your work habits. Cross-outs, blank spaces, and vagueness are minus factors. A personnel director once confided to an interviewer that he always checked carefully to see if the applicant included her ZIP code number. "If she is thorough and accurate, she'll put it in," he claimed. Because little things mean so much when there are so few clues to what you are like, you must take special pains to see that everything is done to the best of your ability. Check carefully to see that all information has been filled in, that any dates and all the names and addresses of references are correct.

"Mr. Employer will see you now," the receptionist says, nodding to you. Smile and take a deep breath as you follow her to his office. Let your posture and your poise show the confidence and self-assurance he is looking for.

If the employer is on the phone or busy as you enter, wait quietly at his door until he finishes or looks up and motions you to a seat. You will, of course, keep your purse and any other belongings on your lap—not on the interviewer's desk. If he offers you a cigarette, it is the better part of wisdom to refuse politely. Some bosses have an aversion to women smokers, and you don't want to upset your chances.

During the interview, the employer must evaluate you to see how you will fit in with the requirements of the work and with the office personnel. In return, you will want to evaluate him to see what type of answers he is searching for. Mentally put yourself in his place and try to emphasize the assets you can offer and the qualities that would be helpful in this particular position. The clever girl tailors her answers to show how he might benefit from hiring her.

Some of the employer's questions may have already been answered in your application form, which he has before him. This repetition needn't be attributed to careless reading. His purpose may be to get you talking and to see how you express yourself. In your replies, try to answer fully enough so that you give the pertinent information he desires without unrelated chatter. For instance, if he asks what type of work you did in your father's office, you won't boost your score any by merely saying, "Oh, anything that needed to be done." How much better a sales technique you'd use if you answered, "I typed letters and bills, did the filing, and greeted visitors. I often described our service and prices over the telephone, and I ran errands." Thoughts of the magnificent luncheons Dad treated you to, crotchety Mr. Adams who always had one more job for you just at quitting time, or your father's handsome young assistant may whiz through your mind, but since these have no relation to the matter at hand, you will wisely avoid bringing them up.

Allow the employer to lead the interview conversation as much as possible. Girls who talk too much, are too self-assertive, or who force their personality into the interview too strongly usually are ushered out rather fast.

Most employers will ask such questions as "Why do you want this particular job?" and "How long do you intend to work?" Be sure you can come up with a good answer by

289

giving these questions some thought before beginning your job search. Some interviewers may also ask what your ambitions are, what you consider your greatest assets, what hobbies you have, and what books you've read recently. If the interviewer should ask what salary you expect, mention a figure that is just a few dollars higher than the going rate for this type of job. You don't want to sell yourself short, neither do you want to price yourself so high as to appear ridiculous.

If you have worked before and are asked why you left your last job, you will want to proceed with caution. Remember, the best psychology is to accent the positive, never the negative. For instance, say that there was not enough opportunity for advancement. *Never* that you couldn't stand your boss. No matter how unbearable a former employer was, you'll be wise not to criticize or complain.

In all your answers you want to appear as alert, polite, and capable as possible. Show by your attitude that you intend to be a good worker and that you are seriously interested in this job. Even if you don't think it is the job for you, be courteous and attentive. The cocky or too-good-for-this-job attitude that some job hunters display might boomerang some day when there was a really exceptional opening in the same concern.

If the interviewer considers you at all qualified, he will probably give you a good picture of the work and will explain hours, company benefits, and other aspects of the job. If you are not certain about any important phase of the work, such as the duties, opportunities for advancement, or the salary, don't hesitate to ask a few polite questions. You should have as clear an idea of the job as possible. However, the applicant who asks how soon she will get a vacation, how many holidays are observed, and whether coffee breaks are permitted will hardly convince a boss that she wants to *work*.

IS THE JOB RIGHT FOR YOU?

If before you began your job hunting you gave some careful thought to the type of work you want, you should be able to decide easily whether this is the job for you.

- Is it a type of business that will be interesting to you?

- Will you be happy in an office of this size?

- Do the personnel seem to be the type of people with whom you would want to work?

Will the fast pace and excitement (or quiet, calm atmosphere) be to your liking?

If the work is detailed and requires careful attention, are you emotionally equipped to handle it?

If it requires dealing with the public, does this appeal to you?

Does this opening offer prospects of a bright future?

Can you learn and grow on this job?

Does the salary compare favorably with that offered for similar jobs in your locality?

Is it a good location? Is the office convenient to transportation? Is the neighborhood safe to walk in after dark?

How well the job fits in with your answers to such questions will determine your decision. Many beginners feel they should jump at the first job that offers the right salary. Careful, selective job shopping is more likely to result in a happy future.

THE JOB CAN BE YOURS

If you are offered the job and are sure this is the one for you, an enthusiastic "yes" should be given immediately. Don't let the good one get away. If, however, you don't want it, thank the interviewer and refuse kindly, perhaps explaining that you are considering another opening for which you feel you are better suited. Any remark that might seem to belittle the job you are offered should be avoided. Let your good impression remain in the interviewer's mind so that he may possibly contact you at a later time if something more desirable should arise.

Perhaps you are a bit uncertain about the position and want time to think and to get better perspective. Or perhaps you want to check other openings. Politely explain that although you are definitely interested in the job, you have some other interview appointments that you would like to keep before making a decision. Offer to let the employer know by telephoning him by a certain time.

IF THE INTERVIEWER IS UNCERTAIN

If the interviewer wants to consider other applicants before reaching his decision, don't give up hope. Perhaps he, too, wants to be sure that he is, making the best possible selection. To help sway him, why not make one more final sales appeal in the form of a brief thank-you note? Just a few lines, thanking him for his time and expressing your interest in the job, will bring you to mind again and do much to please the employer and to impress him with your capabilities.

1 Learn as much as you can about the job opportunities in your area. What types of businesses are there? What specific products or services do they offer? Are any new firms planning to open offices? When you know something about the companies for which you could work, you can aim for one that will be most interesting to you.

2 Ask your employed friends about their jobs. Try to get a picture of what it's like to work for their firms. Urge them also to talk about the work of their departments and what their specific jobs entail. (One department of a firm can be very different from another.) In this way you can learn what departments might be most in line with your interests and abilities.

3 If you will soon be looking for a job, advertise this to your uncles and your aunts, your parent's friends, your employed friends. Job openings have a way of popping up unexpectedly and someone just might happen to hear of one that would be right for you.

A new job is an exciting opportunity, a new and thrilling beginning. What lies ahead may be wonderful new friends, interesting accomplishments—even adventure. There will, of course, be many challenges—new skills to master, new routines to learn, perhaps strange customs and peculiar personalities to adapt to. It's an opportunity that deserves all you can give it. A beginner is in the spotlight the first two weeks. Her virtues and failings are carefully and curiously inspected. Your good beginning will encourage the staff to expect the best from you and will give you a bonus giant step in your climb to bigger and better things.

19

A CHARMING BEGINNING

EARLY DOES IT

It is pretty much taken for granted that a new employee will arrive bright and extra early on her first day on the job. To forestall any unforeseen mishaps, allow yourself a good deal more time than you think you could ever possibly need under normal circumstances, particularly if the commuting is unfamiliar to you. If you haven't timed your trip during rush hour, remember to allow for traffic tie-ups. No matter how legitimate an excuse may be, it won't go over well. And the girl who arrives panting and in a guilty state of jitters is hardly able to apply the concentration that a new job demands.

GETTING YOUR BEARINGS

If you are working in a large office, you will probably be introduced to many people during your first few days. Listen carefully so that you get each name straight the first time. Then repeat it to yourself and try to use the name in your conversation to help fix it in mind. The person who actually makes an effort to remember names usually finds it's quite easy to score a good average.

Once you are back at your desk and have a free moment, go over the names of those you have just met and try to attach them firmly to the proper faces. Some newcomers find it helpful to fortify their memories by devising a floor plan with the names and locations of the people with whom they will come in contact. Then when the boss booms, "Please rush this to Jenkins in Accounting," there's no need to falter, because even if your memory lapses momentarily, a quick check of that handy floor plan will show you the right direction.

Learn as much as you can about your firm. Study the company manuals and advertising material so that you will know about its products and services. The girl who is familiar with the background of her company soon develops the understanding and insight that make her an asset to the staff.

Notes, notes, and more notes • Sound advice for the beginner! Listen as carefully to all instructions as if you were hearing the greatest suspense thriller, for in fact you are. The instructions are the buildup; the will-she-make-it-or-won't-she outcome is up to you. So many things must be crammed into your cranium the first few days that it will be helpful to jot down notes about any instructions, procedures, or operations that might possibly be confusing. Some of your notes may seem trivial, but if they prevent an embarrassing slipup they will be invaluable to you.

Don't be afraid to ask questions when new work is being explained. You aren't expected to know everything right away. And many an experienced staff member is so familiar with the work that he unthinkingly omits details necessary to your proper understanding of the job. Asking intelligent questions when the job is first given often helps prevent confusion and mistakes later on.

The time will probably come, however, when you will be quite baffled by some aspect of the work you're doing. Although your first impulse may be to run for help to your boss or to the person who is training you, sit tight for a moment and see if you can possibly figure out the answer for yourself. If it's a matter of making extra carbons, you'll always be safe if you make the extras. If your question is about some sort of monthly or weekly report, perhaps you can check the files to find the last report to use as a guide. The files often can prove extremely helpful. They can rescue you when the spelling of a name is in doubt and can provide a great deal of information about the business and its operation. A company manual might give you a clue, too. If you still can't find the answer, then don't hesitate to ask someone. Most people are glad to help, particularly if they feel your questions are warranted and you aren't badgering them needlessly.

If you are lucky enough to be broken in by the girl whom you are replacing, you have a golden opportunity to learn all the quirks of your boss's personality as well as of the work. Make careful note of how he likes things done and also of his pet peeves. Do everything you can to make a friend of this girl and to keep her from feeling "pushed out." If you must share the same desk with her, don't usurp her private drawer or in any way try to take over while she's still there. This may be ticklish, but you can't go wrong if you are thoughtful and considerate. Her friendship is well worth cultivating because she can save you many a pitfall.

LEARN THE RULES

If you want to be appreciated by the rest of the office team, you've got to learn the rules right away and play the game straight. The quickest way to arouse resentment is to break office rules or precedents. Don't take it for granted that certain privileges are just naturally given. Find out for sure. Are coffee breaks permitted, grudgingly tolerated, or forbidden? If rest periods are permitted, find out how long a time is allowed so you won't overstay How about lunch hour—is there a specific time you're expected to take yours and is it actually *one* hour? Is smoking at your desk approved? If there is any doubt about any rules, check with your supervisor. The fact that others smoke or take breaks doesn't mean their acts are approved. They may be violating a rule that is not strictly enforced—but is a rule nonetheless. You don't want to be classed with those the boss growls about—merely because you didn't know the rules.

Be especially cautious in regard to smoking. Although some companies have no objection to employees' smoking at their desks, your particular boss may be annoyed by it. In one office where smoking was permitted, a supervisor was allergic to smoke, and out of consideration for her none of those who sat nearby would have thought of smoking at their desks. Don't take it for granted that because your boss smokes—and may even offer you a cigarette occasionally—he approves of your smoking. Many a businessman objects to seeing a woman smoke, particularly if she is likely to come in contact with customers. Courtesy, however, requires him to offer her a cigarette when he lights up, so he does—but he expects she'll have the good judgment to refuse.

If smoking is permitted and you do indulge, be careful that your smoke isn't continually wafted in one person's direction. Smoke and smoldering butts can be very annoying to a nonsmoker or to a person who has a cold. And overflowing ash trays have no place on your desk; they give a bad impression.

What about personal phone calls? In some offices personal phone calls are definitely prohibited. In others there are no set restrictions. If you are lucky enough to work in the latter type of office, be careful not to abuse this privilege. One of the most frequent complaints of bosses is that employees waste too much time with personal phone calls. It's a good idea to do your own telephoning on your own time whenever possible—during lunch hour or breaks—and to keep your calls brief. Your phone call, you must remember is tying up a business line. There's always the possibility that your company may lose business or irritate a customer because he can't make contact. And woe be unto the girl who ties up the phone when her boss's boss is calling! Be considerate about making personal calls after closing time when only a few night lines are available. Try to limit all your calls only to very urgent needs that can't be taken care of at home. The girl who holds long telephone gabfests with one friend after another during the working day may strengthen out-of-office friendships, but only at the expense of in-the-office relations.

THE RULES THAT AREN'T RULES

When Amy started in her new job, she arrived so early that only a few members of the staff were present. She had been shown her desk the day before and so she hung her coat on the coat rack beside her desk and sat down to await the arrival of the others. She noticed that her employer's assistant hung her coat on the same rack and so did one or two others. When her boss came in, he attempted to hang his coat on the rack, made a few blustering noises, and handed his coat to his secretary saying, "Here, do something with this." It wasn't until later that Amy learned, much to her embarrassment, that the coat rack, although right beside her desk, was reserved for her boss and his assistants.

Incidents such as this are sometimes unavoidable, but you are likely to skirt most pitfalls if you ask first and try to be as considerate as possible. When you see a special broad wooden hanger in a closet full of wire ones, you can be pretty sure it is somebody's private property—and that he will feel annoyed if you use it.

In matters involving the office hierarchy a newcomer is wise to tread lightly. Why is the dictionary kept on Ellen's desk instead of on the window sill between you? Why is Connie allowed to cut in at the head of the line when the coffee cart arrives? Why does Miss Priddy keep her rubbers in the catalog file drawer? Why? Because that's the way it's done, that's all. Bit by bit over the years, special privileges have been carefully garnered along with seniority. Trivial as they may seem to a newcomer, they should be respected. Perhaps you may even learn later that there are reasons for some of these sacred rights; but, reason or no, sacred they are, and they should not be trifled with.

Such innocent acts as opening windows, adjusting the radiators, or moving the shades are also likely to disturb someone. Until you can determine the feelings of others on these matters, it may be best to keep hands off. If you feel you absolutely must make some such change, be sure to ask first if anyone would mind. Your thoughtfulness and graciousness in these little matters will do much to charm the staff and win friends for you.

REFORM THEM SLOWLY

As a newcomer, you have the advantage of being able to look at things with a greater degree of objectivity than can those who have been doing the same work in the same way week in and week out. Perhaps it will occur to you that certain procedures seem needlessly involved or have no reason for being done at all. Keep your bright eyes open for ways in which you might improve the methods. Write your ideas down and keep them someplace where you won't lose them. Then say nothing and do nothing about them. At least not for a few months, until you are thoroughly familiar with all aspects of the work.

Any smart employer is eager to receive sound suggestions from one of his workers. Some companies even post suggestion boxes in which employees are invited to place suggestions for improvements; awards are given for usable ideas. You will want to be sure, however, that your idea is *completely* workable and that you know about all phases of the operation that might affect such a change *before* you mention it to anyone. Half-cocked suggestions are merely irritating. Being creatures of habit, office staffs seldom react favorably at first to suggestions involving change. Before you whack the beehive, you want to be absolutely certain your idea is holeproof. Probably the work is performed this way because that's the way it has always been done and nobody has bothered to change it. But perhaps there is a subtle reason that may not be obvious at first. Perhaps a more involved process in your department makes the work easier for another department. Or, perhaps the present method is the pet brainchild of your boss—or his boss—and must be continued at all costs.

Write down your idea so that it won't become submerged in the inertia of routine and bide your time. Meanwhile, try to learn all the whys and wherefores of the work. When you are sure your idea is good, phrase your suggestion as if you were asking advice. Express it in constructive terms of how it might improve the work, being careful not to cast aspersions on the old process and those who have been blindly performing it. If your idea is accepted, you will be one charming lass whose business future will become beautifully rosy.

PLAY IT SMART

One of the first days Lucy had been on her new job in a leather goods manufacturing firm, her boss took her to the reception room and asked her to clean out the display cases, wash the glass counters, and rearrange the display samples. Lucy was horrified. She had just graduated from a prominent business school with top honors, was one of the fastest typists in her class, and had been trained to do better things than wield a duster and scrub cloth. But being a clever girl, Lucy swallowed her pride and obligingly set in. It wasn't until she had finished that she learned that she had been selected because the boss had been impressed with her good taste and felt that she could handle the job of creating an attractive display better than anyone else on the staff. Her cheerful attitude and willingness to work soon won her a promotion.

As a new and inexperienced worker, the beginner is likely to be the low man on the office totem pole. It's unfortunately true that in some cases the more tedious or menial jobs may be pushed off on her. Someone has to do them, and since the other employees have passed their fledgling period, these chores are dumped on the novice. If such is the case in your first crack at the business world, you'll be wise to accept the lowly job cheerfully and pleasantly. Never let yourself feel that any work is too belittling for you. The private secretary to a world-famous author and lecturer told how she once literally waded in and cleaned out his goldfish pond. The Girl Friday to a noted decorator has often wielded a paint brush to convert some bit of gadgetry to the exact blue the client is searching for.

Many secretaries to famous personalities think nothing of preparing lunch for their bosses, taking suits to the dry cleaner's, walking the dog, or even baby-sitting with the children. No matter what comes your way, accept it with good grace. The day will soon dawn when you will no longer be the lowliest, and the less-glamorous chore will be shifted to someone else. The cream naturally rises to the top. The girl who plays it smart by doing her best on *every* job will soon be accepted as an important member of the team, capable of handling more responsible work.

CHOOSING FRIENDS

Although you want to be very friendly to everyone in the office, as a newcomer you will be wise to take a bit of time before aligning yourself with any one group. You don't want, by mistake, to get in with what may turn out to be the wrong clique. This may mean lunching alone the first few days and keeping to yourself slightly more than usual. But soon you'll be able to size up the staff. You won't swallow all the gossip you hear and you'll be able to see who has the right attitude and who will most likely be your brand of friend.

Some girls quickly latch on to a couple of close friends and pretty much ignore the rest of the staff. On the whole, you'll be much happier if you have as many friends as possible. Lunch with different girls and try to make friends with those in other departments as well as in your own. You'll not only have more fun, but you'll learn more about other parts of the company and other work in case you should ever want to make a transfer.

301

END OF THE DAY

Amazing, isn't it, how many people survive the first days on the job! They may be a bit hesitant about them, but usually everything turns out pretty well—and may even seem fun in retrospect.

On your very first day begin the habit of organizing your work at closing time so that it will be easy to start on the next morning. Perhaps you can put all unfinished work together in a folder. As an aid to efficiency, leave yourself a note if there is anything that needs further attention in the morning. This is always a good practice because if you are out the next day for any reason, someone else can follow through on your work.

As you tidy your desk, take a few moments to review what you have learned during the day. Are there any instructions you want to fix in your mind, any names or details you don't want to forget? If you made any mistakes, perhaps you can analyze them to see how they might be avoided. When we can learn from our mistakes, we run less risk of repeating them. Nobody's expected to be the expert her first day, but if she shows a willingness to learn and an eagerness to please, she'll make a charming beginning.

Promptness is a virtue appreciated much more at 9 a.m. than at 5 p.m. Even if everyone else begins an early cleanup as closing time draws near, the girl who is conscious of her good impression won't be eager to be the first one out of the office door. While your reputation is in the making, you should be especially careful that no one gets the wrong idea.

Many experienced workers have developed graceful leave-taking to a fine art. They wash up early enough to allow them to be back at their desks as the clock nears five. Although most of their work has been carefully organized and put away for next morning, one job is still out so that they can continue working until closing time. Although they depart no more than a minute or two later than the girl who stands, hat in hand, foot poised to run, as she watches the clock tick from 4:58 on, these clever girls show a businesslike sense of responsibility that pleases employers.

 FOLLOW-UP

1 The ability to remember names of new people you meet is largely a matter of concentration. Try now to develop the habit of listening for a new name and giving it your full attention. In the excitement of meeting someone new our minds tend to leap ahead to all sorts of questions about the person. Train yourself to grab onto his name and to hold it fast in your mind before it is bumped aside by other onrushing thoughts.

2 The person who can control his mind sufficiently to concentrate well can often surpass the accomplishments of someone with superior intelligence. Those first few days on a new job, when there is so much to learn and remember, concentration is particularly important. Controlling attention is largely a matter of self-discipline and practice. If you have difficulty keeping your mind where it belongs, a little mental exercise will soon help. Practice confining your thoughts to just one thing for at least five minutes. Suppose, for instance, you choose a bird as your subject. Then force your mind to think *only* about birds and bird-related objects. You might think about birds in a nest, swans in the park, hard-boiled egg sandwiches, the feather trim on your new hat, the old-fashioned bird ornaments on a Christmas tree. Don't however, let your thoughts squiggle away to the fun you had Christmastime at your tree-trimming party or to the scarf you want to wear with your new hat. Remember—birds, birds, birds. Keep your mind firmly under control. Practice this sort of thought direction at least twice a day for a week, more often if possible. The mind reacts like a muscle: the more it is exercised, the stronger it becomes and the greater the feats it can perform.

303

How to charm an employer is one of the lessons any would-be successful business girl must master at the start of her career. Fortunately, bosses are people, and for the most part the same rules that work with others will win with your boss.

Try to understand your employer. How does he look at company problems . . . at your work . . . at you? Your boss knows that the only way *he* will get ahead is to do an outstanding job. In a large company, an executive may be under considerable pressure to produce results. Office politics may be such that other young men on their way up are elbowing for his job. In such a situation, he must turn out a stellar performance just to hold his niche on the promotion escalator. Even in a concern that doesn't have stiff internal competition, there are rival firms, rising costs, and operating difficulties to create pressure, making it essential for his department to do its best. This means that his staff must be efficient, must work together well, and must promote goodwill for the company. He is pleased when you fit into this plan and help further these goals. It is his responsibility to see that his staff operates smoothly. Any weak performance or clash of personalities among his employees is likely to disrupt the smooth functioning of the business and is, therefore, especially disturbing to him.

While it's true that he views you as a person in most regards, a businessman is also forced to look at you with dollar signs in his eyes.

"How well does she do her work?"

"Does she fit in with the other workers?"

"Does she possess a competent, polite manner that will help win more business for us?"

These are questions he must consider. The girl who can't measure up to the cold, hard requirements of business efficiency is out of luck. Attractiveness and charm go far and are invaluable assets in helping us work effectively, but alone they will not satisfy a businessman. They must be coupled with honest hard work.

20

RATING APPLAUSE FROM THE BOSS

WHO'S THE BOSS?

There's the distinguished gentleman in the tremendous office with the wall-to-wall carpeting. He's the owner of the company. You can be sure he's the boss. But in the intervening spaces on the company totem pole there may be a lot of executives, minor executives, department heads, and individuals who have merely one or two workers responsible to them. Occasionally, a beginner is a bit dubious about who is "the boss," who should be catered to and given the velvet glove treatment. Actually, every person who is your superior deserves executive respect and deference, whether this be merely a private secretary or a higher clerk. The person who assigns you work and to whom you are responsible is your boss, regardless of his status in the company. Please and impress the person immediately above you and the word will soon travel up and up to all the higher and mightier.

ADJUSTING YOUR ATTITUDE

How you think of your boss can have a startling effect on your success in the job. When Mr. Sullivan, a rather bombastic sales manager, was looking for a secretary, a bright and promising stenographer was suggested to him. "But she's afraid of me!" he objected, and the job went to another girl who, though not quite so competent, had the poise and aplomb to cope with his harmless bluster. This type of boss can unsettle a beginner but, if she's smart, she'll make every effort to overcome her fears. The timid girl makes a man uneasy, for unconsciously he feels guilty about having caused her fear.

What should your attitude be? Bosses being quite varied, that depends on the person you work for. In general:

• Be friendly but respectful. A smile can hide—and help diminish—any timidity.

• Let him set the degree of formality; then, to be on the safe side, be just a bit more reserved than you feel you need to be. The girl who keeps a little distance usually has more chance for job happiness than the girl who is too chummy.

• Call him Mister unless he specifically tells you otherwise, regardless of how he is addressed by others on the staff. Most men prefer to be addressed as Mister, even though they will probably call you by your first name. But if your man suggests you call him Bernie, then by all means do so. Of course, whenever other executives or strangers are present, you will be careful to speak of him as Mister.

• Avoid wisecracks or personal kidding. Although many executives indulge in good-natured banter among themselves, they may resent it, as an affront to their dignity and position, if it comes from their staff. A smart girl will give thought to her chief's reactions before uttering her clever quip.

• Look for his good points; overlook his bad ones. You'll enjoy working with him far more if you do. Be an appreciative audience and a bond of good feeling will develop between you.

• Stifle any tendency to judge. One advertising executive complained that whenever he left early, his secretary's knowing little remarks—"Lovely weather for golf," or "It's a hard life!"—made him feel guilty, despite the fact that he was off to a grueling session with a client. A major portion of present-day business deals are consummated over the dinner table or on the golf course. Not only had his secretary no right to judge, but she should have realized that an employee seldom sees the complete picture and is in no position to judge fairly.

AIM TO PLEASE

The man behind your paycheck is pleased when you do a good job. Here are some work habits about which he is concerned.

Be someone he can count on. Show him that you are as dependable as you are charming. Let him see that you can be counted on to do a job right, that you are thorough, accurate, and careful in the many little details that are so important—spelling, taking messages, writing names and addresses, filing, dealing with figures, or handling money. If you are typing correspondence, check any dubious points—bosses can make mistakes, too, you know. If you must consult him about a correction, you'll want tactfully to avoid calling unnecessary attention to his error.

Be neat in all you do. Such things as smudges, strikeovers, or sloppy erasures disturb the most saintly boss's disposition. And any man is dismayed by the girl whose desk is a flurry of papers, carbons, and files. Perhaps she knows where everything is, but she's not likely to give the impression she does unless her desk has a tidy, businesslike order. If you smoke be especially careful. An ashtray overflowing with lipstick-rimmed butts, smoldering remains, or spilled ashes is distasteful to most men.

Be a self-starter. The girl who tries to find out what she can do to solve a problem, instead of taking a let-the-boss-worry-about-it attitude, will go far. Many a business girl has won her chief's appreciation by helping a customer herself, by gathering in advance information that her boss will need, or by composing answers to letters to save dictation time. You must, of course, be careful not to overstep your authority. You must be sure your employer would want you to act for him. If there is any doubt about your boss's attitude in such a case, submit your idea for approval first. The girl who willingly takes all the responsibility her boss will give her shows that she is capable of handling an important job and quickly lines herself up for promotion.

Be willing to work hard. Let your boss know that you are conscientious, that you care about doing a job right, and that you don't mind taking on the occasional extras that are sometimes necessary. If a task is tough or tedious, be a good sport—don't complain or make him feel like a slave driver.

Be flexible. The girls who get to be private secretaries to top executives and famous personalities work under all conditions. They may take dictation in such strange places as elevators, subways, airports, taxis, or even beauty parlors as they trail their bosses through busy, exciting days. When a last-minute rush job arrives or a change in procedure or hours is called for, adjust to it easily and graciously. Occasionally you may be asked to do shopping for your boss or a personal favor such as a duplicating job for his wife's club. Take on these chores agreeably. Part of the job is making life easier for your chief, even to the extent of obliging his wife.

Be well organized. Plan your work so that you do important jobs first. Collect everything you need before you begin a task so that you can work efficiently.

Show your interest and enthusiasm. The girl who can adopt a "we" attitude in regard to the company and the teamwork required to make it a success will not only please her boss, but she will get more satisfaction from her work as well. Try to learn as much as possible about your concern, about its products or services, about the various departments. Your work will become more meaningful and you will be better informed, thereby better equipped to help your boss intelligently.

Keep your mind on your work. No girl can keep her filing straight when she's deliciously reliving the previous night's date—or worrying why Rod hasn't phoned. She wouldn't waste her own precious lunch-hour shopping time on such unfruitful mental meanderings; and she most certainly should not squander the time she is *paid* to think about business. Personal problems and daydreams are strictly for after-hours.

Keep confidences. When your boss entrusts you with some confidential information, feel flattered and show that you can live up to his trust. Not only must you be discreet and carefully avoid mentioning the subject to others, but you must be sure that your face and manner also reveal nothing.

Don't abuse his goodwill. The boss hires an employee to work a certain number of hours. He expects her to be at her desk (not in the ladies' room) at starting time. He expects her to limit her personal telephone calls and to save long personal conversations for lunchtime. Some offices operate like a classroom, with all but necessary conversation prohibited. Most companies are more lenient, but as one executive complained, "Every day after lunch my girls waste a good part of the next hour comparing the bargains they got during lunch-hour shopping. The time they waste each day in personal chatter would easily add up to another full-time employee!" Viewed from the boss's angle, it becomes apparent that such girls are a company liability. They are taking unfair advantage of his good nature.

DO NOT DISTURB

Every boss has special ways of doing things. Early as possible on the job you want to find out his special likes so that you can cater to them. He'll probably have his own peculiar peeves, too, which you will delicately avoid, no matter how trivial they seem. But the main irritant of most bosses is interruptions. The phone calls, the visitors, the executive conferences that eat away at his time are not your doing, but you *can* help by being considerate of his time in all your dealings with him. Although you will sit quietly—and interestedly—when he has a story to relate, you will be quick to sense his impatience if you are telling a story. Your business discussions should be as brief and concise as possible. Many girls find it helpful to keep a list of subjects they wish to discuss with their bosses. This allows them to dispose of all the accumulated problems in one quick businesslike session and eliminates frequent interruptions.

The considerate worker also tries to avoid distracting her employer. She doesn't barge in and out of his office every two minutes to bring mail, check his wall chart, get material from his file, or deliver finished work. She tries to possess a quiet manner that doesn't call attention to her presence. When someone is trying to concentrate, such things as slamming drawers, noisily ripping paper from a typewriter, tapping a pencil, or uttering exasperated sighs when an error occurs on the bottom line, can be sufficiently disturbing to shatter his thoughts completely. Other irritants: loud talking, singing or humming, gum chewing (loudly or otherwise), a heavy walk, and distractions during dictation. A dictator has enough trouble trying to compose a coherent message without having to contend with a squirming stenographer, a footswinger, a hair fusser, a jewelry twister, or a girl who makes diverting doodles. Obvious boredom, or a superior attitude that implies he is not the world's greatest literary light, gives him an inferiority complex that quickly douses all inspiration.

Your employer wants all letters sent in large envelopes, even though you realize small envelopes would do just as well and would be more economical. He decrees that you get along with one less filing cabinet, although the drawers are bulging already. What to do? Do it his way, of course. Some men want pencils used down to one inch stubs. Others fuss if a slightly tarnished paper clip appears on outgoing mail. Trivial, perhaps. Unreasonable, perhaps; but because your man likes things that way, you do it that way. Otherwise he's likely to find himself someone else who will.

(MORAL:) The boss is boss. Keep him happy.

Jane's employer quoted a price during dictation that seemed far too low. After she left his office, Jane checked on similar work and found that the quoted price was considerably below the usual figure. When she called this to her employer's attention, he said he was aware of the lower price but had his reasons for this. Unsatisfied, Jane continued to press the issue, pointing out the work involved and the foolishness of not allowing for sufficient profit. Although her boss seemed to want to drop the subject, she continued to argue the matter until finally he had to tell her that was the way it was to stand and she should do as instructed.

Although Jane was wise to check the unusual price and to confirm it, she should not have questioned her employer's judgment and argued with him. When a boss makes decisions, we must accept them and let them go. Jane was sincere in thinking she was right and that she was protecting the best interests of the firm, but she should have done as she was told without further protest. There are often considerations that influence an employer's thinking that he may not care to reveal to others.

(MORAL:) The boss is boss. Don't argue.

Lucille's department had a large mailing job to finish. Her supervisor had said that the entire staff was to work overtime tomorrow. With a big date in the offing, Lucille was far from enthusiastic. She pleaded with her supervisor, explaining that if they didn't have to stay late, all the girls would work as fast as they possibly could to finish the work during regular hours. Her boss felt the extra time was necessary and refused. Lucille persisted until she realized he was becoming irritated and then she gave in.

(MORAL:) The boss is boss. Why not comply graciously and not risk causing annoyance?

You cannot go wrong if you remember that you are hired to help your boss do *hi* job better. His idea of how work is to be performed may not be the same as yours; bu because his is the hand that sways your future, his is the idea that counts.

CHANGING HIS WAYS

The exception to the previous advice is the case where the boss is unaware that he is sabotaging your efficiency, as when an employer unthinkingly leaves important dic tation or rush orders until late afternoon. If this is his habit, a girl should have a heart to-heart talk with her boss, tactfully explaining that when she must rush important worl out so fast, she doesn't have time for the careful checking she feels the work deserves and is afraid some error may slip through. When faced with the prospect of better job per formance, most executives will gladly rearrange their schedules.

HOW BIG A LOAD?

Occasionally a worker is so efficient that her boss loses track of how much work she is accomplishing. He merely knows that everything that must be done Meg does—quickly and well. When another involved task looms before him, he unhesitatingly turns it over to Meg, confident that she can be depended upon to handle it properly and accurately But eventually Meg reaches the point where her day becomes a hectic race with the clock and the need for frequent overtime or taking work home is too much of a burden.

How should a girl who is genuinely overtaxed handle the problem? Before raising any objections, she should see if there isn't some way she can possibly handle the extra work. What she definitely should not do is bewail her fate and tell her hard-luck story to every handy ear in the office. Neither should she continually complain to her boss in vague terms about the "tremendous amount" of work she has. Frequent complaints lose their effectiveness with even the most sympathetic ear.

Instead, Meg should analyze her problem as objectively as possible to see how the overall work picture could be improved. Perhaps there are some shortcuts she could try Possibly some of her more routine work could be taken over by a less skilled worker or by the receptionist or the office boy. Would a copying machine, a dictating machine, or some other equipment pay its way in saved time and improved efficiency?

Occasionally, a worker with a good record is reluctant to surrender any of her duties for fear of losing status. As a result, she is so burdened by unimportant routine details that she denies herself the opportunity to look up and ahead, to display the foresight and initiative that would make her stand out as an exceptional, creative worker who is more than just a good workhorse. Any girl with glowing aspirations owes it to herself to keep her eye on the future, to grow with the job. She cannot let herself stagnate either through her own inertia or her reluctance to pass off routine work so that she can help her boss with more involved tasks.

In Meg's case, she would be wise to make a list of all the duties she now performs. (Often a busy boss is unaware of all that an employee handles for him.) Next she should list all additional duties or responsibilities she could take on if she had more time—duties that would relieve her employer of some of his load. Then she should indicate which routine jobs could be delegated to someone else or, perhaps, to a machine. Such constructive thinking impresses an employer that she is not merely attempting to shirk work but is sincerely concerned with helping him more effectively.

CHAIN OF COMMAND

Kay worked in a large department. The procedure for choosing vacation time was to send around a chart on which each employee indicated his preference. If there were no vital conflicts, each person was allotted the time he had chosen. Shortly after the schedule had been made up, Kay learned that the friend with whom she'd been planning a vacation trip would have to postpone her vacation two weeks. Kay envisioned all their wonderful plans spoiled. She rushed down to the department manager's office and asked if the last two weeks in August were available. They were. With her spirits soaring high, Kay returned to her desk.

The next day Kay's boss approached her looking quite annoyed. "Why didn't you tell me you wanted to change your vacation?" he asked. "This morning I promised Ann that time. We can't get along without both of you, so I'm afraid you'll have to make other plans."

If only Kay had gone to her boss in the first place, he would have been aware of her desire to switch her weeks. Once he had approved Ann's time, he would not ask Ann to change.

The executive chain of command is a hallowed business tradition that no employee can afford to ignore. One of the unwritten rules of business is that whenever an employee has a request to make, or a suggestion to offer someone outside the bounds of her immediate working group, she first consult her own boss and work through him. Her immediate superior would feel hurt if he were bypassed, and, moreover, he can often smooth the way for her when he knows her plans.

Even in matters that seem of little concern to your employer, it's advisable to keep him informed of your plans. When the gang is planning a luncheon for one of the girls, the boss may want to be one of the first to know about it—if only as a matter of pride. Bosses usually appreciate being in the know about department activities and may even be a little put out if they are not told first.

Mr. Ames was notorious among the staff for his temperamental disposition. His was a creative job and he was often under considerable pressure to turn out work fast. The list of girls he had tried and rejected was as long as his temper was short. When Alice had stayed with him for three months, the staff was astounded. The explosions from his office were less and less frequent and Alice seemed to be holding up remarkably well. "How do you do it? How do you stand him?" she was asked. "Oh, he isn't half bad once you understand him and realize what he's up against," Alice replied. "He's carrying a terrific load and he really turns out some excellent material."

Alice's experience with Mr. Ames taught her a few important lessons that are helpful in succeeding with any type of boss. Instead of approaching the terrible Mr. Ames as if he were the most unpleasant creature on earth, she decided to accept him as he was and to do her best to put up with him. She made up her mind to look for whatever good points she could find in him—which were many, she discovered—and to make every effort to please him.

Putting up with a difficult person is much easier when you take an objective point of view and realize that often there is nothing personal in his annoyance. Frequently his temper may be aroused by something that has nothing whatever to do with you. Alice was aware of this, and Mr. Ames was grateful when she overlooked his flare-ups. Alice's lack of condemnation had a calming effect in itself, whereas the other girls' show of disdain had provoked him to take out his wrath on them. Alice realized that her boss's nerves were on edge, and she had learned that serious family problems added to the pressure he felt. She endeavored to be as calm, as inobtrusive, and as quietly efficient as possible.

That was six years ago. Mr. Ames has overcome his jittery nervous condition and is now a top executive of a larger company. Needless to say, Alice is still with him. When Mr. Ames was offered the new position, he insisted on bringing Alice along (at a considerably higher salary) for he knew how valuable she had become to him.

If you are confronted with a difficult boss, allow yourself a six month trial period to win him around. Try all the cajoling refinements of diplomacy, subtlety, and tact. Make an honest attempt to like him. Usually this treatment wins.

Even if it doesn't, fate may step in and give you a hand if you allow a little time. Because there is continual change of personnel in every office, it sometimes happens that the disagreeable boss leaves or is transferred to a branch office. Perhaps some other girl will quit, and your good attitude will bring you to the attention of her boss. Don't jump at the first snarl from a nasty boss. Give him a full-fledged try before you cancel out.

If all your efforts are to no avail, but you like the company, perhaps you can find a job in a different department. Learn as much as possible about the various departments of the firm and then ask the personnel manager if you can be considered when an opening occurs in the department of your choice. You'll make a better impression if you phrase your request in terms of your interest in the work without admitting any inability to adjust to your present boss.

WORKING FOR A WOMAN

The nasty rumor that women are difficult to work for was probably started by some man who was beaten out for a job by a female. You're a woman. You're a sweet, kind, thoughtful, charming person, aren't you? And if you were an executive, you'd still be the same, perhaps a bit more harried but basically the same. As with all bosses, individuals vary; but because a woman becomes an executive she cannot automatically be classified as an ogre.

If a poll were taken among girls who actually work for women, the results would probably show overwhelming approval. To win a top position, a woman must be truly exceptional. Even in our progressive era, women executives are greatly outnumbered by the cigar-smoking sex. Approximately only two-thirds of one percent of women workers in our country ever reach a five figure yearly salary bracket. These paltry few must be tops to make the grade. You can be certain that a woman boss has to know her stuff.

A female executive has probably worked her way up through the ranks. As a result, she is likely to be more considerate in many ways than her male counterpart, who entered via the training squad. She remembers what it was like to be an underling—to discover at the end of a long report that the carbon was in backwards, to have the boss's cigar ashes scorch a long and perfectly typed rush letter. In all probability she will be more understanding whenever the going gets rough. She knows, too, what a tragic inconvenience a lunchtime errand for the boss can be on a chance-of-a-lifetime sale day. Being a woman, too, she can appreciate your problems more fully and will probably be more considerate of your personal life.

Loyalty is one of the most valued business virtues. Many a boss is so wonderful that you automatically want to gild his reputation at every opportunity. But even those not-so-wonderfuls deserve—and respond beautifully to—the person who glosses up their reputation for them.

As an employee you are, perforce, your boss's publicity agent. Whether he is heroic or horrendous, nothing but the best publicity should emanate from you. His clients, his superiors, his staff, even the girls at the luncheon table should hear nothing but words of praise. When the office staff resorts to the insidious pastime of let's-pick-the-boss apart, loyal girl that you are, you can deftly change the subject.

Granted, bosses being individuals, there are bound to be a few bad ones. Some may not deserve loyalty and respect. An employee who lacks loyalty loses the respect of others, and her attitude reflects adversely on herself and her work. If you find yourself in a situation where, after considerable effort, you cannot respect your employer, you had better find yourself another job.

Not only do you owe your employer loyalty, but you will find that the benefits are multiple. From a purely mercenary point of view, the faster you help your boss get ahead, the sooner you'll advance, too. No man will want to leave so valuable a champion behind. But for the sake of job satisfaction, nothing improves a relationship more than loyalty and joint respect. You know how a friend's esteem helps bring out your best. Employer-employee esteem is a winning combination that can make a job a joy and can help both live up to the gleaming reputations they make for each other.

 FOLLOW-UP

1 Analyze your employer (or if you are not working, pretend your father or some man you know well is your employer). What are his special preferences and dislikes?

2 Survey five executives of your acquaintance. Ask them what qualities they like most in employees and what qualities they find most annoying. Most employers are delighted to have a chance to air their feelings, and you may be surprised at how much you will learn.

3 Interview a woman executive. Ask her how she got her start and how she has risen to her present position. Does she consider her experience typical of other women executives? What advice can she give you to help you reach the executive level?

The business girl who endears herself to the staff finds her working hours pleasant and exciting. Her job becomes more than so many hours on the timecard at so many dollars a week. It becomes an interesting and rich experience in which friendship and the satisfying bond of joint accomplishment play an important part. Management is forever on the watch for a girl who can win friends and influence the staff. She is the one they want for supervisory positions and for important roles that involve interesting contacts. In the office, it is particularly true that the lass who can get along is the one who will get ahead.

Conversely, as the director of a large employment agency in Chicago put it, "More people lose their jobs because of personality difficulties than any other reason. Many an extremely capable worker becomes classified as unemployable simply because she has not learned the importance of good relations with the office staff." An employee who is disagreeable and ill humored has a hard time obtaining cooperation. When her sales report gets lost, it's likely to stay lost. When she has a rush job, she rushes alone. Few favors are offered and her work becomes increasingly difficult when the staff refuses to cooperate. Management can ill afford to have such a misfit hampering smooth operation.

21 THE OFFICE STAFF

EARNING YOUR LAURELS

Tops on the list of those we appreciate are the girls who work both fast and well. If a worker keeps on schedule, no one is inconvenienced. But let that report be late for Accounting, and listen to the wails of woe! If work isn't done on time, often others must rush or must work overtime to make up for the slowpoke. Occasionally a beginner is so overly conscientious that she holds up work.

Myra had to compile and type daily numerical reports that were needed by the shipping department. Not being very good at typing figures, Myra made frequent mistakes. In her desire to be neat, she usually retyped the report before sending it on. A little lunch-hour practice would have soon improved her typing, but her policy of redoing work merely impeded progress and caused annoyance.

One of the most cherished employees is the girl who is willing to help when someone is busy. A secretary in a large department was so good a worker that she occasionally had free time. Often she used it to study trade literature so that she could learn more about the business or to discover additional ways in which she could assist her boss. But she also was the first to offer help when she saw someone in a jam. She not only won office-wide appreciation, but she learned so much about the various jobs in the depart ment that when an opening occurred for a supervisory post, her knowledge of all th work made her the ideal choice.

Another girl in the same department was also a skilled worker—far better than most— but when she finished her work, she was content to loaf. "I still turn out just as much a anybody else," she rationalized. "Why shouldn't I take time off when I feel like it?" I someone asked help on a special job, she would object, claiming that she wasn't hired to do that work. She hadn't learned one basic fact: no one can play it solo in an office Prima donnas soon find themselves out in the cold.

One of the fastest ways to be blacklisted is to take advantage of other members o the staff: So-Sorry Susie assigned to help cover the phones is consistently late returning from lunch; Edna-the-Excuse-Maker always has a terribly important appointment when she's asked to relieve someone at lunch time; Rubber-Band Rosey stretches lunch hour and rest periods but is aghast at the prospects of overtime; and Nettie-the-Nail-Polishe believes manicures should be done only on company time. These girls may think they are getting away with something, but their few extra minutes are dearly bought. It may be possible to fool the boss for a while, depending on how watchful and trusting he is, bu it is never possible to fool the rest of the staff, which is ever-watchful and far less trusting

How do you win? With the Virtues Every Business Girl Should Have:

Cooperation   **Consideration**   **Tact**

This means being diplomatic and pleasant to those below as well as those above you Perhaps this may be difficult when the office boy ruins *your* single-spaced stencil or when Slapstick Sally squirts Coke on *your* freshly typed letters. But it is essential nevertheless Let your warmth and friendly manner be liberally applied to both the lowly and the high

Often how an employee treats the mail boy or the switchboard operator has more significance than her attitude toward higher-ups. Any rudeness detected in her treatment of a lower-level employee flashes a red light in the executive cerebral structure. How can more authority be given to one who doesn't know how to use what she now has?

When someone ruffles you, do your best to put up with him. If the order clerk has made an error, discreetly show it to her in private. Then call her attention to the need for a correction as diplomatically as you can—avoiding any "*you* made a mistake" emphasis.

The Golden Rule—treating others as you'd like to be treated—has been a standard of conduct down through the ages, and it works as well as ever today. Put into practice, it protects us from being inconsiderate. We remember to work quietly without disturbing or annoying others; we steer clear of gossip; we resist the urge to complain loudly when someone goofs or blunders; we're helpful to other newer employees. In short, we're nice to have around—we earn our laurels of praise.

MATURITY VALUE

One of the best investments a business girl can make is in habits of self-control. She can learn not to give vent to her emotions and to keep a firm and realistic grip on her vanity, temper, and tongue. In the office, a girl just must act like a lady at all times, no matter how much she feels like slinging a stapler at someone. She is expected to be poised and genteel. This may involve keeping a near stranglehold on her emotions, forgetting the oh-so-deep sorrows of her current love life, and maintaining a pleasant disposition despite an onslaught of cranky customers. A big order, true, but one that when filled shows you have the poise to rise above day-to-day disturbances.

Women are often accused of being overly emotional and overly sensitive. Perhaps we are, but it is the girl who keeps the damper on her emotions who fits in best in business— or in any social activity for that matter. The business world, particularly, is a rough-and-tumble place where sensitive feelings may be trampled on and where no one can afford the time or trouble to stop and soothe them. There will be occasions when someone else will get the promotion or be chosen for a desirable task such as modeling for the company magazine photos. Nobody but nobody may compliment you on the outstanding piece of work you slaved over. But such is business life. If you accept it without sulking and apply a bit of good humor, you'll win respect and appreciation.

321

Criticism may seem brusque at times, but we must be prepared to accept it cheerfully and thoughtfully. The girl who interprets criticism of her work as a direct insult had better head for the hills and take up a solitary career of basket weaving.

The best way to minimize trying times at the office is to balance work with outside interests. What seemed like such a mountainous misery at 3 p.m. slides down to molehill size after a happy evening of bowling—and, perhaps, becomes in retrospect just a hilarious anecdote to pass along to the gang. The person whose whole life is her work lacks such insulation and unconsciously tends to exaggerate the importance of every little incident that occurs.

Another quality that is used to gauge maturity—one that some young employees may forget—is dignity. Occasionally a beginner yields to impulse and shouts down the hall to a friend or runs lickety-split through the office. Eyebrows go up; a few frowns appear; and the other members of the staff hope their junior member will soon learn that business has a more formal set of rules than school or home. Pointless practical jokes and elaborate pranks, raucous laughter, and inappropriate schoolgirl clothing all act as a tag that reads, "Do not promote until more fully matured." Most too-cute juveniles are unaware what annoying bores they can be to those who maintain more businesslike standards.

RESPECTFULLY YOURS

The office staff is a conglomeration of human beings thrown together by the accident of their having chosen the same place to earn a living. Many of them may be very different from you in educational background, experience, age, race, religion, politics, and general outlook on life. Perhaps you wouldn't have chosen them as the ideal set of daily companions, but associating with them can be a wonderfully rich and broadening experience. You will probably like most of them, but try to learn from them all and to appreciate their various points of view. Once you step out of the office door you aren't *forced* to have anything to do with those who don't appeal to you, but your nine-to-five hours will be far more pleasant if you make a determined effort to like and respect everyone.

Of all the forms of intolerance that seem to be most prevalent in offices, the most frequent is lack of consideration and kindness for older workers. Perhaps elderly Mrs. Rae objects when someone opens the window not because she wants to be ornery but merely because she isn't feeling very well. When we're young and hale and hearty, we sometimes fail to realize that someone older may be tired rather than dull, or bothered by arthritis rather than fussy. Age brings with it numerous aches and troubles, and many an older person who would be better off resting at home is forced to work because of financial conditions. Youth is a gift that is only loaned to us, and today's young people do well to remember that they may be in a similar situation at some later date.

An older worker may have set ideas—different ideas from you—about how work should be done. If this person is your superior, you should follow instructions even though the method seems old-fashioned. If the older person is not your superior, you will be wise to learn from her and to give any suggestions careful consideration. (Someone who has been doing the job for a number of years surely must know many worthwhile shortcuts.) If you disagree with the suggestions, you won't want to cause hard feelings by raising objections. Perhaps you might unobtrusively check with your supervisor to see which method is preferred.

RESERVED—FOR YOU

While it is wonderful if you can find a bosom pal among those with whom you work, you want to be careful about pouring out your heart to someone at the office until you are sure the friendship has a firm foundation. If suddenly the friendship should crumble, day-in–day-out association with this one who knows *all* can grate miserably.

The business girl who knows her way around wisely puts a "Reserved" sign on all her private affairs. She realizes that, on the whole, the best policy is not to become too involved with office associates. She keeps her relations pleasant but rather impersonal. Of course, she has lunch with the girls or may go to a show with some of them after work; but her family, her love life, her finances, her personal matters—these are strictly private. She doesn't try to delve into others' private lives either; and if someone is so thoughtless as to reveal something of a too-intimate nature, she is careful not to offer advice and to remain as politely—and pleasantly—detached as possible. She doesn't bring up the subject again, knowing that the loose talker may have embarrassing second thoughts about her indiscretion. She also resists any temptation to pass the news along.

As for the Chatty Kathy, who keeps the staff informed on all the "He said; I said," details of each date, and who discusses the family trials and tribulations—she seldom realizes that her stories aren't half as interesting to others as she thinks they are. Her lack of discretion quickly lowers her in the eyes of others, and in a short time she either bores everyone to tears or becomes a juicy subject for office gossip and ridicule.

The girl who maintains an impersonal attitude may miss the full gory details of a few little dramas, but she will also avoid much unpleasantness and will keep herself above unsavory entanglements.

THE SUNNY SIDE

In the office you know well the people with whom you work most closely, but you are observed by many more with whom you may be merely on a "Good Morning" or

"Good Night" basis. They may not know that you saved the day for your department by making what seemed an impossible deadline or that in yesterday's storm you thoughtfully offered Shirley *your* umbrella to save her new Easter bonnet. But they do know that you have a happy manner, a gay sense of humor, that you smile often, and that you are quick to say "thank you" in return for their kindnesses.

The girl who keeps her sunny side on display is sure to attract friends—and, who can tell, perhaps one of them will turn out to be that *most* important man in her life!

 FOLLOW-UP

1 List at least five helpful things you could do to make an office associate like you.

2 List five things you might find most annoying in the behavior of fellow workers in an office.

3 When you are employed, what outside activities can you maintain to help balance the strains of your working day?

A large order? Hardly. Yet employers often have difficulty finding top caliber material among the girls on the staff. If you earnestly try to do the best possible job, you will surely attract notice. To succeed, you need only keep up your good work. Everyone expects the new broom to sweep clean; but some new employees, once they have passed their trial period and feel somewhat secure, go into a slump. All too many girls are content to park themselves in their swivel chairs from nine to five and, with a minimum of work, keep from being turned out in the cold. They just want to get by; they never care enough to try to get ahead.

The business girl who consistently turns out top quality work and who seeks out the helpful extras she can do stands out like an Easter lily in a cabbage patch—she can't help but call attention to herself. Your good work and gracious manners automatically publicize your ability to all those you come in contact with. And, bosses being prone to brag about their exceptional employees, the word spreads fast when plaudits are due.

EFFICIENCY

One of the business traits that is most attention-getting is efficiency. It is also one of the most essential for promotion. The person who flounders through her work can't even carry a full load, let alone the larger load a promotion might entail. Unless a girl is efficient, she needs constant supervision and can't possibly be counted on to direct others.

Perhaps you are naturally efficient and well organized, but even the girls who do not consider this one of their strongest points have been able to develop reputations for remarkable efficiency by following these suggestions.

1 ❀ **Plan your work.** At the beginning of each day make a list of the important jobs that you want to accomplish that day—not every job that's hanging over your head, but the necessary tasks that should be accomplished right away. With such a list to guide you, you'll be sure to tackle the important work first and will be less likely to let trivial matters take too much time.

2 ❀ **Do important work when you're most alert.** Many people have a low ebb period just before lunch and again in the late afternoon. Others are slow starters in the morning. Do your most important or difficult jobs at periods of peak efficiency, leaving chores that require less concentration, such as tidying your desk or filing, for the end of the day.

3 🌼 **Make a note of all instructions.** Lorraine's boss asked her to make a luncheon reservation for him at the Town House. As she approached her desk, her phone jangled urgently. Next came a special-delivery package that required immediate attention; then a visitor arrived. When her boss returned from lunch and asked what had happened to the reservation, Lorraine was horrified. In the rush of little emergencies she had completely forgotten about the reservation. If Lorraine had quickly jotted down her boss's instructions before she answered the phone, she would have been saved. There are times when you just can't afford to let yourself be interrupted until you jot down a quick reminder.

4 �',' **Use a dependable reminder system.** Since memories are fallible, many clever girls leave themselves reminder notes where they are sure not to be overlooked—pierced on a desk pen, clipped to a mechanical pencil, rolled in the typewriter—or, if it concerns an after-hours matter, tucked into a hat band or glove cuff. Many girls use a tickler file (a file with a separate section for each day of the month) to remind themselves of upcoming jobs and chores that recur regularly. The hitch is, of course, that they must remember to look in the tickler file every morning!

Perhaps the least complicated and most valuable reminder system is the lowly desk calendar. On it you can note special work and appointments and can warn yourself a day or two ahead if advance preparations are needed. If you are responsible for once-a-month tasks, list reminders for each month throughout the year when you get your new calendar. You can also include any birthdays or other events during the year that you will want to remember—for yourself or your boss. If your calendar is the loose-leaf type, where the pages are not thrown away, it can prove valuable as a diary, in case you need to check back to a particular meeting or appointment.

5 �',' **Finish one job before you start another.** The girl who has everything at hand before she starts and then works steadily until she completes the chore, accomplishes much more than the girl who jumps from one half-finished job to another. If we stop in mid-letter to order more carbon paper or to check on train schedules, we lose time getting reorientated. If something important comes to mind in the middle of a job, make yourself a note and attend to the matter as soon as you finish. Of course, the telephone or a visiting customer can't be kept waiting, but there are many times when you can postpone interruptions.

6 �',' **Look for shortcuts.** Whenever you have an involved chore, ask yourself if there isn't an easier way to handle it. Perhaps you send out weekly schedules. Would a duplicated form that could be quickly filled in eliminate work? Or, if this isn't practical, could you save time by marking an old copy with tabulator settings and keeping this for reference so that you won't have to refigure each time you make out a new schedule? Perhaps you could compose form letters for replying to common situations. Or would a printed note do just as well? It makes good sense to cut down routine work as much as possible.

7 �',' **Arrange your desk efficiently.** A desk not only looks much more businesslike if it is neat and well organized but also there is less danger of losing something. An efficient way to keep specific jobs together is to use folders; a folder of work always looks much neater than a lot of loose papers. Any pile of papers that must be kept on your desk while you work should be weighted down so that nothing is blown away by a stray draft. Other little efficiency ideas that save time: tying an eraser on each side of your typewriter (one for carbons, one for originals), keeping carbon erasure slips under the left edge of your typewriter, always keeping a pencil and telephone message pad beside your phone, making a list of frequently used phone numbers. If you handle correspondence, it's also a great advantage to have your own copy of a dictionary and a secretary's handbook. If you must make frequent calls, obtain a phone book for your own desk.

8 ✿ Check supplies frequently. You want to have enough on hand so that you won't run out in the middle of a rush job. You don't, however, want to be so overstocked with any item that it clutters up your desk and your drawers and yellows with age before it can be used.

A GROWING GIRL

One of the quickest ways to speed up the promotion process is to demonstrate how much you've grown (mentally, that is) while you've been on the job. Many a bright young miss has furthered herself by taking courses after hours. Such business courses as accounting, economics, letter writing, retailing, public speaking, or something specifically related to your firm's particular industry will give you a broader background for your work. An industry-related course also helps you gain the confidence and air of authority that comes from being well informed about your field.

Let your boss know about your courses. Perhaps you might ask his advice in selecting the best ones. If you have a report to make for school, try to do it on some phase of your own company's operation. Perhaps your boss will set up interviews for you with other executives who can give you the information you need. Not only does this provide you with material for school, but it also helps you learn more about the company and, just incidentally, happens to bring you to the attention of other important people in the concern. The young person who sincerely wants to learn has a magnetic appeal. Human nature being what it is, we all seem to love to play teacher. Many a busy executive has been known to take considerable time and trouble to help someone who was genuinely interested in learning from him.

One additional advantage of your classes is, of course, the many friends you make among those who have interests similar to yours. You probably don't need to be told that many a marriage has blossomed from night school cultivation.

Even without taking courses, you can increase your knowledge of the business. You can learn as much as possible about the various departments of your firm and how they work together. Find out where and how the materials used in making your products are secured. What happens to the products after they leave the company portals? You might also learn how the company got started and what was responsible for its growth. Keep up with your company's new products and with those of its competitors. This is the bac[k]ground information that makes a girl more than a cataloger of thingamajigs. She ma[y] instead consider herself an authority on inventory for the control mechanisms vital to o[ur] newest space program.

You want also to improve your general knowledge. You want to be up on curre[nt] events, important television shows, new plays, music, books, and all that is going on abo[ut] you. Learn all the skills you can. Even such an unrelated skill as flower arranging help[ed] one girl move up to become secretary to the top art director—he was impressed by h[er] artistic ability.

BE PROMOTION-MINDED

We all know that it's easier to hit what you aim at if you keep your eye on the targe[t]. The same applies to your business future. Set a goal for yourself; look ahead and try [to] decide the type of position you would like to attain. Then go about learning as much [as] possible about it. You may never get this job—you may be selected for something f[ar] afield—but the fact that you are striving toward a goal will give you an advantage. Amb[i]tious girls always keep an eye on the job directly above theirs. Volunteer to help [or] substitute for a girl in a higher-rated job whenever the opportunity presents itself. Yo[ur] acquaintance with the work marks you as a likely candidate when a promotion [or] vacancy occurs.

But all promotions don't result from changing desks or bosses. Many smart girls ha[ve] made themselves more important by taking on increased responsibility. One girl su[g]gested an additional way for her company to profit by offering a supplementary servi[ce] and she was put in charge of the operation. Although the new service started out in [a] small way, she now has a force of twenty in her charge.

Other workers have advanced because their bosses were promoted. If you are t[he] girl who helps the assistant manager, he may be moved up to manager and you m[ay] become the assistant manager yourself. Or you can advance without even changing yo[ur] title. Suppose you are secretary to a department head who is appointed vice preside[nt]. When he is promoted, you, as his secretary, go up a notch right along with him. [By] helping your boss do his job better, you are actually helping yourself. Keep this in mi[nd] and overtime seems less of a burden.

The time may come when you feel your good works should be rewarded more fully than they have been. You believe that you deserve a raise or promotion and none has been forthcoming. How can you induce the powers-that-be to favor you?

Before you approach your boss, do a little clearheaded planning. When confronted with any sort of employee request, bosses invariably have the somewhat discomforting habit of wanting to know *why*. In the case of a pay increase, it's not that he wants to put you on the spot. Most likely, higher approval is required for a raise, and your boss may want some reasons to substantiate his recommendation. You can't reply, "Because I want more money." This he knows, of course. Wiser psychology suggests that to influence his decision most favorably you play up not what *you* want but rather how *he* has benefited by having you on his staff.

Suppose you want a raise and your company has no policy of regular pay increases for deserving employees. Or perhaps you have reached the maximum salary for your particular job. In such a case, you'll want to prepare a sales talk that will show why you *deserve* more money. Here are some of the reasons you might offer to show that you are of greater value to your company.

You have taken on more responsibility. (Perhaps you've relieved your boss of certain tasks or enlarged the scope of your work.)

You handle more complicated work. (Be sure to give specific examples. Perhaps you now handle alone certain jobs formerly supervised by someone else. Don't overlook them.)

You've increased your knowledge of the company. Its methods and its products are familiar to you, and, therefore, you can make more intelligent decisions about the work.

You have helped build goodwill for the company. (Can you name specific instances when you have pleased customers by giving them special help? Can you quote compliments received from customers? Any appreciative letters?)

You are familiar with the particular preferences of many customers. You can help provide the individualized service that they have come to depend on.

You have made suggestions for improved work methods that have been put into practice. Or you have submitted ideas for obtaining more business, for pleasing customers, and so on.

You have improved yourself. (Can you cite any courses you've taken, lectures you've attended, or books you've studied—anything that has added to your business skills or personality development?)

Your appeal for a raise will be more impressive if you type out your reasons in outline form. Every salesman knows that a written presentation enhances and emphasizes his sales pitch. A boss will also be impressed by your thoroughness and by the business-like manner evidenced by a typed presentation.

If you are seeking a promotion, it is most important that you write out your qualifications. Perhaps you know the prospective boss very well—even to the point of exchanging daily comments on your favorite baseball team. Even so, it's advisable to prepare a résumé. In all probability he has only a vague idea of the work you do. In your résumé, you can enumerate all the exact types of work you handle (transcribing, filing, record keeping), all the contributions you have made to your present job, and how you can best help your prospective boss in his work. You also have an opportunity, in a résumé, to describe past experience and accomplishments and to mention other abilities that you may have no chance to use in your present position. You are able to bring to his attention many details he may not be aware of or may have forgotten. Also, since you may be competing with outsiders who are applying for this job, your neatly typed presentation will help you compare favorably with them.

POPPING THE QUESTION

Any girl who has approached her dad for an advance on next week's allowance knows that the best time is when he's in a good mood. The same applies to your boss. Watch for a time when he's been telling jokes to the staff, has just returned from a pleasant luncheon, or has received good news. If he's trying to get out a rush job, troubled about difficult work, or seething from some sort of annoyance, keep away from his door.

When you do confer with your boss, aim for the happy medium between overselling and underselling. A good salesman knows just how far to push so that he seems smart and ambitious without becoming annoyingly aggressive. He lets the facts sell for him and does not try to exert high pressure tactics.

In the course of your conversation bring out the length of time that has elapsed since you received your last raise. (In most instances, an employee is not expected to look for a raise unless she has not had one for at least a year.) When you do so, state it without any sarcasm or complaining chip-on-the-shoulder attitude. This merely annoys a boss. The situation is difficult at best, and you want to keep relations as pleasant as possible.

Occasionally an employee lets herself become so worked up over a promotion or raise that she threatens to quit unless her request is granted. Some bosses bristle at this type of ultimatum and are just likely to take the attitude, "If that's all the loyalty she feels for us, let her quit!" Although we don't like to face up to the fact, no one is so vital to a company that she can't be replaced. Sometimes the idea of getting a replacement may even have a certain tinge of appeal to an angry executive. A newcomer is usually someone who is eager to please and, also worth considering, she is someone who will probably settle for a lower salary.

On the whole, bosses want to please. They want to grant raises, and they want their employees to stay around long enough to qualify for 25-year award gold watches. There are times, however, when a slump in business or a squeezed budget may make a raise impossible. One girl who liked her job thought it would strengthen her case if she threatened to quit unless she got a raise. She didn't—and found herself backed into the position of having to resign because the company couldn't afford to pay her more. A few months later, when business had picked up, she was chagrined to learn that her former co-workers had all received salary increases.

If a raise is refused, a worker is perfectly justified to turn the tables and ask why. She will inspire respect when she explains that she wants to know if something is wrong with her work so that she can correct it. There have been times when the refusal of a raise was such a jolt to the so-so worker that she snapped out of her lethargy and got down to business, soon deserving—and receiving—the raise she had been denied a short while before.

RED LIGHT AHEAD?

There are jobs, of course, where nothing looms before you but a big red stoplight. It's obvious that you can't get ahead and that your employer can't afford—or won't pay— more money. You realize that your only course is to get another job. If this is your decision, by all means say nothing about it. Then quietly go about the business of hunting for another position. No matter how much you'd like to dramatically hand in your resignation, resist the temptation.

There are many advantages to holding on to a job until you have another. For one thing, you still have a steady salary rolling in and you can afford to be choosy about selecting the work you really want. A girl faced with starvation is likely to jump at any job, perhaps one even less promising than the one she has left. Another advantage is that you have an opportunity to survey the field. It sometimes happens that a job hunter comes to realize that she is a lot better off in her present company than she thought she was and decides that her own job is well worth holding on to.

Don't, however, be afraid to change jobs. Some girls who have the ability to go far stay in low-paying, unchallenging work year after year merely because the job is pleasant. There are many other pleasant positions to be had—and they become much more pleasant when accompanied by a promising future and a more substantial salary! Look quietly and choose carefully before you make the break. If you have high career hopes, a dead-end job is merely a waste of precious time.

Too-frequent changes, however, are also bad. The fickle job-hopper who flits from one position to another, never satisfied and never staying long enough to give the job a chance, soon finds herself blacklisted. Employers scare off easily when confronted with a job record of frequent changes.

FINDING ANOTHER JOB

Hunting for a new job while you're employed is more complicated than when your days are your own. You don't want to annoy your present boss or arouse his suspicions by stretching lunch hours or taking time off. You can save much time and fruitless effort by working through an employment agency (though this usually involves a fee that may wipe out the advantages of a better salary for several paychecks to come). Many girls manage to follow up newspaper ads without too much difficulty. Most would-be employers are glad to set up lunch-hour or after-five appointments to accommodate working girls.

If there are certain firms in which you are specifically interested, don't just walk in cold. You can make a faster and more direct entrée by first sending an application letter that requests an appointment and by including a résumé. Aside from demonstrating your efficiency, a résumé is often very helpful in saving time for the job hunter with a job. It can sometimes eliminate the time-consuming filling out of application forms and can quickly emphasize your best selling points, thereby cutting down interview time.

A GRACEFUL EXIT

After you've obtained a new job comes the problem of severing ties with your old employer. You'll want to do this in as graceful and as fair a manner as possible. Even though you might feel quite sour about your present job, you'll want to leave like a lady. Stormy tell-him-off scenes never are wise. They slam the door tightly behind you and leave an unpleasant memory in case recommendations are needed in the future.

Be fair to your present employer by giving him sufficient time to find a replacement. (Two weeks' notice is customary.) Even though your new boss may want you to start immediately, he'll respect your consideration for your present boss.

1 Survey some of your friends who have been working a few years and have advanced in their jobs. Ask them about the types of promotions they received. Did they move up with their bosses? Did they change bosses or departments? Ask what factors they considered were responsible for their being selected for a promotion.

2 Discuss how you would go about finding a new job while you are still employed.

PART SIX: MAKING THE

MOST OF FIVE-TO-NINE

The big city has a magnetic attraction for the small-town girl with the brains and the ability for a bright career. It's a place of varied opportunity, bigger salaries, glamorous jobs. And, of course, there's always the excitement of city life—fascinating places to go and things to do, more people, more parties, more frantic fun.

Many a business graduate with her new diploma in one hand and a suitcase in the other immediately heads for the city, considering it the ideal place—the only place—to make her fortune. Perhaps it is, for living in a big city has many advantages—if you are the right type of girl.

The girl who has a loving family and wide circle of friends whom she would miss might *not* be the type. And the girl who has grown up loving the beauty of the outdoors and the fun of outdoor sports may feel as deprived in the city as the stunted trees that struggle to grow beside the shadowed, unfertile, grime-laden streets. Another wrong-type girl might be the young miss who would find the fast pace of city living too hectic. Life on your own has many more problems than the one you lead when you're cozily ensconced in the love and comfort of your family home. There's no one to pass out the knowing advice a mother or father can offer, no one to cook or clean or mend for you, no one to soothe away troubles and to remind you that you've always been such a wonderful girl—no one who really cares as much about you as your family does. You have to be able to depend entirely upon yourself.

Perhaps one of the problems that bothers transplanted small-towners most is the continual need to prove themselves. At home you've achieved your status. Everybody is aware of your virtues and accomplishments. Your family is known and respected, and you, in turn, fit into the town and are respected. A city is too big for this type of acknowledgement. There you can easily get lost in the crowd. You may have been a diving champ, the girl voted most likely to succeed, and a gold-medal shorthand winner, but to your city neighbors you are merely the girl in 8A.

HOME OR ROAM?

With an increasing number of industries moving to the suburbs, there are many more good jobs available within easy commuting distance. These deserve thorough consideration. Perhaps an interesting and exciting job can be found close to home, even right in your own town.

23
WHERE YOU LIVE

But, if you long for city life and possess the independent spirit, the maturity, stamina, and ability to manage money that living alone requires, you'll probably have a marvelous time. And your single business girl years are the time to try it. (Most married couples prefer to bring up their children in the country.) If possible, persuade one of your best friends to go with you. Someone else to share your adventures makes life easier—and more fun.

A HOLE—OR HEAVEN?

When you're city-bound, your first concern is a place to live. Before you make the move, try to learn as much as possible about the city of your choice. If you are not familiar with it, you may want to make a preliminary visit so that you can become acquainted with the various sections. Can you consult any friends who live in the city and can advise you? If you're planning to enroll for courses in one of the schools or colleges in the city, you will probably be eligible for student housing or may be able to obtain recommendations for other approved places. It's much easier to make the move when you have some idea of where you will live once you arrive. There are several types of nonschool housing found in most cities; each with definite advantages and problems. It is wise to check them against your own needs and desires before you leave the nest.

A hotel · On the plus side, a hotel offers you a place to park until you can get the lay of the land. It requires no furnishings, linens, or entangling leases that make moving away difficult. The cleaning, bedmaking, and cooking problems are nonexistent. However, hotel living is usually hard on the budget. Many cities have hotels that cater to women, such as the Barbizon in New York, or those run by the YWCA, which are less expensive. But even if the rates are reasonable, eating out isn't. Some girls also feel that hotel living soon pales when they must make the effort to get dressed and go out for each meal. They are also faced with the problem of no place to entertain, no facilities for parties. And hotel living lacks the settled, homey feeling that gives a sense of stability.

Boarding or rooming houses · These are usually less expensive and less elegant than hotels, but offer the same freedom as hotel living as well as many of the same disadvantages. They vary widely from excellent to miserable and should be investigated carefully. Some are run specifically for young women and are managed by a housemother type of supervisor. Some boardinghouses provide meals; some have kitchen facilities where the girls can eat, cooking and cleaning up for themselves. A boardinghouse of this type enables you to make friends easily.

Rooming with a family · When you rent a room in someone else's home, a great deal depends on the family you live with. They may be marvelous, a pleasant substitute for Mom and Dad, or they may be either of two extremes: ever-present, allowing you too little privacy; or ever-absent, letting you alone to such a degree that you almost feel like a trespasser. The life of a roomer can also be lonely if there are no other young people nearby. Living with the right family can be most enjoyable, but they must suit your needs and your temperament.

The advantages of this arrangement are similar to those of hotel or boardinghouse living. All the necessary furnishings are supplied and usually the cleaning is done for you. In some cases meals are included. Rates are often quite reasonable.

A residence house · If you're lucky enough to get into one of the residences run for business girls, you'll have the fun of college dorm living at quite low expense. Because most such residences are run by religious groups or other nonprofit organizations, they are usually subsidized. Some have restrictions as to age (often under 35), salary (low), religion, education, and occupation (some are specifically for apprentices in art, ballet, music, or drama). The most desirable houses may have long waiting lists. It is usually advisable to send in well ahead of the time you expect to come to town and to make other plans to tide you over in case a vacancy doesn't materialize in time.

The advantages of a residence house are many for the new arrival. They are particularly desirable as a first step because they allow you to gather the courage and the cash for apartment living. It's easy to make friends and to find a prospective roommate there. You are surrounded by girls who have the same interests and problems. Usually a happy community life prevails, with the girls finding dates for one another, swapping hats and jewelry, and pitching in when someone has a big job to finish. There's always someone who's good at setting hair or altering dresses and always someone who has plans for fun that can include you. A maid takes care of the cleaning, meals are usually provided, and often there is a recreation room of some sort in which you and the other girls may entertain dates.

347

On the minus side, you may find that the setting isn't as homelike as you'd desire and that at times there are simply too many people around. Occasionally you may yearn for silence, for privacy, for the pleasure of enjoying a good black mood without having someone attempt to jolly you out of it. By the time these feelings take on any sizable proportions, a residence will have served its purpose. You'll no longer be Little Girl Lost in the big city. You'll have made a slight niche for yourself; you'll have a circle of friends and a job and perhaps a raise or two to make apartment living more financially feasible.

CONSIDER THE APARTMENT

If you dream of having a place of your own, you must reckon with the cold hard fact that apartment living, fun though it is, is usually more expensive and more time-consuming than a residence or other accommodation. Rents in the better locations are usually amazingly high. Most rents do not include gas and electricity; some even leave it up to the tenant to provide heat. A high rent can sometimes be offset by taking in one or more roommates, but the problems of cooking and cleaning and doing the laundry are ever present. You man the mop, lug the groceries, and wash the dishes. Usually, though, because it's a place of your own—a place to take pride in—you don't really mind. You have every little girl's dream of a chance to play house come true. You know it will only last until your Shining Knight on the White Charger comes to carry you off to his own castle, but for the time being it's fun to play house any way you want, and you'll learn much from the experience.

Furnished or unfurnished? · Will you want a furnished apartment or an unfurnished one? Rents are higher for furnished apartments, but all furniture and most necessary household equipment are included. This makes it easier to move, to give up the apartment, or to split up with an altar-bound roommate. Of course, a furnished apartment may not be a decorator's dream, but much can be done to give it a personal touch by adding a few of your own accessories and pictures.

An unfurnished apartment is the choice of the girls who yearn for a chance to fix up their apartments in a manner a bit advanced for Mother's taste. It allows them to express their individuality—and to play with the puzzle of decorating on a budget. But your budget must include more than just the furniture. While the rent is lower than that of furnished rooms, an unfurnished apartment is merely bare walls with a ceiling and bare floor. You provide everything from spoons to beds, from scouring powder to vacuum cleaner. Possibly the family attic will yield a few treasures you can use and you can borrow some things from home, but there will be many things that must be purchased— a problem to finance and a problem to divide up should you and your roommate part. Tip: *Never* buy anything together, as *both* of you are sure to want it when the time comes to split up.

Tracking down an apartment · In apartment hunting there are several methods you can try.

· Consult friends. When you've decided upon the section of town you want to live in, spread word of your search among all the residents you know. Many of the most desirable apartments pass from friend to friend and are never advertised.

349

- Go to a real estate agency. This is the quickest and easiest method, but it involves a fee that is often substantial.

- Follow the real estate ads. The newspaper ads supply many good leads—especially those in the Sunday section. When you find something that sounds right, go after it as early as possible. Good places go fast. Perhaps you can even obtain the classified section the night before so that you'll have a head start on other apartment hunters.

- Scout the area. Since many of the best apartments don't need to be advertised, you may be able to find what you want by walking through desirable neighborhoods and watching for vacancy signs. This can prove tiring and time-consuming, especially for a girl with a busy workday schedule.

• Leave your name with the superintendents of several buildings you are interested in. In any large apartment building the turnover is fairly frequent and superintendents are often glad to have a waiting list of applicants. If you are anxious to move in, don't just list your name and then forget about it. Call up frequently to remind the superintendent of your interest. Another possibility to speed up the process is, of course, to use the mighty power of a tip, distasteful though it may seem.

It pays to look highly respectable on apartment-hunting expeditions. You want to convince the landlord that you are the type of tenant he wants. Many landlords are reluctant to rent to single women and some won't consider renting to more than two girls.

RENTAL TECHNICALITIES

When you live in a hotel, a boardinghouse, a room in a private home, or a residence, you can move in with no more financial outlay than a week's rent in advance and, when you wish to leave, a week's notice or less is usually acceptable. Renting an apartment, however, can be much more involved. Usually a lease (see pages 352–353) is required.

A lease is a contract between you and the landlord, giving you the right to live in a specified apartment at a specified rent for a specified period of time. A lease for more than one year must be in writing or it is unenforceable. The lease lists the duties and responsibilities of both the tenant and the landlord. The landlord benefits by being assured of steady income for the period. In return, you are assured of having the apartment for the length of the lease at a fixed rent.

A lease usually requires that before a tenant takes possession the landlord be given a certain payment (generally one month's rent) as security against damage to the premises or cancellation of the lease. Before you can move in, therefore, you must be able to pay the equivalent of two months' rent—a month's rent in advance plus an equal amount as security. The security payment is returned at the end of the lease. Some landlords will deduct from the security any damage done by the tenant—even such minor things as nail holes in the wall or a chip in the sink enamel. In most cases, however, the security is returned intact.

Most leases contain clauses that allow the tenant to sublet an apartment to someone else should she be forced to move. Usually the landlord reserves the right to approve the new tenant. Some leases, however, specify that the security is lost if the tenant moves

351

This Agreement, made the...day of

....19.......... Between...

....as Landlord, and

....as Tenant ;

WITNESSETH, that Landlord hereby LEASES to Tenant, Apartment No...........................

on the...floor of the premises known as No...................................

....

City of..., for the term of...

unless sooner terminated as hereinafter provided, to commence..,

19.......... and to end..., 19.........., to be occupied as a strictly private
dwelling apartment by Tenant and Tenant's immediate family consisting of
only and not otherwise. And the Tenant hereby covenants and agrees to pay to the Landlord,

the TOTAL RENT OF $.............................. in equal monthly payments of $..............................
each, in advance, on the first day of each and every month during said term.

Tenant shall pay the said rent at the time and in the manner above provided without
demand therefor.

THE SAID PREMISES ARE ALSO LEASED UPON THE FURTHER COVENANTS AND CONDITIONS:

1. Tenant shall take good care of the apartment and fixtures therein and shall at Tenant's
own cost and expense make, when needed, all repairs, replacements and decorations
therein and thereto, whenever damage or injury to the same shall have resulted from
misuse, or neglect by Tenant, Tenant's family, employees, or visitors. Tenant shall not
drill into, drive nails, install new locks or change apartment entrance lock or deface in
any manner any part of the building, or permit the same to be done, and at the end or
other expiration of the term, shall deliver up the demised premises in good order and
condition. Tenant shall indemnify and save harmless the Landlord for and against any
liability or any injury to person or property resulting from any negligence or improper
conduct on the part of Tenant, Tenant's family, employees or visitors. Landlord is
exempt for any and all liability for any damage or injury to persons or property caused
by or resulting from steam, electricity, gas, water, rain, ice or snow, or any lack or flow
from or into any part of said building, or from any damage or injury resulting or
arising from any other cause or happening whatsoever unless said damage or injury be
caused by or be due to the negligence of Landlord.

2. That any and all shelves, locks, plumbing fixtures, or any other improvements that
Tenant may place or cause to be placed in the said apartment shall immediately become
a part of the house and the property of Landlord.

4. That Tenant, and Tenant's heirs, executors, or administrators shall not assign this
agreement, or underlet the premises, or any part thereof, or make any alterations in the

352

apartments or premises without Landlord's or Landlord's authorized agent's consent in writing, or to permit or suffer upon the same, any act or thing deemed extra hazardous on account of fire ; and shall comply with all the rules and regulations of the Board of Health and City Ordinances applicable to said premises ; and that Tenant will not use or permit the said premises or any part thereof to be used for any purpose other than above mentioned.

5. That Tenant shall, in case of fire, give immediate notice thereof to Landlord who shall thereupon cause the damage to be repaired as soon as reasonably convenient ; but if the building or demised premises be so damaged by fire or otherwise as to require rebuilding, the term shall, at the option of Landlord, cease, and in case it so ceases, the rent shall be paid only up to the time of the fire, unless such damage be caused by the negligence or improper conduct of Tenant, or Tenant's family or servants.

10. That Landlord will furnish, without additional charge, hot and cold water ; heat during winter months only. Neither Electricity, Gas or Telephone service is included in the rent, but shall be paid for separately by the Tenant. There shall be no allowance to Tenant for a diminution of rental value, and no liability on the part of Landlord by reason of inconvenience or annoyance arising from the making of any repairs, alterations, additions, or improvements in or to any portion of the building or demised premises.

21. That Tenant has this day deposited with the said Landlord the sum of $........................... as security for the faithful performance of and compliance with all the terms, covenants and conditions in the within lease. That if Tenant fails to comply with each of said terms, covenants, and conditions, or surrender said premises without the written consent of Landlord, or be dispossessed therefrom prior to the expiration of this lease, then, and in that event, the sum herein deposited aforesaid, shall belong to Landlord, as a part payment of the disbursements, attorney's fees, costs, and expenses that Landlord may undergo for the purposes of regaining possession of the said premises and preparing same for renting ; and the same shall not be considered as payment for any rent due, or to become due by reason of these presents, or in any manner release Tenant from such rents herein reserved, or from any of Tenant's obligations. If, however, all the terms, covenants, and conditions be fully complied with by Tenant, the said security shall be returned to Tenant after expiration of the term.

IT IS FURTHER AGREED that the character of the occupancy of said demised premises as above expressed, is an especial consideration and inducement for the granting of this lease by Landlord to Tenant, and in the event of a violation by Tenant of the restriction against assignment or sub-letting, or if Tenant shall cease to occupy the premises or permit the same to be occupied by parties other than Tenant, Tenant's immediate family and employees, or violate any other restriction or condition herein imposed, this lease may, at the option of Landlord or Landlord's agents or assigns, be terminated in the manner hereinbefore recited.

In Witness Whereof, the Landlord and the Tenant have hereunto set their hands the day and year above written.

Signed and delivered in the presence of :

Witness ....

....

out before a certain period of time has elapsed. The tenant is also expected to pay the costs of advertising the vacancy and of rerenting the apartment and of any redecorating that may be required.

Many leases contain clauses stating that if the tenant doesn't want to renew her lease, she must notify the landlord in writing a certain number of weeks or months before the expiration of the lease or it will be automatically renewed. Should a tenant forget to give such notice, the lease automatically renews itself for another term (not to exceed one year).

If a tenant overstays the time mentioned in the lease, the landlord can, if he desires, hold her to the lease for another term. One girl who planned to move out the last day of the month changed her mind because it was raining too hard. Although she moved the very next morning, she found herself faced with a lease for another year. (A delay is permissible only in extreme cases of serious illness or death in the family.)

If a tenant wants to stay on after the expiration of a lease and the landlord accepts the next month's rent, the landlord is considered to have renewed the lease and can't change his mind or try to evict the tenant, even though he may have others waiting to move in.

CHOOSING ROOMMATES

Much of the fun of living on your own depends on your success in finding a congenial roommate. Ordinary activities become fun when shared with the right person, but a personality that grates will blight even paradise.

Two roommates, Joan and Barbara, who are an especially happy pair, summed up pretty well what they want in a roommate: "She should like the things you like—at least the big things—so that you have someone to share your interests," said Joan. "She should be considerate and fair," added Barbara. Both girls agreed that a sense of humor is most important.

The areas which seem to cause the most strife should be discussed between you beforehand. Do you *both* like to entertain? Do you enjoy similar types of recreation (theater and concerts or rock and roll and baseball games)? Is one of you a chatterbox, while the other prefers peace and quiet most of the time? Do you have similar ideas about money? Is at least *one* of you easygoing?

As Joan and Barbara agreed, you don't have to match up like two buttons on a blouse, but you should have somewhat similar standards and viewpoints on life. The serious-minded miss who wants a career had better not team up with the party girl who comes to the city for the sole purpose of tearing a few years into confetti. Similar standards about housekeeping, although sometimes hard to assess in advance, are important in helping a relationship click smoothly. Barbara commented, "I lived with one girl who left her clothes all over the place. Our apartment was always such a sloppy mess that I couldn't stand it. And my roommate thought I was unbearably neat!" But you can't be a perfectionist, the girls added, pointing out that sometimes you have to put up with an unmade bed or a less-than-gourmet dinner when the pressure of time or finances interferes.

Independence is another quality that roommates need. Occasionally there is a girl who likes to play momma, but difficulties usually arise when one girl leans too heavily on the other. Often the stronger roommate rebels against too much responsibility, or the weaker objects because she feels stifled by being subjected to unwanted authority.

Most trivial differences can be *kept* trivial if you respect these differences and resolve to put up with them. Barbara goes to night school and must occasionally study late. Joan, who likes to go to bed early, has obligingly outfitted herself with an eye mask to keep out the light. On the other hand, Joan can't bear conversation before breakfast, so Barbara saves her thoughts until the morning coffee has perked up her roommate's sluggish spirits.

Most girls who come to the city alone seem to find roommates either in the residences or other places where they live or work. Many also have found kindred souls among those they've met through such activities as choir, hobby groups, dramatic clubs, or through classes they attended. The consensus of opinion seems to be that if roommates work for the same firm, they'll be less likely to become oversaturated with each other's company if they work in different departments and have different workday experiences.

Whether to take on a roommate or to live alone is a decision each girl must make. Living alone is considered peaceful by some, deadening by others. Those in favor like the freedom of not having to cater to someone else and of not having to compromise at every turn. You're your own boss, responsible only to and for yourself. No one can object to what you do or how you do it.

But lonely it can be. As it has been said, there's security in numbers, even if the number is only two. Another person to confide in, to help you out if you're sick or broke or don't know the ropes is mighty comforting. Needless to say, learning to live with someone else is excellent training for marriage.

Aside from the matter of compatibility, the big dark shadow that hangs over most twosomes is usually that of the man on the horizon. If one roommate marries first, quite an upheaval takes place—both emotional and financial. The girl who's left behind will certainly need a quick replacement unless she can swing both halves of the bills herself. For this reason, some girls prefer having more than one roommate.

THREE IS A CROWD

Four is more so, especially when it comes to roommates. Before you get involved in a three-or-four roommate deal, make sure you're the gregarious, flexible soul who can thrive on life *en masse*. Getting along with one roommate can sometimes be a strain—and each additional roommate can be just one more source of friction. Also, one less chance for privacy. But, on the brighter side, also one more source of close friendship. Many such relationships have been known to work out beautifully. Just make sure you're the girl for them and they're the bunch for you before you hop aboard the merry-go-round.

If there is a choice between having three or four roommates, often it's easier to be part of a foursome. Multiple roommate setups have a way of separating into groups. Threesomes sometimes split into a two versus one faction. When there is a division among four, it may not be even, but a two and one and one split is less uncomfortable.

RULES FOR ROOMMATES

If you want to foster a happy relationship with your roommate, you'll want to observe the following:

🌼 Don't make a play for your roommate's date. She snagged him first and you're honor-bound to direct your allure in some other direction.

🌼 Don't poach on her preserves. Keep your belongings separate—separate drawers, separate shelves, separate halves of the closet. Overflow into her premises will surely be resented. Just because she isn't using all of her space doesn't give you the right to take over.

🌼 Have equal facilities whenever possible. If there's only one comfortable chair in the place, or only one good spot for writing, there's likely to be discord. Try to borrow or buy (secondhand if necessary) whatever you need so that you can both be comfortable.

🌼 Be considerate of her sleep. Some people need more sleep than others. If she likes to go to bed early or snooze later in the morning, tiptoe quietly so that you won't disturb her.

🌼 When there's housework to be done, pitch in. If one girl slaves while the other relaxes, there are likely to be hard feelings. For the greatest harmony, try to arrange your cleaning chedule so that you both work at the same time. One idea that has worked well is to ssign each girl to a room or job and rotate on a weekly basis. This way, the cleaning ,ets done and you have clearly defined areas of responsibility. It saves trouble and empers!

Seldom a borrower be. If you've earned her devotion, she'll probably suggest that ou wear her tangerine scarf with your beige outfit, but asking for it may not go over vell. People usually lend you what you ask for, but often with a degree of resentment.)nly borrow in real emergencies, and never ask for anything valuable or perishable; ou'll worry so much that you won't enjoy it anyhow.

Don't exude overmuch about the man in your life. She's glad for you, yes, but too 1uch is too much. Also, if her life is a bit low on masculine affection at this point, some-ne else's continual man prattle may make her feel just that much more dejected.

Don't decide to throw impromptu parties. Check with her first. The one time you ecide unexpectedly to invite the gang in she may have just washed her hair or may be uffering from a seething headache.

Respect her need for quiet. If she's cramming for a course or is just in no mood for onversation, give her the peace she needs. Be judicious, too, in your timing of television.

 FOLLOW-UP

If you live in a small town, compare the good and bad points of local job opportunities ith those of a city. Can you find the work you want near home? Will it have the type f future you want? How do salaries compare with those of city jobs? Check a city news-aper want-ad section to get an idea of the work available and the salaries offered. Would : be possible to commute to a city job or would the time and expense involved make it 1ore advisable to live in the city? How much would commuting cost? How long would take round trip?

Learn as much as possible about the housing available in the city you might want to vork in. Study the real estate section of the city's newspaper and, if possible, the classified ection of the city telephone book. What type of housing is available? Are there any laces that cater to young women for which you might be eligible? Compare the rates or the various types of hotels, boarding or rooming houses, and residences. What prices re asked for a room in a family home? How do apartments, both furnished and unfur-ished, compare?

Charm grows most successfully when it is nurtured in a happy, well-ordered existence. If our lives run fairly smoothly, without hair-tearing emergencies and avoidable crises, we can devote our energies more fully to concentrating on charm.

The girl who never quite manages to get caught up with herself has too many distracting annoyances pricking at her poise. To make the most of the opportunities life offers, you must manage your energy, your time, and your money so that the routine matters of daily living quietly fall into line. Then you can devote full attention to the BIG things that make life worth living.

24

HOW
YOU LIVE

BE GOOD TO YOURSELF

A lovely Southern belle came to New York a few years ago to have a fling at city living. Marylou was completely captivated by New York. She was fascinated by the plays, the opera, the ballets, and the continual round of activities available. She seemed determined to see and do everything that was going on.

Evenings after work found her dashing off to a box office for standing room tickets (the only kind her salary permitted). Supper was often a drugstore hamburger or the meager nourishment of hors d'oeuvres at a cocktail party. Because she was well liked, weekends were equally hectic, with gala dates and parties that lasted until early morn. Marylou was in a gay, exciting whirl. She hadn't time to sleep. She barely bothered to eat. This went on for a little more than a year, when suddenly all came to a jolting halt. Marylou's health gave out. A doctor quickly shipped her back to the old plantation, where Marylou underwent a long and frustrating recuperation, followed by a strict regime of careful diet and early curfew.

It seems so easy to pass up sleep or to ignore meals once in a while, but a series of such physical punishments can do serious damage—damage that may not turn up until years later. There are many cases of stomach troubles, anemia, nervous disorders, heart conditions, and even blindness in people in their late twenties and early thirties who lived at too fast, too careless a pace a few years earlier.

BE GOOD TO YOUR CAREER

Being healthy has a lot to do with everything in life. When you feel below par, your whole outlook sours. It's hard to be alert and accurate at the office when you haven't had **361** enough sleep, and hard to control your emotions when you're hollow inside because you've skipped a meal. Any job seems dull, any chore too much, and no promotion worth striving for if you feel miserable. Maybe an extremely good-natured boss will put up with you if you have a low day now and then; and, if there are no upsets, you can coast through safely. But, oh, how risky! There's always the unexpected to contend with—the really big job you might muff or the sudden promotion interview you might mangle. Opportunity doesn't wait until the morning after a girl has been to the beauty parlor, had ten hours sleep, and eaten a country style breakfast. For business girls *any* day may be an important turning point, and you always want to be ready.

There's also the little matter of playing it square. It's hardly fair for an employee to overspend *her* time and energy on fun to such a degree that she must rest up on her boss's time and can't function efficiently. It's even more unfair for her to neglect her health so that she's forced to stay home. No one should come to work if she is seriously ill or has a bad cold that she might spread to others, but it is possible to work when you have a slight headache or a sore knee. Every worker who stays out not only costs the firm money but also puts an unfair burden on the rest of the staff. Many firms can't afford to carry someone with a high absentee record and may be forced to let such persons go. Your attendance and the state of your health are, of course, important considerations in evaluation for promotion. The more responsible your job, the more others depend on you and the more necessary it is for you to be at your desk, in top form, each day.

Being overly conscientious to a fault is unwise, however. No one should overspend her energy on work and office worries to such a degree that she overtaxes her nervous system and bankrupts her health. The girls who lead the happiest, best-balanced lives know the wisdom of leaving office problems behind them when they close their desks at night, and of offsetting work strain with weekends of sports and relaxation.

For the sake of your charm, your health, and your job:

🌷 Resolve to get eight hours sleep at least four nights a week, with no more than one wee-hours bedtime a week, and this on a Friday or Saturday.

🌷 Resolve to eat three nutritious meals a day. Never skip a meal, especially breakfast. Stoke up on foods rich in vitamins, minerals, and proteins rather than "empty" calories.

🌷 Resolve to get some exercise in the fresh air each day and to indulge in some active sport at least once a week.

HOW TO FIND TIME FOR EVERYTHING—ALMOST

Probably nobody has found time for everything she wants to do. With most of us, "everything" is just too big an order for any measly twenty-four hour day. But an amazing number of girls seem to pack a tremendous amount into each day. They're the ones who are never too tired, never have a messy-hair day, a nothing-clean-to-wear problem, or any of the other troublesome trivia that interfere with important doings. They're the girls who lead busy happy lives, dress with shopwindow perfection, and manage it all calmly and efficiently and economically.

Regulate your time so that each day allows sufficient time for each of the following:

- A well-groomed appearance.
- Doing a good job for your employer.
- Leisurely meals.
- Reading and learning something new each day.
- Fun and relaxation.
- Sufficient sleep.

How can you streamline *your* living? Think about your own daily activities—what do you do? How do you do it? Which of the following time-savers can you make use of, so that you will get greater advantage from your free hours?

Decide what you want most to do · Part of the problem is that sometimes we try to do too much. We can't stretch time; we can only eliminate some of the nonessentials that are squeezed into our schedule. If you want to read some good books, for instance, but never can seem to get around to it, figure out what less interesting recreation is taking up your time. Many people spend more hours than they realize reading so-so magazine stories, watching mediocre television programs, or doing something else they don't really care much about.

Some girls get so wound up with trivial puttering that they miss half the fun. One girl who took a Western vacation tour completely baffled the rest of the group. Every time they returned from exploring some scenic wonder, they would be met by Ethel who would proudly announce, "I feel so good—I just shampooed my hair" or ". . . did all my laundry" or something equally commendable but tedious. The Grand Canyon, Yellowstone, Mount Rainier—nothing could divert her for long from her craving for cleanliness. While the rest of the group were a bit more grimy, they saw and did much more on this wonderful vacation.

Everybody has to decide what's most important for her. If it's cleanliness, then be antiseptic and enjoy it; but make sure this is really what you want most out of life. More worthwhile goals for a young girl might be education for career advancement, cultural development, improvement of talents, preparing for marriage, helping those less fortunate, and so on. When you really want something, you will be able to find or even make time for it.

Get the necessary chores out of the way as quickly as possible · Because you must eat properly and look presentable and live in an orderly place, you can't skip chores. But some people tend to waste time trying to find excuses that enable them to avoid doing unpleasant things now. Instead, if they'd just do the chores *first* and get them over with fast, there would probably be time left for something more enjoyable.

Streamline your surroundings · Some time ago, in a TV interview, Elsa Maxwell uttered some sage advice that hits home for many of us. She said that her amazing ability to accomplish so much was due largely to not letting herself become overburdened by possessions. It takes a strong constitution to resist buying some fascinating little knickknack or to throw out an especially becoming but outdated hat. And how often have you bought two of something to save a penny, even though you wouldn't need the extra for six months? The nuisance value of such clutter cancels out thrift. You have to clean around it, find room for it, care for it. Such unneeded extras are permissible for women who live in roomy houses and have nothing more urgent to do with their time, but business girls are wise to simplify their lives as much as possible.

Parting with still useful possessions hurts much less if you can give them away. In one apartment house the tenants, mostly young office workers, made a practice of leaving on the newspaper pile any good items they felt forced to part with. This allowed other occupants free choice of anything of interest. Such a system seemed to be a much more satisfying solution than heartlessly dumping some charming but useless possession down an apartment incinerator. Many charity organizations are delighted to accept your castoffs. If you keep in mind that someone desperately needs an item you use once in a blue moon, it's much easier to discard intelligently. A good measurement for most items: if it hasn't been used in three years, discard it.

Don't clutter your life with too many activities · Some girls try to do everything at once—drive themselves wild with four night courses instead of two, feel compelled to accept every offer of fun, never say no to any appeal for assistance. Remember, there's next semester, next week, or tomorrow. It's good to be active, true, but some girls overdo to such a degree that nothing comes out right. Concentrate your energies on a limited number of worthwhile endeavors if you want to get most enjoyment from them. A practical rule to follow was devised by a group of big city cliffdwellers for their weekly activities:

1 night course ❀ 1 volunteer job ❀ 1 "wash and sew" night ❀ 1 free night

Do it the easy way · Everybody must decide how important her time is. When you're pressed for time, time can be as precious as money. Then how wasteful extensive bargain shopping, running to several stores to compare prices, or searching doggedly for just the perfect gift becomes. Sometimes you *have* to settle for something less than the greatest value or the very best choice.

Another way to make life easier is to use as many easy-care items as possible: drip-dry and soil-resistant fabrics for clothing, curtains, and other household furnishings; no white collars unless the outfit can also be worn without the collar; dark shoes instead of white; no fussy fabrics. Perhaps each such special care item takes but a few minutes extra work, but the total time lost can assume amazing proportions.

Don't make double work · Some girls, when they come home after a busy day, are tempted to throw their coat, purse, umbrella, and what-have-you on the nearest chair. As they change clothes, they may strew what they take off on the bed. Then, when they're all ready to relax, what happens? They're faced with the depressing chore of picking up everything and putting it away. Actually, it's a lot easier and quicker if you make a habit of putting away the coat, hat, and other clothes as you take them off—while they are in hand. This way, the room looks much tidier and you avoid an extra cleanup later.

Schedule your chores · Many girls find it helpful to have some sort of plan for the week's activities. If you live with roommates (or sisters), a work schedule simplifies the problem of who gets to use the iron, when to do the cleaning, and so on. A schedule that two roommates, Lois and Julie, have worked out for themselves is on the next page.

Since Julie and Lois are a very harmonious twosome, they usually cook and clean up together. Other roommates, especially if three or more girls live together, find it more convenient to divide up the work. One group of four, with a very small kitchen, worked out a schedule where each girl shopped and cooked for a week and the others cleaned up.

In any event, it's important that each girl does her share. Many otherwise happy relationships are strained because one girl feels she is stuck with too much of the work.

SUN	MON	TUE			FRI	SAT
			SCHEDULE FOR THE WEEK			

Monday—As this is a good TV night, the girls do chores that enable them to be home if they want to watch. Julie does her hand laundry, mending, and ironing, while Lois gives herself a shampoo, set, and manicure.

Tuesday—Lois has a class. Julie is a volunteer reader for the blind.

Wednesday—Choir practice for both girls, followed by study or reading.

Thursday—Weekly marketing, followed by "TV chores"—shampoo, set, and manicure for Julie; hand laundry, ironing, and mending for Lois.

Friday—Dates or "Y" activities.

Saturday—MORNING: cleaning and machine laundry.
AFTERNOON: shopping, errands, studying, or fun.
EVENING: dates or parties.

Sunday—MORNING: church.
AFTERNOON: If dateless, they try to plan fun (skating, bowling, bicycling, a walk; sometimes a trip to a museum, zoo, or art gallery).
EVENING: Devoted to special cooking—perhaps a small roast or chicken and a more elaborate dessert; occasionally a casserole is made and stored in the freezer for week-night use. The girls often have guests for Sunday night dinner.

1 What timesaving suggestions could you initiate to make your life more enjoyable? For the next three days see how many spare moments you can save from mundane activities to put to use doing something you really care about.

2 Take a good look at the place you live in. Is it efficient and well organized? Or is it cluttered with good but unused items that use up precious space or that require extra care? See what you can do to streamline your surroundings.

369

For any girl with less than six oil wells, money management is one of the most important skills to master. Your own peace of mind, your smart appearance, your way of life, and your future wedded bliss (money problems being one of the chief causes of marital strife) can be greatly influenced by your ability to handle money wisely.

It's a nice feeling to be financially independent—to know that your paycheck will stretch far enough to cover the necessities with, perhaps, something left over for fun. Some girls who have developed sound money habits through their school years have little difficulty living on their income, yet others seem to be continually broke no matter how large their salaries become. The secret? Those sound money habits. Like saying thank you, brushing your teeth, or keeping to the right, good financial habits should become an automatic part of your life.

It's easy to be overwhelmed by your first salary check, particularly if it is for a two week or longer pay period. How marvelously rich it makes you feel to have all that money in hand! But—how much it has to cover! For most girls, earning a paycheck brings with it several new obligations. Instead of receiving an allowance from Dad to cover your clothes and other necessities, you will probably not only pay for them yourself but will contribute something to the family treasury to help pay for your room and board. If you live on your own, you will learn mighty fast how easy it is to overestimate your paycheck and how fast those dollars do a disappearing act. There are a multitude of items those lovely, lovely dollars must cover, and only careful management will enable you to maintain the happy state of solvency from one pay day to the next.

25
DOLLARS
AND SENSE

BLACK IS BECOMING FOR BUDGETS

Two of the most important lessons any novice with a paycheck can learn are:

1 Live within your income.

2 Don't let yourself get into the red.

A beginner's salary is bound to be rather low, and it may not allow you to live as comfortably and as luxuriously as you are accustomed to, particularly if you have left the family home to seek your fortune. Your new dwelling may be a bit stark at first, and you may not be able to afford that darling suit with the $60 price tag. If you embellish your living quarters and your wardrobe gradually, bit by bit as each paycheck allows, you will take special pride in each new acquisition. Every cash purchase will be a tribute to your earning ability and to your success in handling money.

From the day you receive your first paycheck, decide to keep your financial status in the black as much as possible. Liberal credit terms, generous charge accounts, and installment plans make it sound so easy to own anything you want merely by signing your name. But woe to the inexperienced miss who gets herself in beyond her means! Being in the red is far from rosy. Some girls find themselves in the miserable state of having each new paycheck already gobbled up by last month's debts.

BEWARE THE DEBT DEMONS

If you want to assure a safe start, avoid all types of borrowing and debt, which is what installment plans and charge accounts actually are. Many of the girls who've had financial difficulties feel that the biggest mistake they made was opening a charge account. A charge account can be particularly treacherous if it is the revolving credit variety that allows you a certain credit limit (usually $100) but charges $1\frac{1}{2}$ percent interest per month on the unpaid balance. When you stop to do some arithmetic, this can be a whopping bite unless you pay up fast.

Even a regular charge account, where your bill should be paid in full each month, has its risks, because it's so easy to go overboard, so tempting to sign your name to the salescheck and walk out with your lovely purchase. When the time comes to pay up, the total bill may be something of a shock.

Installment buying is another unhappy system that is best avoided. Interest charges for items bought on the "easy payment" plan usually run a big fat twelve percent a year. Unless you absolutely need the item immediately, you'll do much better to save up the money first. After all, the person who can manage to pay installment payments after the purchase should be able to pay the same amount into a savings account beforehand so that she'll have the money for a cash purchase. *She who saves first, saves most.* Remember, too, when you are paying off a loan, the interest charges you must add on reduce the amount of money you have for other pleasures. Who wouldn't rather have a new hat than pay the same money in carrying charges!

A sound policy to establish is never to purchase luxuries unless you pay cash. Of course, there may be times when it is imperative to take out a loan, such as when you must have a car in order to get to work. If you merely want a car for fun, better pass it up until you have saved up the money. In regard to cars, another reason to resist is the high upkeep and operating costs involved, which can be too much for a limited budget. If you must borrow, read your contract very carefully and investigate all the hidden charges before you sign on the dotted line. Usually it is advisable to go to your bank— or a couple of banks—first when you need to borrow money. A bank is always reliable, while some finance companies may not be, and bank rates usually are lower than those charged by loan companies.

If you owe money, don't let your debts become overdue. Only if you pay your bills promptly can you establish a good credit rating—something very necessary if you ever expect to borrow money again, to obtain a lease on an apartment, or to take out a mortgage someday to buy a house of your own. When creditors go unpaid, they may also become so impatient that they take the matter to the indebted person's employer—all of which does nothing for her standing on the job. A person who can't manage her own money affairs has little chance of being recommended for a more responsible position.

MISER OR SPENDTHRIFT?

We all know the girl who's paid on Friday and broke on Monday. She realizes money is merely a means to an end but, unfortunately, her means always seem to end too soon. She blows it all on whatever whimsey catches her fancy, then spends the rest of the week lunching on fingernails.

The opposite is the money hoarder, who considers money as an end in itself. She carefully stores it away, afraid to spend it and worrying over every purchase she is forced to make. She may even lose friends because she can't help being a tightwad with others as well as herself. She causes herself much unhappiness because she has completely lost sight of the fact that money is meaningless except for what it will buy.

Somewhere between these two extremes is the sensible approach—that of the girl who knows how to make her money work for her. She is the girl with the clear-eyed view of what she has to use, the well-thought-out plan for spending it, and the self-discipline to follow through.

A BUDGET CAN INCREASE YOUR BUYING POWER

One of the chief virtues of a budget is that it helps you keep track of where the money goes. When you know what your expenses will be, you can see how much money will be left for fun and can plan intelligently how best to use it.

A budget needn't be adhered to as a matter of life or death. It shouldn't oblige you to keep each sum strictly quarantined for the sole purpose it is set aside for. A budget is merely a guide, and it should be flexible. There should be enough leeway so that you can occasionally skimp a bit here to splurge a bit there. The value of budgeting is that it gives you a clear picture of exactly where you can skimp and how much you can splurge.

Most important of all, a budget shouldn't be grim. It should be realistic and should allow room for at least a few minor indulgences. The girl who lives a Spartan existence so that she can save an exorbitant amount may soon make herself miserable. Better a more normal amount saved and a little extra allowed for fun if the budget is to be practical and workable.

Here is how a typical young office worker, named Wilma, might spend her money if she lived according to the budget shown. These figures are based on reports of the United States Department of Labor and show the cost of *adequate* maintenance for an average business girl. (Costs and salaries may be higher in some cities, of course.) Wilma the Working Girl will have to pinch pennies, and she may not live quite as well as she did at home, but she should be able to manage nicely if she is careful.

BUDGET

	WEEK	MONTH	PERCENT
Rent	$10.00	$ 45.00	17½
Phone and Utilities	1.33	5.99	2½
Food and Household Supplies	10.00	45.00	17½
Clothing	6.00	27.00	10½
Clothing Upkeep	.75	3.38	1½
Personal Care	1.20	5.40	2
Medical Care	2.00	9.00	3½
Transportation	2.80	12.60	5
Recreation and Reading	2.00	9.00	3½
Incidentals	4.00	18.00	7
Hospitalization	1.11	4.99	2
Insurance	2.00	9.00	3½
Savings	3.50	15.75	6
Federal and State Taxes	10.31	46.39	18
GROSS SALARY	$57.00	$256.50	100

Wilma shares a three-room furnished apartment with another girl. She pays half the costs for rent, phone, utilities, and household expenses. The roommates cook their own breakfasts and suppers and, to save money, take their lunches to work, buying only a beverage.

The *clothing upkeep* figure covers laundry, which the girls do in coin-operated washer and dryer machines. It also includes laundry supplies, dry cleaning, storage, shoe repair, and any clothing repair or alterations.

Personal care includes such items as Wilma's cosmetics, toothbrushes, toothpaste, shampoo and hair supplies, deodorant, soap, tissues, manicure supplies, and either two permanent waves a year or four cut-and-set hair stylings.

The *medical care* figure covers dental care, eyeglasses, and all the cough drops, aspirins, and other medications Wilma buys.

The girls live fairly close to their jobs so that transportation costs are low. They need pay only 20 cents fare each way; two extra round trips per week for shopping or entertainment purposes are allowed in the estimate.

The figure for *recreation and reading* covers half the cost of five daily newspapers and a Sunday paper per week, because the roommates share this expense, and allows a dollar a month for Wilma's own magazines and books. This leaves, for a year's recreation, something like 18 games of bowling (including shoe rental), eight movies, six trips to the beach, and $18 for Wilma's share of TV, radio, and record player repairs. As the girls' recreation is often paid for by their dates, this figure isn't as skimpy as it may seem.

The estimate for *incidentals* includes donations for church and charity, personal gifts, contributions for office gifts, stationery, postage, and an occasional sundae or soda.

Some of the items not provided for in Wilma's budget: further education, cigarettes, operation of a car, a vacation, travel expenses for visits home, weekend jaunts, purchase of furniture or appliances.

TAPERING A BUDGET TO SIZE

When you begin planning a budget for yourself, you will follow these steps:

1 Estimate your monthly income. If you are not working, find out what salary you can expect in the job for which you are preparing. (Keep this estimate on the low rather than the high side.)

2 Estimate your fixed monthly expenses. There will be certain fixed expenses—rent, car-fare, taxes—that occur regularly each month. If you will have any additional large occasional expenses such as tuition for schooling, insurance premiums that are paid quarterly, automobile license and registration fees, or other similar costs, you should break these down into an average monthly figure and add them to your fixed expenses. Then subtract your total fixed expenses from your monthly income.

3 Next take a look at your flexible expenses—those such as food, clothing, and personal care that can vary from month to month—and see just what you are spending for them. The best way to get a good picture of these costs is to keep track of them for a month or two by keeping a tally in a little notebook that you carry with you. Use a separate page of the notebook for each of the flexible categories in your budget. These would probably be Food and Household Supplies, Clothing, Clothing Upkeep, Personal Care, Medical Care, Recreation and Reading, Incidentals, and Savings. Then jot down every expenditure you make under the proper category heading. Such a record gives you a good idea of how those dimes and quarters actually disappear.

At the end of the month you will add up the figures in each category. The totals for some categories may be a bit surprising. Then add up all the categories to find what your flexible expenses total. Subtract this figure from the money remaining after you deducted your fixed expenses.

Then comes the big question. Surplus? Deficit? If you're lucky enough to have a little money to spare, you will have a cushion for the extra expenses that crop up. If, however, your expenses tower above your income, you'll need to revise your spending habits or see how you can adjust your budget so that it is better suited to your needs.

If you are not familiar with prices of foods and household items, accompany your mother on shopping trips and note how much she pays for the soap, facial tissues, shoe polish, and other supplies that you take for granted. Note what the food bill comes to. Even if you have no intention of taking yourself off to live in an apartment, you'll find this sort of investigation quite valuable and revealing to you as a future wife and homemaker.) A United States Department of Labor report for New York State estimates that a working woman living with her family and paying her share of expenses would have to figure on spending about $20 a month toward rent and $40 toward food, plus another $20 for household expenses and repairs.

There will undoubtedly be many personal factors that will influence the budget you make. Costs and salaries vary considerably in different parts of the country. The climate you live in and the type of job you have will also affect your needs. You will want to analyze each category of your budget to see how you can adapt it to best suit your way of life.

Rent · If you plan to live away from home, you will not capsize your budget if you heed the advice of the financial experts. They say that your rent should not exceed one week's salary. Sometimes a more desirable location is important enough to make you choose living quarters with a higher rent, but you must then be prepared to trim other budget allowances.

If you live at home, you will probably want to contribute something toward your keep; but this is likely to be a more nominal figure.

have difficulty giving yourself a permanent, perhaps you can enlist the aid of a friend—or plan a permanent party in which all the girls help one another.

You may have noticed that the difference between some expensive, nationally advertised cosmetics and the dime store brands is largely in the expensive advertising and more luxurious packaging. If you experiment, you may find the cheaper brands of many items are quite satisfactory.

Medical care · This figure will vary considerably depending on your general health, the condition of your teeth, and whether or not you need glasses. It covers medicine, drugs, and medical appliances as well as doctors' fees.

Transportation · Although transportation has been considered as a fixed expense, you may be able to save here if you can walk part or all of the way to work. Nevertheless, a little leeway should be allowed in case a sudden downpour or a late start makes a taxi an essential luxury.

If you own and operate a car the *minimum* annual cost will be:

Insurance	$ 50
Taxes, license	20
Depreciation	200
Gas and oil (10,000 miles)	200
Tires	35
Repairs, etc.	50
	$555, or $46.25 per month

This is the minimum cost you can expect; the actual figure will probably be higher. Nothing has been alloted for tolls, parking, or garage rent—to name a few of the extras you may have to contend with. The tax and insurance rates may differ, of course, depending on where you live.

Recreation and reading · The amount you allot will be influenced by whether you need any sporting equipment, what types of recreation you prefer, what organizations you belong to, what reading you do, whether you plan to continue your education, and so on.

This is an individual matter that only you can decide. In this category, cuts are always possible, but here they often hurt most. Much good entertainment is free or low cost, however, and you can borrow books from the Public Library. While you may not be able to do everything you want, try to include some good sports and some stimulating activities, such as occasional trips to the theater.

Incidentals · Church and charity contributions, personal gifts, donations for office gifts, stationery, postage, and your occasional petty indulgences (such as special snacks) are included in this category. You know pretty well what your personal gift-giving schedule is and can guide yourself accordingly. Office collections are not so predictable. Weddings, approaching blessed events, retirements, and other leave-takings are often celebrated by luncheons, parties, or gifts financed by contributions from the staff. A newcomer should not be expected to join in on these unless she knows the person well, and her contributions need not be as much as those of someone with a higher salary.

In some offices the problem has been lessened by collecting a quarter or so from everyone each payday. This money is then put into a general fund to be used for all parties and gifts. In a few organizations the employees have received the permission of management to have candy and soda vending machines installed, and the profits from these machines are used for such celebrations.

Hospitalization · Everyone should have some form of hospitalization. In these days of staggering medical costs, this sort of protection is particularly advisable for the young working girl who has little financial reserve. Many companies have set up group plans for their employees. A group plan has lower rates because of the large number of members in the plan. Some corporations even pay part or all of the hospitalization insurance for their employees.

Insurance · Because life insurance and annuity contracts are forms of enforced saving as well as financial protection for your family in case something happens to you, you may want to make this part of your budget, too. Single women with no dependents and many present needs may prefer to forgo life insurance and keep their savings in a bank, where it is more easily accessible and where interest rates are higher than those offered by insurance companies. However, if you choose some form of annuity plan where your money is available to you about the time old age cuts your earning capacity, you're *sure* of having the money at a time you're likely to need it. Unless you are concerned with death benefits for dependents, the pro and con of insurance boils down to this: intelligent foresight and the determination to maintain a good nest egg can get you a better bargain in savings, but for the average, less strongly fortified person, insurance is a good buy.

Many firms have set up group plans that provide their employees with life insurance at very reasonable rates. Group life insurance plans are usually term insurance. These provide low-cost coverage during your employment, but they terminate when you leave the company and they do not build up any cash value as straight life insurance does. They are therefore not to be considered a form of savings. You are merely getting insurance. The advantage of a group plan is that you are insured at much lower rates than are otherwise available. Before joining any company insurance plan, you should ask yourself whether you are more interested in life insurance at bargain rates (a group plan)—with savings left to your own initiative—or in an individual straight life insurance policy which, though more expensive, accumulates a monetary value that can be cashed in should you need it.

Don't, however, overload yourself with such a steep policy that you weary of paying it and let it lapse, which happens all too often. One advantage of taking out life insurance when you are young is that the premiums you pay are lower. The rates go up each year as you grow older.

Savings · The time is sure to come when you will need some ready cash. It is advisable to build up as soon as possible a cash reserve of at least two to three hundred dollars for such emergencies. A minimum of five percent of your salary should go into savings. Ten percent or more is preferable, at least until you have built up a substantial reserve fund.

The experts advise that your goal should be to maintain a rainy day fund equal to half your yearly salary after taxes. This may seem pretty high, especially from your present financial vantage point; but if you intend to rely strictly on the sweat of your lovely brow, this is none too much to allow for peace of mind regarding future emergencies.

Taxes · Social security (F.I.C.A.) taxes and state and federal income taxes will probably be deducted from your pay check by your employer. Some states have more taxes than others, so this figure will be determined by where you live.

Any other categories? · If you are planning to continue your education, you may also want to set up a category to cover this figure. How about a vacation allotment? And one for Christmas gifts? Many banks have Vacation Clubs and Christmas Clubs to help you save the amount you desire. You agree to pay a certain amount each week (even as little as 25 cents) and the bank holds the money for you until the proper time. Club accounts usually pay no interest, and you can't withdraw the money until the end of the time agreed upon. Some girls with a good supply of financial self-discipline prefer to add this money each week to their regular savings account, which does pay interest; but the little nudge a club account offers is very helpful to those with less resoluteness.

GLAD MONEY

If you've ever watched your last quarter go rolling down a drain as you were waiting for the bus on payday morning, you know the woes of letting yourself get flat broke. To avoid this sort of tragedy, many girls like to carry a small emergency fund—glad money—that they can dip into if necessary but which they always replace so that it is ready for the next emergency. One girl who received a dollar in a gift wallet tries never to spend this last dollar. Another girl who once found a five dollar bill used this for her emergency fund. Carry your glad money with you, but keep it in a separate change purse or envelope—isolated in some way so that you won't spend it by mistake. Probably the time will come when it will save the day for you.

HELP YOURSELF TO SAVE

If, after figuring out your budget, you've come up with the conclusion that there's just nothing left for a vacation or for Christmas gifts or any other special spending, you probably need a saving scheme to help. Many a girl who's made just such a complaint is now sporting a new fur coat or enjoying an exciting, romantic, adventurous vacation in Mexico.

The first step in any saving plan is to have a goal—something tangible provides the most incentive. You might want to start out with an item that's not too expensive, such as a bowling ball of your own, an overnight bag, or a hair dryer. Once you have a goal, you will probably discover all sorts of ways to catch money that has been slithering through your hands. When you stack up that afternoon piece of cake against your savings goal, it may be easy to pass up the cake. In a month, that daily fifteen cents can add up to something like three dollars, saved just from this one item. Every time you are tempted to spend money on something you really don't need, think of your lovely savings goal and it will be much easier to resist.

Once you've achieved a small goal, you'll have established saving habits and will have the zest to start yourself off on other, perhaps larger, goals.

SAVING DEVICES

Everybody has her own way of making herself save, but here are methods that have helped other girls.

❧ Keep-the-change method. Each night deposit in your piggy bank all the change you've accumulated during the day.

🌸 Dime collector. Decide to save every coin of a certain denomination for your piggy bank. Instead of dimes you may want to begin with nickles—or, if you're feeling flush, with fifty-cent pieces.

🌸 Splurge box. This is a technique roommates like, to help save for special splurges. Agree to deposit a certain amount each week in a special box or bank. It may be only a quarter or fifty cents, but it will soon mount up to enough for dinner in an elegant restaurant, or maybe theater or concert tickets.

🌺 Give up some regular expense. Perhaps it's only a candy bar each day, perhaps luncheon dessert (the latter is recommended only for the very determined), or the extra bus you take for the last few blocks. Even a small daily saving, when multiplied by the number of days in a month, becomes a figure to be reckoned with.

🌺 Count your bargains. Every time you get an unusual bargain (a blouse reduced one dollar, hosiery purchased at a semiannual sale) deposit the amount saved in your piggy bank.

🌷 Slice it off. This more drastic method involves deducting a certain amount from your pay as soon as you get it, then trying to do without the extra cash until next payday. Some sturdy souls guard against backsliding by immediately depositing this money in their savings accounts. One girl who did this was forced to withdraw some money one week to carry her through. When she confronted the teller with her withdrawal slip for two dollars, he smiled and asked innocently, "How do you want it?"

(P.S. She eventually saved enough for a trip to Europe.)

EARNING EXTRAS

The easiest way to have more money is, of course, to earn more money. If an increase in salary is not in the immediate future, you may wish to take on an extra job to add to the exchequer. For a girl with good typing skills, there are many opportunities. Try inserting a classified advertisement in your newspaper, offering to type letters, business reports, manuscripts, class papers, thesis papers, and to do other typing chores. Many small businessmen often need part-time services of this kind. You could also contact political and charity organizations which have occasional busy seasons, and your local government and school offices, which may sometimes farm out rush jobs.

Some girls prefer a change from their office work and forsake the typewriter for selling jobs. One girl who worked in a department store on Thursday nights and Saturdays said that, although she didn't earn a great deal, the saving she made on clothing purchases, through her employee discount, helped bolster her savings considerably. Another girl who worked in a music store on Saturdays said she loved the job so much that she hardly considered it work and actually looked forward to it. Another refreshing change from office work can be helping out in the local library evenings or Saturdays. "That's where I keep up on all my friends," explained one library assistant. Baby-sitting is also popular because even though it is low-paying work, it usually isn't very demanding, and your time can be put to good use on your own projects while the children sleep.

Another girl used her car to earn money, changing it from a deficit to an asset. She had driven her car to work but realized that the convenience cost her much more than the bus fare. To turn this into a paying proposition, she advertised for riders, took on four at bus-fare rates, and got herself a free ride plus something for the savings account besides.

1 For one month keep an account of your actual expenses (including those expenses paid by your family but that you will assume when your salary permits). Use a separate notebook page or piece of paper for each category. At the end of the month total up your expenses in each category. You may be surprised at how much it costs you to live.

2 Plan a budget for yourself based on the information in this chapter. When you have completed your month's accounting of your actual expenses, compare this with your budget to see what changes are necessary to make your dollars do most for you.

3 Do a little investigating as to what carrying charges amount to for installment plan purchases. Compare the cost of a TV set purchased for cash with the total cost for the same set purchased on the installment plan.

4 Find out what type of work might be available in your area for an office worker with your skills who wished to earn extra money in her free time.

During childhood you probably often had more time on your hands than you knew what to do with. "What can I do now?" is an all-too-frequent wail from youngsters. As you became more occupied with school activities, your spare time dwindled. Now, as a full-time working girl, your free time will be at a premium. It's positively precious. You'll want to use it cleverly so that it can do the most for you. Squander it on the same old routine activities in the same old places and you add little zest and freshness to your life. Cram it brimful of the best in fun—especially fun that will help you develop greater understanding and knowledge—and your reward will be ever-increasing charm and sophistication.

Sophistication is the highly admired polish that comes from being acquainted with the many things that interest intelligent people. It's being in the know about what's going on and about the important names and happenings, past and present, that affect our society and culture. It's also knowing what to do when. How much do you tip a redcap? Would a nineteen-year-old miss look smartly dressed for a luncheon date if she wore her mother's sable fur skins? How do you eat oysters on the half shell?*

The sophisticated person is admired because she has learned what to do and how to do it gracefully. You learn sophistication from many sources. Mostly you absorb it bit by bit from what you do and observe. Invest your spare time in activities that will help you learn and grow and you will add to your sophistication. You will develop a brighter, richer personality.

26

FUN WITH
A FUTURE

FUN WELL SPENT

How do you usually spend your evenings? If it's watching TV programs you don't particularly care about, chatting or playing bridge with the crowd whose every thought you already know, or just puttering around the house, you might give heed to ways in which you could get more value for your time. Is there some subject you don't know about that gives you an uneasy feeling of inferiority whenever it comes up? Would a course in music or art appreciation or just reading some good books help fill the gaps in your background? Would you like the creative satisfaction of expressing yourself through

---

* In case you've any doubts about the answers, see page 397 for the first question, page 430 for the last. Fie on the fur skins! Not only are skins rather dated, but any dangling fur piece or stole is too mature and tends to make a young girl appear overdressed.

hobbies such as art, craftwork, playing a musical instrument, or performing in a theater group? Look around for activities that will give you solid satisfaction and inspiration.

Some criteria that might be used in planning your free time:

- Will I learn something new and interesting?
- Will I obtain practice in some of the social graces about which I'm a bit shaky?
- Will I be improving my health and physical well-being?
- Will I be doing something worthwhile that will help others?

392

And, of course, to each of these must be added the further qualification: will it be enjoyable? On this last point, however, don't cross out something you haven't tried until you've given it a fair chance.

One further suggestion: keep your activities varied. Tennis is an excellent sport—good fun, good for the figure—but the girl who spends every weekend on the tennis court takes care of only one of her needs. Her backhand returns may be great, but her head may rattle emptily when the conversation ball bounces her way.

Susan Sawyer had lived in a suburb of New York all her life but felt that despite her closeness to the metropolis she was provincial and inexperienced in the ways of any but her own immediate set. To develop more smoothness and confidence, Sue enlisted her friends in her project of absorbing the sophistication that could be gleaned from New York. She went to plays, lectures, TV broadcasts, concerts, foreign movies, museums, art exhibits, and attended some of the famous churches to listen to their celebrated clergymen. If she was hesitant about something—such as how to act at the Stork Club—Sue found out by going there on her own. (Lunch or tea doesn't put as big a dent in your pay as dinner, she advises.) She and her friends also tried foreign restaurants so that they'd have an acquaintance with unusual foreign foods. Wherever she went, Sue watched and learned and evaluated so that she would develop naturally a cosmopolitan air.

WONDERFUL WEEKENDS

In each year we have 49 free weekends, assuming the others are taken care of by vacation plans. Each is a marvelous opportunity for special fun. When the budget permits, you might take off on a special weekend excursion—perhaps to a ski resort in the winter, a lakeside resort in the summer, a riverboat excursion for spring or fall, or a hiking or biking trip (especially inexpensive for American Youth Hostel members who can stay overnight at one of the A.Y.H. hostels for $1–$1.25). Good anytime is a weekend of sightseeing: a visit to some historical area or to one rich in local color, such as the Pennsylvania Dutch country around Lancaster, Pennsylvania, the Indian reservation at Taos, New Mexico, or historic Williamsburg, Virginia. A sports area like Sun Valley, Idaho, Lake Tahoe, California, or the Dells in Wisconsin, can be varied and exciting. With so many wonderful opportunities available to all of us, no girl should let her weekends sink into an uninspiring sameness.

TWO WEEKS TO PLAY

Vacation time, those precious two weeks of your very own, offer a chance to do something very different. After being attached to a job for nearly a year, you're off the leash to run far and to live it up as you please. Take advantage of this once-a-year opportunity to get an invigorating change of routine. The girl who hangs around the local haunts all vacation, perhaps even joining the office crowd for lunch, misses the marvelously refreshed feeling to be gained from new places and new faces.

Start your planning in the early spring. If you want to stay at a specific place for several days, you had better make advance reservations, and the earlier the better, to be sure space will be available for you when you want it. If you are planning a trip that will mean overnights in certain cities, you might do well to make reservations ahead of time. The joy of a vacation can be ruined if you must spend time searching for lodging and transportation when everything is booked solid because of a convention.

How do you decide where you want to go? The travel sections of the large newspapers offer many suggestions; and if you have decided on a certain locality, you can write to the state or city chamber of commerce for more information. Whenever possible, it is best to consult a travel agent. A travel agent is an expert on vacation opportunities, and his services cost you nothing. Tell him what you want and he can probably suggest the right place for you—and for your budget. He will also save you time by making travel reservations and booking accommodations. You pay nothing for this service because his commission comes from the other end—from the bus line, hotel, or whatever. Consulting an agent can often get you more for your money because he may know of tour plans that give bargain rates and include features not available otherwise.

Look for a change of pace · If you sit at a desk all day and don't need a rest, there's little to be gained by spending your vacation sitting on a beach or lolling on a hotel lawn. How about a dude ranch, a windjammer cruise, a riverboat tour, or a resort that is noted for lots of scheduled activities? If you want the latter, pass up the glamour hotels and consult a travel agent or study the advertising literature that promises hayrides, masquerades, amateur nights, and the like. If the resort brochure plays up facilities for children, probably you can rate it as more of a quiet, restful family place.

As you make plans, ask yourself if the main feature of this vacation idea is something you enjoy. If you don't like roughing it, a camping trip will hold little charm for you.

Look for congenial company · Check the age group. Does the place seem to cater to young people? If you want a young crowd, study the pictures and other clues in the advertising matter. Better yet, consult a good travel agent. It's his business to know about the atmosphere as well as the facilities.

Sample new places · Whenever possible, try to get away from the type of people you associate with each day. If you live in Boston, don't follow the rest of the Bostonians to Cape Cod or the Berkshires each year. Go where people think a little differently from you.

When you travel, try to absorb the color and flavor of the area. Talk to the people who live there, read the local newspaper, and eat the regional specialties so that you can get a good picture of the place. Don't act condescending, however. No tourist who has a we-do-it-better-back-home attitude is appreciated. Your trip will also be more enjoyable if you read up on the area before you go. If New Orleans is your goal, for instance, how much more fascinating it will be if you know something about the early French and Spanish settlers, understand the Creole heritage, can tell stories about such pirates as the dashing Lafitte, and have read a story or two about the French Quarter.

In many parts of the country there are special festivals such as the Maine Seafoods Festival at Rockland, Maine, or the Cheyenne Frontier Days in Cheyenne, Wyoming. Perhaps you can make your vacation even more interesting by scheduling it at festival time.

If you live and work in the country, a city vacation may be your ticket for fun. Treat yourself to a glorious week of theatering, dining grandly, sight-seeing, shopping. Perhaps you can pamper yourself with good-for-the-morale beauty treatments at one of the elegant (though expensive) beauty salons. A city vacation is an excellent idea for the girl who entertains thoughts of coming to work in the city at some future date. She has a good opportunity to look it over and examine job opportunities firsthand.

Gather new thoughts · If you want an inspiring vacation, you might consider a place like Aspen, Colorado, which is noted for its plays, concerts, and lectures. Lenox, Massachusetts (in the Berkshires), features the Tanglewood Concerts, and nearby is Jacobs Pillow, noted for its modern dance group, and also the Berkshire Playhouse. At Isomata (Idyllwild School of Music, Idyllwild, California) you can take short courses in music or the arts as well as enjoy being part of the audience.

If you are a Sunday painter or musician, you can investigate the art colonies and music resorts where you can receive expert instruction along with your vacation fun. Consult your newspaper travel section or advertisements in magazines catering to these fields.

Go with a good companion · If you want a change, don't go with the gang from your neighborhood or with the girls from the office. Vacation time should let you get away from it all. Choose one or two good friends who will keep their good spirits through thick or thin. Or don't be afraid to try it alone. If you're planning a resort vacation, your chances of making new friends will probably be enhanced if you go solo. Conducted tours are often a good choice for lone vacationers because you travel with a group and because the tour director handles all the details of reservations and transportation. Some tours are limited to single people, with further classifications according to age.

WHAT NOT TO LOOK FOR—A HUSBAND

It's sad but true that very seldom do wedding bells chime tidings of a vacation romance that actually "took." As with adult vaccinations, the reason few vacation romances take is that many of the men at resorts are already immune—they have the Ideal Girl back home. Men on vacation are looking for fun—for someone to have a good time with. They feel free to ask anyone out, with no strings attached, for they are far from hometown gossip and may want to have a bit of a fling. You, too, have a chance to expand your knowledge of people, to break out of a rut. But be casual about it, be yourself, don't lower your standards just because you're on vacation. If he's really interested, he'll call you again, and then you can judge each other in more prosaic surroundings. If he's just having a fling, you won't get hurt, and you'll have a wonderful memory of fun.

TRAVEL TIPS FOR TRAINS

In addition to regular coach seats, there are several types of accommodations available for long trips. These usually must be reserved in advance. Many trains have special streamlined coaches with reclining seats that make them fairly comfortable for sleeping; these are available for a small additional charge. The least expensive accommodations with beds are Pullman cars, which have upper and lower berths, the lower berths costing more. A roomette, which contains a washbasin and toilet and a bed you can let down yourself, costs a little more than a lower berth. Larger versions are bedrooms, compartments, and drawing rooms, which hold up to two, three, or four persons, respectively.

Managing your luggage · The secret of easy travel is to avoid taking too much luggage—never more than you can carry if you don't want to risk being stranded when no porter service is available. A redcap or porter is handy as a guide if you are in a large, unfamiliar station. He will steer you quickly through the labyrinth of tunnels and find you a seat on your train, determining your correct accommodation if you have a reservation. Redcaps receive a standard fee of 35 cents for each piece of luggage, regardless of its size or the distance it is carried. If you'd rather tote your own, you need feel no qualms about politely refusing a redcap's services.

Don't let your luggage become a nuisance—to you or to anyone else. You are entitled to half of the overhead luggage rack by your seat. If this is not room enough, ask the conductor where you can put the rest; don't leave it in the aisle. In a Pullman, the porter usually puts large suitcases on shelves in the rear of the car, unless they fit under the seat; an overnight bag is kept handy for your nighttime needs. A roomette or compartment has space for hand luggage. Large or heavy pieces (up to 150 pounds) can be shipped free if you check them at the baggage room at the station. Be sure that all luggage bears your name and address—inside as well as outside—to guard against mishaps.

Mealtime manners · You can bring a box lunch or eat in the diner, where prices will be somewhat higher than usual restaurant prices. Some trains have snack bars, which are less elegant and less expensive; most have someone who goes from car to car selling sandwiches and beverages. Eating in a diner is similar to a restaurant except that you write out your order. Also, people are more likely to chat with each other than in a restaurant.

Pullman etiquette · Because the lower berth passenger pays a higher fare, he has the privilege of riding forwards during the day. The passenger in the upper berth rides backwards unless the lower-berth passenger offers to share his seat with him, which a considerate traveler will do.

When the berths are made up, the seats can't be used. If at night your berth hasn't been made up by about ten o'clock, you might ask your seatmate if he would mind if you asked the porter to do so. A passenger who wishes to stay up later can go to the club car or observation car. These are usually at the rear of the train. You ring for the porter, and while you are waiting for your berth to be made up, you can move to an empty seat or to another car; or you can take your toilet articles to the ladies' room and prepare for bed. If you have an upper berth, you must ring for the porter to place the ladder for you. A passenger is not allowed to move a ladder, even if it is right across the aisle.

Once you are in your berth, you close the curtains and undress, using the hangers and net hammocks provided for your clothes. If you must leave your berth during the night, you will wear a robe (or your coat) and will take your valuables with you. Leave the curtains open and the light on so that you can find the right berth when you return.

In the morning you usually dress first, call the porter for the ladder if you have an upper, and then go to wash. Be sure that all personal articles are removed from your berth before you go to breakfast, because it will probably be folded up by the time you return.

Other services a porter will perform if requested: call you at a specific time, bring a pillow or a table for writing, shine your shoes, send letters or telegrams. When you reach your destination, he will brush your coat, take care of your luggage, and help you off the train. You will tip him 50 cents to $1 for a night berth (more for special service), $1 to $1.50 in a roomette or compartment, slightly less per night for longer trips.

TRAVELING BY BUS

Long-distance travel by buses is popular because it is less expensive and because it often allows you to see more interesting scenery than the freight-yard-end of towns. Reservations are made in advance for most long-distance buses, though no reservations are required for most intercity buses that leave regularly every hour or so.

Etiquette for bus travelers boils down pretty much to being considerate of the driver and of other passengers. Don't disturb the driver by talking to him unnecessarily, and do take with you a small bag that contains everything you'll need during the trip. No driver will appreciate the backbreaking job of trying to extricate your suitcase from the luggage compartment because you forgot your makeup kit. Be considerate of other travelers by not taking too much time at wayside stops, by not disturbing sleepers at nighttime, and if you smoke, by being careful that your smoke and ashes do not annoy others.

AIRPLANE TRAVEL TIPS

Most air flights require reservations, which can be made through a travel agent or at the airline terminal. At the time you make your reservation, check the amount of baggage allowed on the flight and whether meals will be served. Complimentary meals are served at meal hours on all first-class flights and on some tourist flights. If they are not, bring something to eat or purchase a box lunch at the airport. You will also want to inquire about transportation to the airport. Generally there is a bus or limousine service that leaves from the airline terminal or some specified central place in the city; the charge for this is usually much less than the cost of a taxi.

Checking in at the airport · First you take your luggage to the desk to be weighed. (If a porter carries your luggage, he should be tipped 25 cents for each bag unless there is a sign specifying a standard porter's fee. No one else at the airport need be tipped—*never* a stewardess or other uniformed airline employee.) Forty pounds is allowed free on any class flight in the continental United States. Even hand luggage (except for your coat, purse, and camera) is included in this total, so you will want to travel lightly. A high charge is made for excess weight.

Suitcases will be stowed in the plane's baggage compartment, but you are allowed to keep with you your coat, camera, binoculars, and a small bag for personal grooming essentials. Many women prefer to use a large purse for this purpose. The attendant at the desk will verify your ticket and give you checks for your baggage. Then you will wait while your plane is being loaded. Be sure you know your flight number, because this will be announced over the loudspeaker when your plane is ready. Then you will go to the gate specified and board the plane.

400

Which seat? · Unless the seats are reserved, you will be wise to arrive early so that you have a better choice. Seats in the rear of the plane have the best view but may be bumpy in bad weather; seats over the wing offer a smoother ride. If you suffer from motion sickness, you'll be wise to take one of the preventive pills before you leave. Special plastic bags are hung on the back of the seat in front of you for use in emergencies.

Mealtime manners · Despite cramped facilities, delicious meals are served on planes. If the flight is at all rough, it is considered perfectly proper to tuck your napkin under your chin.

After you land · Your baggage may be claimed at the baggage enclosure, where you surrender your baggage checks. If you are planning a return trip by air, it is a good idea to check your return reservation while you are waiting for your luggage.

ETIQUETTE ON THE BOUNDING MAIN

If a sea voyage is in your plans, you should make your reservations months in advance, especially if you plan to go during the peak vacation season. Reservations can be made through your travel agent. He can also arrange for your table and deck chair assignments. (You will have your choice of early or late sittings for meals and of the location of your deck chair, sunny spots usually being preferred.) As soon as you embark, you should check with the stewards in charge of these services to confirm the reservations. You will sit at the same table throughout the trip, unless you want to change for some reason. The livelier crowd usually prefers second sitting—breakfast is later and the time between dining and dancing is shorter!

On shipboard all the luggage that you will need during the voyage can be kept in your cabin. The ship's advertising material will probably contain information about the type of clothes to be worn and your travel agent can also advise you about what to take. If you share a cabin, you will want to be careful about keeping your belongings neat and not usurping too much space.

A resort atmosphere prevails on shipboard. Most people are friendly and congenial and you will be expected to chat casually with them.

Tipping is usually done at the end of a voyage or weekly if the cruise is a long one. Ten percent of your fare is the usual amount to count on for a transatlantic trip. (Those traveling first class tip proportionately more.)

Cabin steward—$1 per day

Night steward—$1 per day (if you utilized his services, such as coffee and sandwiches at 2 a.m.)

Dining steward—$1 per day

Deck steward—$2 to $3 (Tipping in advance may result in a more desirable position.)

HOTELS AND MOTELS

In this country, most hotels and motels operate on the European plan, which means that rates are quoted without meals. Often resort hotels quote rates on the American plan, which means that three meals (two at some beach resorts) are included. If you are traveling on a limited budget, don't hesitate to ask about a minimum-rate room. In a large metropolitan hotel, you wouldn't ask to see your room before you engage it, but if you find it unsatisfactory, it wouldn't be out of order to ask if something else is available. In small hotels and in motels you will probably want to look at your room before registering. When a woman signs the register, she includes either "Miss" or "Mrs." before her name. You are expected to tell the clerk how long you will be staying. If you are merely staying overnight at a motel or tourist home, you usually pay when you register, particularly if you plan to leave early the next morning. At a hotel it is more customary to pay when you leave.

A bellhop will usually take your luggage and show you to your room. The standard tip is 25 cents for each bag, no matter how many or how few you have with you. Pay him separately for extra service. Bellhops who deliver telegrams, newspapers, or small items to a room usually receive a dime; 25 cents is given for larger deliveries. Any such room service can be obtained by phone by asking the operator.

Hotel manners · When you are staying overnight at a hotel, it's a good idea to bring some sort of suitcase, even if all your personal needs can fit in your purse. Hotel management is inclined to view with suspicion any young woman without luggage. Similarly, for the sake of your good name, you would not invite a man into your room alone nor go to his alone. Most people, unless they have a suite with a sitting room, entertain in one of the public lounges or dining rooms.

Incidentally, when a secretary or other female employee is traveling with an executive, reservations are requested for two single rooms for "Mr. John Craig and secretary." This indicates to the hotel staff that the two rooms should be on different floors or at least not next to each other. If work is to be done, the secretary goes to her employer's room. He does not come to hers.

Metropolitan hotels are quite formal, and usually the guests do not chat together or greet each other. Resorts, on the other hand, are much less formal, and it is expected that guests will introduce themselves and be friendly.

When you leave, please don't collect any of the hotel property as "souvenirs." Although many respectable people consider this good sport, walking off with hotel towels, ashtrays, stationery, or other supplies is just as much stealing as if these items were taken from a store counter.

Tipping · Other types of tipping that you might run into during your stay at a hotel are:

Room service waiter—15 percent of the check but not less than 25 cents. This can be paid in cash or, if you sign the check indicating that the bill is to be added to your hotel bill, you can note that a certain amount is to be added as a tip for the waiter.

Chambermaid—no tip for a very short stay, probably $2 for four or five days (leave it on the dresser or under the pillow). At a resort hotel the maid is usually tipped when you leave, at the rate of about 50 cents a day.

Doorman—25 cents if he calls a taxi for you, more if he lets you leave your car near the entrance for a short time or has it parked for you.

SAFETY FIRST

Traveler's Checks · If you are planning to carry large sums of money while you are traveling, you'll be wise to use Traveler's Checks. These can be purchased from your local bank or Railway Express office. They are easily converted into money by countersigning at the time you wish to cash one. Since your second signature is proof that the Traveler's Check belongs to you, it should never be countersigned beforehand. Follow the instructions for recording serial numbers in case of loss or theft.

Protection for valuables · If you have any large amount of money or valuables with you, you will be wise to leave them in the office safe if you are staying at a resort or hotel. On shipboard, you can leave them with the purser. Most hotels caution you to keep your room locked at all times, for the sake of your privacy as well as your valuables. Never leave anything precious in your room when you go out.

Strangers · Mother has surely warned you about strangers, and you'll do well to remember her advice. It's fine to be friendly and pleasant to fellow travelers, to chat with your seatmate in a train or bus if he is in the mood to talk. (You won't, of course, be forward or force conversation on someone who'd rather keep to himself.) To avoid embarrassing situations, keep the conversation impersonal and don't obligate yourself in any way by accepting favors. If a stranger offers to pay for your meal or to give you a lift in his car, it's better to thank him but to refuse politely. Most strangers mean well, but every Little Red Riding Hood may not have a handy hunter to come to her rescue if the stranger turns out to be a wicked wolf.

Need help? · If you have lost your wallet or run up against some other difficult problem while you are traveling, you can consult a policeman or the Travelers Aid Society, which usually has a desk in large stations and terminals. If you are on a train or plane, the conductor or stewardess will help you. It's always best to seek help only from an authorized person.

You'll be a welcome guest in someone else's home if you can show the consideration and thoughtfulness you'd like a guest to show in your own home. This means being careful about the furniture—no suitcases on beds (the floor is always safe), no wet glasses on wooden tables, no wet bathing suits on chairs. When there are dishes to be done or other work in the offing, the thoughtful guest pitches in. She also praises the cooking, even dutifully downing the turnips she abhors. She wouldn't think of raiding the refrigerator and accepts her hostess's preference in records, television, or radio programs.

If you're visiting at the family home of a friend, you'll win her parents' appreciation by relating complimentary stories about her. (You can discreetly skip any stories that might embarrass her, no matter how hilarious they seem.) Enter enthusiastically into her plans and show your appreciation of her friends. You shouldn't accept a date, however, unless you're sure your hostess has one, too.

Find out when you're expected to rise in the morning and make an effort to get up on time, taking your turn in the bathroom as quickly as possible so that you won't interfere with others. A hostess appreciates guests who stick to family timetables, particularly regarding meal hours.

You should also abide by family bedtimes. If the hour grows late, you should gracefully let the conversation ease off at intervals in case your hostess wants to suggest retiring. Resist the urge for a midnight swim, a wee-hours walk in the rain, or any other unorthodox whim, because you would not want to upset family routine any more than is necessary.

When the time comes to leave, do so on schedule. Don't be tempted to linger. The menus and weekly routine were planned around a certain length visit. Though your hostess may say with sincere sorrow, "Oh, I wish you didn't have to leave," exit smiling.

A thank-you note for any visit of overnight or longer should be sent within a day or two after you return. If you hadn't taken a hostess gift with you, it would be thoughtful to send something at that time—a record or book you had discussed or something else pertaining to your hostess's home or interests.

PACKING TIPS

The experienced travel knows the wisdom of traveling light. One woman who is noted for her attractive appearance spent two months in Europe with a total wardrobe of three basic dresses and a limited assortment of carefully selected accessories. When you are choosing clothes for travel, be guided by their versatility, soil resistance, and wrinkle resistance.

Next time you take a trip, try the following suggestions for organizing your suitcase efficiently:

• Put jewelry in pockets of a sectional silverware bag to prevent scratching and scattering. When the bag is rolled up, it fits compactly in a corner.

• Use plastic jars for cosmetics. Store spillables in plastic bags for extra insurance.

• Use a plastic bag (or shower cap) for washcloth and toothbrush in case they are still damp at packing time. Carry an extra plastic bag in case things you have washed out don't dry in time.

• To save stockings, tuck them in gloves and socks; put gloves and socks in shoes. Put shoes in plastic bags.

- Use plenty of tissue paper in shoulders and folds of dresses and suits to prevent creases.

- Pin blouses to shirt cardboards to keep them smooth.

- To pack a suit, fold the skirt lengthwise with the hem end hanging out over the side of the suitcase. Place the upper half of the jacket in the suitcase on top of the skirt at the waistband end and fold the sleeves across. Now fold the hem end of the skirt over the jacket top; then the bottom of the jacket up over the skirt. The resulting layers of skirt top, jacket top, skirt hem, jacket bottom act to cushion each other and to prevent creases.

- Arrange your clothes in this order: shoes and heavy items on the bottom, then lingerie, accessories and blouses, suit, and dresses on top.

- If you are making several overnight stops, keep your nighttime articles together where they are easy to get at. Grooming items can all be kept in one plastic bag so that they can be carried to the bathroom easily.

- Include several clip clothespins. When clipped over wire hangers, they make excellent dryers for hosiery and other wash.

- Extras for emergencies: your own version of a first-aid kit with aspirin and indigestion remedy, sewing kit (plus a roll of cellophane tape for loose hems), also scissors, a miniature clothes brush, shoe polish, razor.

- Nice to have—travel iron, travel alarm clock.

Before you begin your packing, make a list of all the things you will take. This makes the job of assembling all the items much easier and, if you carry the list in your suitcase, provides you with a ready reference at homecoming time to make sure nothing has been left behind.

 🌹 FOLLOW-UP

How could you make your life more interesting? What new activities could you try? What different places could you visit? Plan to spend your next free weekend doing something special. Perhaps it can be a sight-seeing trip, maybe a lunch at an interesting restaurant, an evening at the theater, or possibly just a try at a different sport. Any worthwhile change of place or pace will put more zest in your life.

A thorough grounding in the basic rules of etiquette is just as vital to the success of a business girl as knowing which key is which is to a typist. Good manners should be completely automatic, like touch typing. If you are to appear poised and socially mature, manners must be something you just do, something so second nature that you don't have to think about them. Being constantly aware of the situations that call for special actions and taking the trouble to follow correct procedures will result in a smoothness that sets you off as a cultivated, well-bred young lady—qualities that cannot be overestimated.

Good manners make a person vastly easier to get along with, whether at work or play. They are also taken as an important gauge of personality, for good manners are an indication of other virtues—and lack of them is an indication of many other lacks.

27 SOCIAL GRACES

THOSE LITTLE THINGS

There are many small courtesies that rate high when it comes to making a good impression. They are rules everybody knows but which, sadly enough, are not always observed.

- Someone who is speaking should not be interrupted.
- Privacy must be respected. Knock on a closed door and wait for a response before entering. (Business is an exception, however. You would not wait for an invitation to enter your boss's office. You would merely knock and walk in.)
- Mail addressed to someone else, whether family, friend, or fellow worker, should never be read unless you've been told to do so, even if the letter has already been opened. One secretary antagonized her department by opening all incoming mail, no matter to whom it was addressed. Although she may have meant well, she infringed on others' rights and was heartily disliked for this.
- Walk around, not between, people who are talking together.
- When in a hurry, be careful not to cut off others who may be strolling down the street or corridor.
- Don't push when attempting to enter a bus or elevator.
- Avoid making a scene of any sort in a public place—no shouts or calls to friends in a restaurant, no noisy complaints about poor service, no unpleasant digs at the other team during sports events, no loud to-do's in the office.

- Gum chewing is permissible only at extremely informal affairs, *never* at business or more formal social functions.
- Quiet is essential during a meeting, speech, or performance. Jokes and other side remarks or rattling of papers disturbs others and is discourteous to those on stage.
- A sneeze or cough should be covered up with your hand or a handkerchief and your head turned away.

INTRODUCTIONS MADE EASY

The important thing about introductions is that we should not neglect to make them. While there are many technicalities regarding the exact wording, few are vital. The fact that you make an introduction is often more important than the precise words you choose. Introductions should always be made whenever you talk with someone who does not know the others with you. If you are with some friends and another acquaintance joins you, you would introduce her to the others. If you are walking with someone and pass an acquaintance on the street, you wouldn't bother to make introductions unless you were to stop and chat. If you are hostess at a large gathering, introduce a guest to a few people to make him feel at ease; don't attempt to have him meet everyone at once.

Wording the introduction · The basic rule to remember is that *the person you mention* FIRST *is the one you are honoring.*
- A MAN IS PRESENTED TO A WOMAN: "Mrs. Hendricks, this is Mr. Briggs" or "Debby Campbell, I'd like you to meet Jerry Jackson." In each case the woman's name is mentioned first. (An exception to this rule is usually made in business when a woman employee is presented to an important executive of the firm. In such situations respect is shown to the executive by mentioning him first: "Mr. Gilbert, this is our new receptionist, Ann Bartlett.")

When you are introducing members of the *same sex*, the guiding factors are age, rank, or degree of distinction. Again, the person to be honored is mentioned first.
- PRESENT THE YOUNGER TO THE OLDER PERSON: "Mr. Elder, may I introduce Mr. Young."
- PRESENT THE LOWER IN RANK TO THE HIGHER: "Mr. Aldridge, (vice-president of your firm or another firm) this is Mr. Adams" (a junior executive of either your firm or of another firm).

410

- PRESENT A LESS DISTINGUISHED PERSON TO A MORE CELEBRATED PERSON: "Miss Celebrity, may I present Miss Smith?"
- PRESENT A LAYMAN TO A CLERGYMAN: "Father Higgins, Mr. Hudson." Protestant clergymen should be addressed as "Mister," or, if they have a degree, as "Doctor." A few Episcopalian clergymen are called "Father." For Jewish rabbis, "Rabbi Stein, this is Mr. Hudson," is the correct form.

Usually you would honor your mother and father by presenting others to them. This applies to your employer, to instructors and professors, as well as to other acquaintances: "Dad, this is my friend Carol Welles." "Mother and Dad, I'd like to introduce Professor Carlson." The only exception would be some very distinguished person, such as a college president or the president of a large corporation.

When two people of the same sex are approximately the same in age, rank, and prominence, it doesn't matter who is mentioned first.

411

The following forms of introduction are all acceptable:

"Sally Green, Herb Thompson."

"Sally Green, this is Herb Thompson."

"Sally, this is Herb Thompson. Herb, Sally Green."

More formal but equally correct are:

"May I present . . . ?"

"May I introduce . . . ?"

"I should like to introduce . . ."

If you are not sure whether they are acquainted, you can forestall any embarrassment by saying:

"Do you know . . . ?"

"Have you met . . . ?"

Acknowledging an introduction · The best acknowledgment to an introduction is "How do you do." Mentioning the person's name in your reply helps fix it in your mind. With people your own age, you might reply informally, "Hello, Karen" or even "Hi."

If you have heard a great deal about someone and are especially glad to meet him, you might add sincerely, "It's a pleasure to meet you," or "I'm very glad to have the opportunity to meet you." You'll want to avoid such crass phrases as "Pleased to meet you," "Charmed, I'm sure," or that immortal exclamation of the lightning bug who bumped into the lawn mower, "De-lighted no end."

In the rush-rush of business, it is not likely that your employer will introduce you to many visitors, even if you are his private secretary. If he does, you should merely smile and say, "How do you do, Mr. Jones?" (even if he was introduced to you as Dick Jones), and you would quickly return to your work unless the men have something further to say to you.

Shaking hands · Shaking hands when introduced is not quite as customary for women as it once was. Although a man always shakes hands when introduced to another man, he may merely nod to a woman, and will shake hands only if she offers hers. Usually you would not offer your hand to someone your own age or to another woman unless she was considerably older. You would, however, be alert to the possibility and would be ready to shake hands should the other person offer. If you are introduced to an older man or

412

woman, you would want to extend your hand. Let your handshake be brief, firm, and friendly, neither a painful grasp nor a limp, unresponsive one.

If you are wearing gloves at the time of an introduction, it is much better to shake hands with your gloves on than to delay the proceedings by hurriedly fumbling to pull off your glove. When possible, it is preferable to remove the right glove as a mark of sincerity and respect for the other person.

When do you rise? · While it is proper for a man to rise whenever he is introduced to someone, a girl is not expected to rise unless she is introduced to an older woman, an elderly man, or to someone of great distinction whom she wishes to honor. However, whenever you are a hostess or are in a hostess situation (such as when you greet your boss's visitors), you would probably want to stand up to welcome callers. When in doubt, you can't go wrong by getting to your feet.

The same rule about rising for introductions can be applied in social situations to persons entering a room in which you are seated. Again, a young woman need not rise except for an older woman (especially if she is a housemother or instructor or the mother of one of your friends), a much older man, or to honor a very distinguished person. In the office, you would not be likely to rise unless someone very important came to your desk specifically to talk with you. Neither should you expect men to stand up when you enter an office. Convenience overrules chivalry in the business world.

WATCH YOUR SMOKE

Where there's smoke, there's ire—unless the smoker takes care. Those who smoke are seldom aware of the annoyance that this habit can cause.

Smoking still evokes frowns, not because it is naughty but because of the nuisance it creates. Tobacco odor can be very annoying to nonsmokers, and the hazard of accidents is ever present. A smoker is literally playing with fire. If you smoke, you should be very careful and very considerate of the feelings of those around you.

Careless handling of cigarettes is the Number One cause of fires. The office smoker who hasn't a good ash tray with secure resting places for her cigarette should hie herself to the nearest dime store and buy one. A rolling cigarette gathers no friends—especially if it happens to scorch an important report, a desk, or a brand-new suit.

A few good rules to follow:

- At the office, never smoke in the presence of customers or visitors, even if smoking is allowed at your desk.

- Put out your cigarette before going into your boss's office to take dictation or to discuss work.

- Between puffs, remove a cigarette from between your lips. A cigarette drooper or the person who talks with a cigarette in her mouth looks undignified and cheap.

- Always snuff out your cigarette carefully. Smouldering butts give off an unpleasant odor.

- Empty your ash tray often; a heap of lipstick-smeared butts is a definite eyesore. However, be sure matches and old butts are completely out before putting them in the wastebasket.

- When you smoke, air the room out occasionally to counteract stale tobacco odor.

• Avoid blowing smoke in other people's faces, and take the prevailing winds—or drafts—into consideration so that your smoke won't trail in someone's direction.

• Watch your ashes. Don't keep others hypnotized as the ash on your cigarette grows longer and longer.

• Don't gesture with a cigarette. That is a sure way to flick ashes where they may be damage.

• Avoid playing with your cigarette. Affected mannerisms and excessive hand movements give a smoker away as unsophisticated.

• Tote your own supply of cigarettes and smoke them. A cigarette moocher is no joy to have around.

• Guard against cigarette stains by holding the lighted end up so that smoke does not trail through your fingers. (Tobacco stains usually can be bleached out with lemon juice.)

Office parties • Christmas, a wedding, a lamented resignation—throughout the year there are a goodly supply of office parties. Some may be merely department cocktail parties at the close of the day; others may be elaborate dinner-dance affairs. Good spirits soar freely, and so do the alcoholic ones. This is a time when all is good cheer, yet it's also a time when each employee is on display—an occasion that influences management's opinion of staff members and provides grist for office gossip for weeks to come. Your most charming, ladylike manner is called for.

• WHAT DO YOU WEAR? For a normal after-work party you would wear your usual business clothes. If you are the honored guest, you might wear your prettiest outfit, but certainly nothing more dressy. Even a company dinner-dance would not be the occasion for a low-cut bouffant cocktail dress. A better choice would be a simple dressy style with a discreet neckline. Let the festive touch come more from elegant fabric or jewelry than from cut.

• HOW DO YOU ACT? Act basically the same as you do when you're in the office. Of course, the talk is gay, and business is forgotten, but you will show the same deference to those above you and the same dignity and poise that is expected of you on the job.

Management is more likely to mingle with lesser employees at these times. If the man in the formidable office guarded by a gauntlet of secretaries should happen to chat with you, don't let yourself become shy or embarrassed. The great man must talk to someone and, perhaps, he feels a little uncomfortable out of his usual office element. Be cordial and friendly and *interested*. Part of the reason he has become so successful is that he is a charming person.

Occasionally some executive may, under the mellowing effects of the occasion, become quite chummy. He may even suggest that those he is with call him by his first name. Although they may do so for that evening, the status shifts back to normal on the next working day and the "Mister" and other usual formalities apply once more. Just remember: keep the party apart from the job.

• TO DRINK OR NOT TO DRINK? When you are as much in the spotlight as at a company party, you want to present the very best image you can. Whether you drink socially or not, it is wise to refrain when you are with business associates. Then, of all times, you want to be in complete command of your tongue and actions. The girl who becomes a little too high may be the life of the party for a while, but she will probably drop a notch or two in the estimation of those who control her future. If you don't want to drink, don't feel you must. Most men actually respect a girl who doesn't drink. Request a glass of ginger ale, which in appearance is a reasonable facsimile of more potent libations, or nurse one cocktail along all evening so that when Fill-'Em-Up Freddy comes your way you can blithely reply, "Still have some, thanks." Let your own good spirits eliminate the need for bottled ones.

• WHEN TO GO HOME? Office parties have a way of becoming more sticky and more difficult as the hour grows later. Those who come off best usually leave fairly early in the evening.

Office luncheons • If a large group from the office holds a luncheon to celebrate some auspicious occasion, they will need to make a reservation. In some restaurants it's possible to obtain a menu in advance so that each person can sign up for her luncheon selection and can pay her money beforehand. If not, one girl usually takes care of the bill and collects from the others later.

A luncheon cocktail? Even though the boss may have no objection, there's always the danger of treacherous aftereffects—drowsiness, carelessness, a loosened tongue, or emotional eruptions. You'll be wise to refrain. No girl who meets the public should ever risk giving offense by a liquor-tinged breath.

CHRISTMAS ETIQUETTE AT THE OFFICE

Many companies give bonuses at Christmas; some executives give presents to their secretaries. Whatever gift-giving occurs is done down the scale, not up. Employers are never given presents by staff members. You would, of course, probably want to send your boss a Christmas card. If he is married, it should be addressed to "Mr. and Mrs."

MANNERS AND MEN

There are many rules of etiquette governing the behavior of men and women. Some are delightful gestures of gallantry that make a girl feel special and appreciated, such as

417

when your date opens a door or pulls out a chair for you. Some are, however, a bit inconvenient at certain times. Maybe he's digging for change at the precise moment he should be helping you on with your coat. Maybe in your rush to make curtain time he didn't stop to run around to open the car door for you. Don't make him conscious of his lapse. Manners in the social world, as well as in business, often succumb to convenience. By all means, give a man a chance to show off his gallantry. (No man appreciates the brusque I-can-do-it-myself attitude of the girl who beats him to the door knob. Even in the office, nine times out of ten, a male associate will be pleased to hold a door for a girl if she gives him half a chance.) But no charming lady will stand there waiting in an obviously expectant pose so that he feels like an oaf if he's preoccupied or his timing isn't fast enough for these little things.

Good manners are born of consideration and thoughtfulness. They are not something artificial we hold up on display merely so that we can say, "See what lovely manners I have." Make sure you know what to do, be ready to let him do his part, but don't embarrass him if he slips up in some way.

When a date is not a date · In offices where a young crowd works together, the boys may treat some of the girls as part of the gang. "Say, Beth, we're all going over to try that new Chinese place for lunch. Want to come along?" Or some night when she's working overtime, one of the fellows may suggest taking time out to get something to eat. Such casual invitations, a girl should realize, aren't dates; she's lucky enough to be considered one of the boys and should pay her way accordingly. If one check is presented for a mixed group, the girls as well as the men will each put enough money to cover the meal and tip in the center of the table for whoever is going to pay the check. If she's dining alone with one of the fellows and a single check is presented, she should offer to pay her share. Some men are embarrassed about having a woman in their company plunk down cash in public; and if she realizes he will be annoyed, she shouldn't insist. Instead, she might tell him she'll settle with him later, which she'll be sure to do promptly—and inconspicuously. A good way to avoid any misunderstanding is to qualify your acceptance of such an invitation by saying, "Sure, if we can go Dutch."

Who goes first? · The business of who goes first and who stands where shouldn't be bothersome. Usually it boils down to this: the lady goes first except in those cases where the man precedes so that he can offer some sort of help or protection, theoretical though it may be.

• Entering bus or taxi—girl goes first.

• Exiting from bus or taxi—man goes first and helps her out.

• Walking on sidewalk—man is on the outside (a protective shield from splashes or other street or sidewalk conditions).

• Theater or movie—while her escort is purchasing tickets, the girl waits inside in the lobby. If there is an usher, she follows him down the aisle. Otherwise, the man goes first or they may walk together to find seats. The man then steps aside so that she can enter first. When they leave, he waits in the aisle while she steps in front of him and precedes him up the aisle.

PARTIES ARE FOR FUN

No matter what kind of an affair is planned, from a hayride to a formal dance, you can relax and enjoy yourself if you have that little extra security of knowing that you have answered the invitation properly and understand what kind of behavior is called for. You won't be thrown for a loop by the receiving line at a graduation, tea, or wedding if you expect it to be there and know what to do. And you won't be the only girl without a hat at the President's afternoon reception.

ANSWERING INVITATIONS

An invitation to a party should be answered, whether or not R.S.V.P. (short for "répondez s'il vous plait," the French equivalent of "please respond") or a similar request for a reply is indicated. An informal invitation can be answered by a phone call or brief note on plain white paper.

Formal invitations use very formal wording and they are usually engraved, although they may be completely or partly handwritten. Formal invitations are used mainly for weddings, dinners, luncheons, and dances.

In regard to wedding invitations, an invitation to the church ceremony doesn't require an answer, but you are expected to acknowledge an invitation to the wedding reception. A reply to a formal invitation must always be handwritten. Use plain white notepaper, and follow the same phrasing and setup of the invitation. Other formal invitations, and your response to them, follow the same pattern.

If you are unable to attend an affair, your reply will state very simply that you regret that you cannot accept the kind invitation.

PARTY MANNERS

If you have been invited for a meal or if planned activities have been indicated, you should be sure to arrive on time. After greeting the hostess and any parents, you will join the others. Remember that you were invited because you were expected to contribute to the fun. If you can play the piano, sing, read palms, or perform in some other way, comply without too much coaxing. (Don't begin on your own, however, unless you're sure your hostess wants you to.) When the hostess has planned games or other activities, enter enthusiastically and lend support wherever you can.

Mr. & Mrs. Richard Greene
request the honour of your presence
at the marriage of their daughter
Linda Karolyn
to
Mr. Donald Garner
Saturday the first

Saint
Co

and to the reception
following the ceremony
The Country Club
Brook Road

R.S.V.P.
231 Highland Avenue

Miss Joanne Burnell
accepts with pleasure
Mr. and Mrs. Richard Greene's
kind invitation for
Saturday, the first of June

The surest way to have a good time at a party is to get your mind off yourself and to concentrate on seeing that others have a good time.

WEDDINGS

Although a wedding is a formal affair with a special set of rules and traditions, you can be poised and ready to enjoy yourself when you know what to expect.

What to wear? An afternoon wedding calls for a simple dress or suit in an elegant fabric, a hat, and gloves. An evening wedding is more formal—wear your dressiest dress, but not necessarily the one with the plunging neckline.

Arrive at the church in good time—at least five minutes before the ceremony is scheduled to begin. You don't want to delay the bride and you want to be present for the whole ceremony. One of the ushers will come up to you and ask "Bride or Groom?" What he means is, which side of the aisle will you sit on—a friend of the groom sits on the right, a friend of the bride, on the left. (If you are friendly with both of them and the groom is from out of town, you might sit on his side because it is less crowded.) The usher will offer his arm; you put your hand inside the crook of his elbow and rest it lightly on his arm. He will escort you down to a pew and stand aside while you enter.

When the ceremony is over, it is customary to wait until the families of the bride and groom have been escorted from their pews before you leave. Usually you will find your own way out, but if those in front of you wait for an usher, you wait too.

At the reception the first thing you do is pass through the receiving line. You will give your name to the first person in line and she will pass your name to the person on her right, by introducing you to her. All you have to say is "Hello, isn't Mary beautiful?" or some similar comment. No conversation is necessary—there may be a hundred people behind you. What you say to the bridal couple depends on how well you know them. Shake hands with the groom and say "Congratulations"; shake hands with the bride, or kiss her if you know her very well, and wish her happiness (*never* congratulate her on securing a husband!). Then move on. You can chat with them again later if you want to.

The reception lasts anywhere from an hour to several hours, depending on the time of day, the number of people, and whether or not there is dancing. If you don't know many people, simply go over and begin talking to someone about the bride or the groom—this is what you have in common, after all! You do not have to stay until the end, but usually you should wait until the bride throws her bouquet—you might even catch it!

TEAS AND RECEPTIONS

Teas or receptions are usually given in honor of some person or event, or, in business, to introduce some new product or development. They are usually held for a specified time period, such as from three to five in the afternoon, and you may arrive any time during these hours. You will probably stay about a half hour unless some form of entertainment or presentation is to take place.

Correct attire would be an afternoon dress or dressy suit, hat, and gloves. Hats are kept on but gloves should be removed when refreshments are served. You will greet your host or hostess when you arrive. When there is a receiving line, your hostess will be first and will present you to the guest of honor on her right, who will, in turn, present you to the person on *her* right, and so on. You will shake hands and say, "How do you do?" A longer conversation would hold up the line and can be saved until later. If there is no one to present your name, you will introduce yourself.

When you want refreshments, you will go to the table. The person who is pouring may ask, "How do you like your tea?" In a cup, obviously, but she wants to know whether you prefer lemon or cream. (An inexperienced young tea drinker once tried both together, much to her chagrin. The curdled mess that resulted is not recommended fare.) You will help yourself to a couple of cookies or fancy sandwiches and can either stand or find yourself a seat while you eat. At a business reception the fare is more likely to be cocktails and canapes. Waiters often circulate with trays of refreshments. If this is a self-service affair and no gentleman is available to get your refreshments, it is quite proper for you to go to the serving table yourself.

DANCE ETIQUETTE

If it is a formal affair, there are a few taboos you will want to abide by. Your entire outfit must be keyed to the occasion. Sporty or fraternity jewelry of any kind is out, and wristwatches are not worn unless they are very dressy or jeweled. If you are lucky enough to be given a corsage, remember that the flowers are worn blossoms up, as they grow.

At the dance, if you and your escort use the same cloakroom, he takes care of the stubs. If separate checking facilities are provided, you take care of your own stub. After a quick checkup on your appearance, you will meet your date and will then greet the hostess or chaperones. If there is a receiving line, you will go down it together, the girl preceding the boy.

The first and last dance and the one following the intermission belong to your escort. You will usually share refreshments with your last partner before intermission. If there is a mixer, be a good sport and join in. In like manner, you and your date should not refuse cut-ins. If you are on the sidelines and someone with whom you do not wish to dance asks for a dance, you had better have a pretty good excuse before you refuse—and then do so as kindly as possible. During a dance, keep the conversation light; controversial subjects and long, involved stories are out of place. At the end of a dance, your partner will thank you and you can reply with a compliment to his dancing technique or a light pleasant remark along the lines of "It was fun."

If you must cross the ballroom for any reason, you will go around the side. No one should ever walk across the floor when a dance is in progress. At the end of the evening, you and your date should be sure to thank your hostess or the chaperones, if it is a school dance, before leaving.

Wallflower problems? · If you've been applying what you have learned so far in this course, the fault can't be your grooming or posture. If you have any doubt about your footwork, try to get in a little extra practice or take a course. A good dancer seldom sits one out. But remember that despite all sorts of allure, even the greatest charmers have occasionally adorned the sidelines for uncomfortable periods. If this happens, don't slink behind a potted palm or hightail it to the powder room for a lengthy stay. Courageously sit out where you can be seen, preferably not huddled with a lot of other girls (or even with only one other). It often requires quite a lot of courage for a boy to ask a girl for a dance. He's much more likely to choose the girl who's sitting alone than the one who is flanked by a group of other girls who are all hopefully wondering if he's going to ask them.

TABLE MANNERS

Table manners are basically a matter of courtesy. They developed from a desire to make mealtime a pleasant social occasion, not just a refueling stop. Eat neatly and quietly and you will not have to worry about your manners. The bothersome questions of etiquette at the table are covered generally here, but if you are eating out and in doubt, just watch your hostess or an older woman and do what she does.

Much of this information you may already know, but it is included to give you a quick checkup on any points that may have been puzzling or may have been forgotten.

When you are a guest for dinner, you wait behind your chair until the host or hostess invites everyone to be seated. In many homes grace is said before the meal is begun. You will be saved possible embarrassment if you watch your hostess for a cue. If no grace is said, guests can begin eating when the hostess starts. If there are many people, such as at an office luncheon or company banquet, you would not begin eating until those around you had been served. It wouldn't be necessary to wait until the entire group had been served, however, because your food would become cold.

❀ It is perfectly proper to reach for dishes directly in front of you, but ask your neighbor to pass you the salt if it is in front of him.

❀ Salad greens may be cut with a knife, but using a fork is preferable.

❀ Only one or two bites of meat should be cut at a time. You are not running an assembly line.

❀ Take a portion of butter and place it on your bread and butter plate (if there is one) or on the side of your dinner plate. If you wish to add butter to vegetables or potatoes, take it from the bread and butter plate with your fork.

❀ Bread should not be cut with a knife. Break off a small piece of bread or roll with your fingers and butter it, on the plate, with your butter knife. Take only one piece at a time.

❀ At no time should silver dangle off a plate.

❀ Since it is very impolite to talk with your mouth full, avoid the problem of being caught by a question in mid-chew by taking only small bites. In any event, you would finish chewing before you replied.

❀ If some food needs to be removed from your mouth, don't hesitate to do so. Clean things, such as fish bones, olive pits, and fresh fruit pits, can be removed with the fingers. Other items, such as a bit of gristle or sticky pits from stewed fruit, should be removed the way they went in—with the fork or spoon you are using—and should be placed on the edge of your plate.

❀ No well-bred young lady should ever chew with her mouth open or smack her lips as she eats.

🌹 Whenever you take a mouthful, lean slightly toward your plate. Then, if anything drops, it lands on your plate, not on your lap or your hostess's tablecloth.

🌹 Don't gesture with silver in your hand—you'll stir up nothing but trouble.

🌹 In a restaurant the vegetables that accompany the main course are often served in side dishes, and should be eaten directly from these dishes. Sometimes a main course, such as a stew, or a chicken pie, or a chef's salad, may be served in a side dish. In this case you would spoon a serving onto your dinner plate.

🌹 Elbows should never be a hazard to table partners. Keep them close to your sides, especially when cutting food.

🌹 If finger bowls are used, they are served on the dessert plate, although they are not used until after dessert is finished. Remove the finger bowl, with its doily, and place it on the table at the upper left of your plate until dessert is finished. Then dip the tips of your fingers in the water and wipe them on your napkin.

HOW DO YOU EAT IT?

• ARTICHOKES. Use your fingers. Take off one or two leaves at a time, dip the soft end into the sauce, and scrape off about a third of the leaf by drawing it through your teeth.

Don't try to swallow the whole leaf; it won't digest well. Pile the used leaves on the side of your plate. When all leaves are removed, cut away the thistle part with your knife and fork and eat the heart with your fork.

- ASPARAGUS. Break off the tender part with your fork, eating it in several sections. Eat only what can be cut with your fork. (At home you might pick up the end in your fingers and nibble a bit more.)
- AVOCADOS. No problem if served cut up in a salad. When they are split in half and the seed cavity filled, you scoop the fruit out of the shell with your spoon, as with a melon.
- BACON. If it is crisp, eat it with your fingers; otherwise use a knife and fork.
- CAKE. Dry cake may be eaten with the fingers. A layer cake or gooey cake should be eaten with a fork. Cake or pie á la mode is eaten with a fork rather than a spoon, although a spoon may be used to come to your rescue if the ice cream is very runny.
- CANDY. When a box is offered to you, take the frilled paper cup as well as the candy.
- CHICKENS. Use a knife and fork in public. At home or at a picnic you might pick up the bones, but you should always get off as much meat as possible first.
- CLAMS ON THE HALF SHELL. Lift the clam from the shell with your oyster fork and dip the clam in the sauce. Put it whole into your mouth. (Steamed clams may be eaten with the fingers.)

- CORN ON THE COB.   Eat it with your fingers. Butter only a few rows at a time.

- CRABS.   *Hard-Shelled:* Pull off the small claws and suck or chew the meat out of the open end. Then lift out the body meat, cut it with a knife and fork and eat it, dipping each piece into the sauce. The coral and green part is also good. If a nutcracker is served with the crab, you may want to crack the claws more. Break the claws with your fingers and take out the meat with your oyster fork or a pick, dip it into the sauce, and eat it.

   Soft-Shelled: Everything is edible.

- LOBSTERS.   Same technique as for crabs.

- MUSSELS.   Use a fork to take them out of the shells, or pick up the shell and suck them out of it. Shells go on a side plate so that you can spoon up the sauce afterwards.

- OLIVES.   Eat with the fingers. Pits go into your hand and then onto your plate.

- OYSTERS.   *On the Half Shell, Raw:* Eat like clams. *Cooked:* Use knife and fork, dip in sauce, if any.

- POTATO CHIPS OR STICKS.   If no spoon is served with them, help yourself with your fingers. Eat with your fingers.

- PICKLES.   Whole pickles and pickles served with sandwiches are eaten with the fingers. Sliced pickles served with meat are eaten with a fork.

- PINEAPPLE RINGS.   *Fresh:* Use a knife and fork. *Stewed:* Use spoon.

- RELISHES.   Put them on the dinner plate beside the food they go with and eat them with your fork along with the bite of food.

- SHRIMP COCKTAIL.   Eat with oyster fork. Sauce may be served on shrimp or in a separate small cup. If the lettuce on which shrimp is served is hard to manage with a fork, skip it. Although on other occasions you might cut lettuce with a knife, it looks rather awkward to attack a cocktail glass with a big dinner knife. If the shrimp is too big to eat in one bite, bite a piece off and then redip the remaining portion in the sauce and eat that

- FRIED FANTAIL SHRIMP.   Using your fingers, pick it up by the tail, dip in sauce and eat, leaving the tail.

UNSHELLED SHRIMP. Shell with your fingers and eat.

SPAGHETTI. If you've acquired the knack of rolling your own, good. To do this, hold the spoon in your left hand, take a few strands with the fork in your right hand and wind the fork, keeping the prongs against the spoon. The result should be a neatly wound mouthful. Only a few strands should be used or you'll end up with much too much. If you can't do this expertly, it's better to cut up the spaghetti with a fork.

DINING OUT

Most fashionable restaurants have checkrooms, where a man will check his hat and coat. A woman usually keeps hers and slips the coat over the back of her chair; she might, however, check packages or an umbrella or raincoat.

If there is a headwaiter or hostess, the girl precedes her escort and follows the headwaiter to the table he indicates, taking the seat he offers and allowing him to help her with her chair. If there is no one to direct you to a table, your escort will choose the table. You will keep your purse and belongings in your lap or, if there is an empty chair at your table, you could put them there. They should not be put on the table itself.

If you are dining with a man, you will give him your order and let him relay it to the waiter. A girl on a date should be considerate of her escort's financial state. If you don't understand the menu, don't be ashamed to consult the waiter for help.

Unless the check advises patrons to pay the cashier, the waiter is paid. Usually, when the waiter is to handle payment, the check is presented on a small tray. This tray will be returned with the change, and the tip (usually 15 percent, see page 437 for details) can be left on the tray. When checks are taken to the cashier, a tip should first be left on the table. If you haven't the right change for the tip, you can obtain it from the cashier and then go back to put it at your place. If you are with a date, wait by the door while he does this. When a couple leaves a restaurant, the girl precedes her date.

On a date, a good time to repair makeup damage is while your escort is waiting for the check. Any face or hair fixing should, of course, *always* be done in the powder room, as the name implies. The sight of a woman applying makeup in public is distasteful to most men.

431

Menu

RESTAURANT TERMS **YOU SHOULD KNOW**

Table d'hôte	—complete dinner is served for the price indicated.
À la carte	—each item is priced separately.
Entrée	—the main dinner course.
Smorgasbord	—a buffet-type meal in which you help yourself to a variety of hot and cold dishes, taking as much as you like and returning as often as you wish.
Demitasse	—a small cup of coffee that is usually drunk black.
Pâté de foie gras	—a finely ground goose liver canapé.
Julienne	—cut in long, thin matchlike strips.
Au jus	—in its own juice.
Au crème	—with cream
Au vin	—in wine.
En brochette	—cooked on a skewer.

French cookery

• SOUPS

Bisque	—a soup made from shellfish.
Consommé	—clear, thin broth of vegetables, meat, and chicken.
Potage	—a thick, rich soup.
Vichyssoise	—creamy potato (and leek or onion) soup, usually served cold.
Bouillabaisse	—a dish ranging between soup and stew consistency, made with various fish, saffron and wine.

• MAIN DISHES

Poulet	—chicken.
Veau	—veal.
Boeuf	—beef.
Ragout	—stew.

Haricots verts   —green beans.

Petit pois   —small green peas.

● DESSERTS

Fromage   —cheese.

Crêpes suzette   —dessert pancakes served with grated orange rind and flaming liqueur.

German cookery

● MAIN DISHES

Wienerschnitzel   —veal cutlet.

Schinken   —ham.

Kalbfleisch   —veal.

Wurst   —sausage.

Geflügel   —general term for poultry.

Sauerbraten   —pickled beef stewed in sweet-sour gravy.

Hasenpfeffer   —rabbit stew.

● VEGETABLES

Grüne Bohnen   —green beans.

Kartoffelklösse   —potato dumplings.

Erbsen   —peas.

● DESSERT

Kuchen   —cake.

Borsch	—soup of beets and other vegetables, served with sour cream.
Shashlick or shish kebab	—cubes of meat and vegetables cooked on skewers.
Beef stroganoff	—slivered beef in sour cream sauce.
Pilaf	—rice dish, served with shrimp, chicken livers, and seasonings.
Blini	—pancakes served with sour cream and caviar or smoked salmon.

• MAIN DISHES

Chop suey	—mixture of cooked bamboo shoots, bean sprouts and other vegetables with some form of cut-up meat, usually pork, chicken, beef, or shrimp.
Chow mein	—similar to chop suey but served on fried noodles.
Sukiyaki	—mixture of cooked vegetables with some form of meat or fish.
Foo yung	—eggs and vegetables cooked together (similar to omelets). Also obtainable in meat varieties.

Zuppa	—soup.
Minestrone	—thick vegetable soup.
Antipasto	—plate of mixed appetizers.

● MAIN DISHES

Pollo	—chicken.
Manzo	—beef.
Bistecca	—steak.
Vitella	—veal.
Agnello	—lamb.
Prosciutto	—smoked ham, sliced very thin.
Scampi	—shrimp (large).
Chicken cacciatore	—chicken cooked in oil with tomatoes and wine.
Chicken tetrazzini	—creamed chicken on spaghetti.
Lasagne	—broad noodles baked in layers with sauce and cheese.
Manicotti	—noodles stuffed with cheese and served with sauce.
Risotto	—rice dish.

● VEGETABLES

Fagiolini	—green beans.
Patate	—potatoes.
Piselli	—peas.

● DESSERTS (dolci)

| Spumoni | —sliced frozen dessert similar to ice cream, with fruits and nuts. |
| Gelato | —any ice cream dessert. |

435

| Sopa | —soup. |
| Gazpacho | —cold soup dish of raw vegetables. |

- MAIN DISHES

Pollo	—chicken.
Cerdo	—pork.
Ternera	—veal.
Vaca	—beef.
Cordero	—lamb.
Tamales	—highly seasoned corn mixture, stuffed with ground meat.
Tortillas (Mexican)	—thin flat cornmeal cakes.
Tortillas (Spanish)	—Omelets.
Enchiladas	—Mexican tortillas stuffed with meat, other ingredients.
Paella	—rice dish with chicken, pork, shrimp or other seafood, tomatoes, pimento, and so on.
Chili	—kidney beans and meat in spicy sauce.

- VEGETABLES

Frijoles	—beans.
Guisantes	—green peas.
Arroz	—rice.

- DESSERTS

| Empanda | —small filled pastry. |
| Flan | —egg custard with caramel sauce. |

How you tip is almost as important as how much you tip. Let your manner as well as your money express your thanks for the service that has been given to you.

Whom should you tip? You only tip employees who have served you personally. The owner or manager should not be tipped even if, as in a beauty parlor, he does the same work as his employees.

As an average you would tip about 15 percent of the bill, more for special services. The amounts suggested below are approximate standards.

- Taxi—15 percent or more, never less than 10 cents for a minimum fare.

- Lunch counter—10 percent to 15 percent but no less than 10 cents. No tip necessary for just coffee, sundae, or soda.

- Waiter—generally 15 percent, but at least 15 to 20 cents per person. For a check over $15, 10 percent is sufficient.

- Headwaiter—no tip for seating you. If he performs special services such as making advance arrangements, $1 to $5 (always paper money) so that it is about 10 percent of the bill. If the location of the table is important, tip before dinner. Otherwise a tip for special services is given after the dinner.

- Cigarette girl—10 to 25 cents.

- Hatcheck girl—15 to 25 cents per person.

- Rest room matron—for towel and soap 10 to 25 cents. More for special service.

- Beauty parlor—for a permanent 10 percent or $1, whichever is higher; for a set, 15 percent but not less than 25 cents; a shampoo 25 cents; a manicure 15 to 25 cents, depending on the bill; for hair coloring, facial, massage, or other involved treatment 10 percent but not less than 50 cents.

- Shoeshine boy—10 or 15 cents.

- Parking lot attendant—if he parks or retrieves your car 15 to 25 cents.

- Telegraph boys, messengers, store delivery boys—15 to 25 cents.

- Moving men—for a large load such as an apartment or house full of furniture, $5 to $10 to be divided among the men. Less for single item.

- Tennis—locker room attendant 25 to 50 cents at a public court; at a country club $1–$2 a month for members, $1 per visit for guests.

- Golf—$1 to $2 per round. Consult the starter or pro, as sometimes the tip is included in the caddy fee.

- Riding—groom at public stable, 50 cents after you ride.

1 For the next week or so, look for opportunities to make introductions. The more practice you obtain, the smoother and easier introductions will become.

2 Are there any problems regarding introductions, dining etiquette, party or dance etiquette, or any other subjects not covered in this chapter that you have some doubts about? If so, go to your library and look up the correct procedure in a complete etiquette book. Don't let any etiquette problems threaten your poise when they can be settled so simply.

3 Practice using your very best table manners at all times. If you have been making exceptions at home, try to avoid this as much as possible.

Breathes there a career woman with purpose so strong that she has never dreamed of a rose-covered split-level equipped with loving spouse and family? Although you want a career, you probably have no objection to love and marriage as pleasant accompaniments. Charm has its rewards, and dates and romance are usually high on the list.

The office has long been considered the happy hunting ground for the two-legged dear and many a marriage has incubated within those gold-lettered portals. But this is one case where success goes not to the fearless hunter. Subtle allure is the best female weapon, and it is the charming trapper who, most likely, brings home her man.

The girl who makes it evident that she is on the prowl and who eagerly eyes every eligible man as a possible conquest is least likely to bag one. The men in an office are exposed to a large number of women. They have a chance to compare, to observe carefully, and to check the office grapevine to find out what kind of girl she really is. In the office the surest way to catch the heart of a man is to build yourself a reputation for being a mighty wonderful girl. The old-fashioned virtues of kindness, consideration, efficiency, and dependability—in short, character—carry the weight here.

OFFICE ATTRACTION

Men like cheesecake when it's doled out by movie queens, but in the office it's poor taste and becomes the subject of nasty jokes. Flirting and coyness are also likely to curdle a man's interest. There's nothing more embarrassing than watching a girl go into an act, determined to dazzle a man. And in an office, *someone is always watching*. Such action makes man wary and arouses the resentment of other girls. The light, delicate touch— the friendly gaiety, the quick kindness—will succeed where the desperate bid for attention falls unbecomingly flat on its face.

HEART TROUBLE

One of the unhappy differences between work and school is that many of the men you meet on the job are not eligible for matrimony. Some girls cause themselves much remorse by developing crushes on unattainable men. If he's married, don't waste your time. Forget him. No matter how attractive he may seem and no matter how interested in you he may be, the girl who's smart will look for unclaimed territory. Maybe his wife **441** *doesn't* understand him, but no girl should risk entanglements with even an unhappily married man until a divorce decree is final. Too many girls miss wonderful opportunities for real love while waiting for the misunderstood guy to make up his mind whether or not to fly the coop. And all too often he never does. Probably, if he's not appreciated by his own wife, there may be many good reasons why he soon won't be appreciated by you either.

Another variety of male to be leery of is the older Don Juan. Smooth, polished, sophisticated, he can sweep you off your feet. If you're young and impressionable, he may astonish you with his glamour and perfection. Eligible though he may be, in ninety odd cases out of a hundred nothing comes of it. All too often this suave glamour gent has no intention of settling down. He gaily flits from one flower to the next, enjoying its loveliness for a time but soon passing on to another. Aside from the dent this leaves in your heart, such an affair is likely to set your standards of male sophistication so high that you are spoiled for all the other young eligibles who have yet to acquire the experience and the money for the extravagant elegance that makes Don Juan so alluring. Such a girl is likely to end up with nothing but daydreams of glamorous gray-templed phantoms, while the flesh-and-blood boys her own age give up the fight, one after another, and marry someone else.

In business, if a girl is top-notch, she's likely to meet some dynamic, brilliant men. They are challenging to work with. Her job becomes exciting and important. She becomes indispensable, perhaps so dedicated that she willingly works overtime and devotes so large a share of her time and energies to her job that there's nothing left for fun. "Who cares?" she asks. "I'm doing something *BIG!*" Big it may be, but all-consuming it should not be. An exciting job and the stimulation of a great mind are fine from nine to five, if they don't warp her perspective or jade her taste. Companies have a way of thriving long after Miss Indispensable departs, and most brilliant minds either are already married or are too busy—too one-track themselves—to consider the matter of matrimony. Sooner or later everybody goes home from the office, and even Miss Indispensable will find it mighty lonely unless she has someone to go home to. If she consistently compares all young men with her dramatic boss, she's lost before she starts. The driving executive, fascinating though he may be, often makes a rather poor husband and father; she will be wiser to look for younger, more versatile men among her friends who are still at the lower end of the ladder.

THE OFFICE WOLF

There are several varieties of office wolves. They range from young nobodies to dapper dignitaries. Some are basically nice guys, actually quite harmless, who because of some inner insecurity have to keep testing their batting average on every girl within sight. Just don't let yourself become their favorite testing ground. Although they may mean nothing by such action, it lowers a girl if she lets someone take advantage of her. In a modern office in this day and age a girl can't go Victorian and declare her virtue slandered by the cad who tells her a slightly off-color joke or puts his arm around her shoulders. But expressing displeasure at this stage (either by a feigned look of alarm or by coolly and quietly moving away) will probably discourage further advances. Act natural, change the subject, and ignore it. The circumstances and the person have a lot to do with how you react, but the wisest course for a girl who's new to the office game is usually to head off any trouble before it has a chance to start.

Serious nuisances can usually be discouraged if you become desperately busy whenever they hover on the horizon. They, too, realize that work must be done and will usually head for less hectic pastures.

Suppose some night when you are working overtime, Mr. Already-Married suggests you have supper with him. It seems a very natural thing to do, so you agree. About dessert time, all thoughts of finishing that important rush job somehow vanish from his mind and he suggests that instead of returning to the office you go on to another gay spot for some dancing. Such extra-curricular activity is dynamite when a married man is concerned. You needn't act outraged or prissy about it, however. Simply state that you already have plans for the evening and are counting on getting home soon. He'll get the point. And he'll respect your discretion. A married man looking for a little outside amusement usually is quite easy to discourage, just because he *is* married. No matter how high his rank in the office, you hold the upper hand in such situations and should use it. Even though you might be quite infatuated with him, *don't let anything start*. There's nothing in it for you—except trouble. When the affair cools and the executive tires, it becomes inconvenient to have the girl around. She's the one who'll be out of a job, not the boss. As with all such moral detours, it is always the woman who is considered in error, always the woman who pays.

If some roving-eyed menace who is too important to squelch becomes a serious problem, you might as well start looking for a new job. Actually, very few bosses have dishonorable intentions. They realize that they are in the limelight, and they value their prestige and position too highly to risk providing opportunities for unsavory gossip. Usually the girl who takes everyone at face value and assumes he has no dark underlying motives will find that she is quite right. Even if she isn't, a naive, see-no-evil attitude will usually discourage anyone who might be contemplating unwholesome advances.

DESK-SIDE ROMANCE

Office romance, you should understand, has a mighty rocky road to travel. Although many girls consider the business world a good place to meet a mate (and, granted, it is,), extreme caution and discretion must be used to bring an office romance to a happy ending. And to a happy beginning, for that matter.

A happy beginning is usually the result of your being observed by someone who liked what he saw well enough to wangle an introduction. Somehow the odds seem to be against the fellow at the desk next to yours. This only serves to point up the fact that you should always be on your most charming behavior; you never know who's watching, and it may be that most important *he*. Ironically, romance slips away if a girl tries too hard, and it usually sneaks up on her when she least expects it. If you want Cupid on your side, be ever ready by always being your best self, but don't deliberately go after every unattached man. Such an approach is always transparent, always self-defeating.

Conducting an intraoffice romance requires great skill and delicacy. Mere proximity can be a serious problem. It's hard enough to keep your mind on your work when you're in love, but when the object of your affection is sitting there in full heavenly view, any sort of concentration requires superhuman effort. Your boss—and your beau's boss—are aware that love and efficiency don't mix, and any little slipup is likely to be attributed resentfully to your romance. In some cases, promising careers have suffered unpleasant setbacks because of a lovesick daze. For just such reasons, some firms prohibit a husband and wife from working for the same company in hopes that if confronted with loss of a job a worker will think twice before becoming serious about a fellow employee. When the staff knows of the interest you and another employee have in each other, you must both be extra careful that your work is above reproach.

As sometimes happens, even the most torrid romance may fizzle out. The end of an office romance is especially painful. Not only is there the necessity for daily contact with the lad who once played such beautiful music on your heart strings, but there is the added torture of watching from the sidelines when he takes up a new romance with someone else.

All the world loves a lover, and office staffs are no exception. You and your heart-throb will be a major source of interest and entertainment to the entire staff unless you are extremely cautious. Any courtship is more difficult when it is being scrutinized by too many interested observers. Some couples have managed to conduct a flourishing romance by keeping it entirely secret until they could flash the news via an engagement ring. Though this requires great restraint, it assures privacy and avoids criticism. It means, however, that the young man can't hover around her desk, can't phone her at the office, and can't be conspicuous about meeting her after work. Couples who have managed this sort of discreet romance are usually highly respected.

Although the boss-loves-secretary theme is a popular one for movies and magazine fiction, actual cases are extremely rare. Probably this is due partly to the fact that the rising executive is sometimes lowered in the eyes of his peers if he marries one of the girls from the office, unless she, too, has some higher standing. In view of this, should one of the young bachelor executives take an interest in a lesser employee, she would most definitely want to keep the romance private so that nothing could spoil her chances before his feelings had become strong enough to counteract any possible criticism.

MEETING NEW MEN

If you're new in town or feel your date list needs a little rejuvenation, make a special effort to get out and meet men. How? The girl who sidles down the street in attention-getting short-shorts uses a sure-fire approach; but girls who play with this kind of fire usually get burned. The fellow in the flashy convertible who spots her signals and picks her up expects her to be an easy mark. Men have little respect for a girl who allows herself to get picked up, and she may well find herself maneuvered into a situation that may be difficult to extricate herself from. A good reputation is so important an asset in meeting the right man that no girl should risk spoiling her chances by some impulsive or foolish behavior. Even if you are with other girls who want to do something you don't entirely approve of, have enough self-respect not to let yourself be talked into it. Stick to your own high standards and you'll save yourself much unhappiness and remorse.

One of the best ways to meet new men is through clubs, classes, hobby groups, church organizations, employee social groups, drama or choral groups, and sports activities. Often a girls' residence house or some similar organization will sponsor a party or dance for members and their dates. This provides an opportunity for a girl to invite the man who hasn't quite got around to asking her for a date but whose interest she'd like to encourage. When an activity of this sort is planned, some girls panic and hesitate to ask a boy they haven't dated before. Actually, this is a golden opportunity to help the fellow who's a bit shy to find out how much he's been missing. The worst he can do is refuse, and then she knows once and for all that she might as well cross him off her list of prospects and not waste further thought on him. More likely, he'll be flattered—and delighted.

A party of this sort is most successful if there is plenty of planned entertainment and lots of mix-up activities. If not, get yourself and your date on a work committee. Any first date is usually less strained if the couple can do something active, such as working together, playing games, or engaging in sports. A first date spent bowling is much easier than a movie date, where the only opportunity you have to get to know each other better is usually devoid of conversation-prompting activities. Then the impression you make depends too heavily on your skill at conversation and the relationship is likely to be stiff and self-conscious.

In this getting-to-know-you stage, talk will flow more readily if you keep the conversation on general subjects and steer clear of too many personal allusions, which can be awkward.

When you are out with a man, let him know if you are interested; but don't give him the impression he's the *only* great interest in your life until he's expressed his sentiments in no uncertain terms. The girl who develops a vine-covered-cottage look after the fourth date soon sends a man scurrying. The surest way to a man's heart (good roast beef not withstanding) is through his ego. If you can inspire him or give him a higher vision of himself, you have presented him with the most marvelous gift any man could desire. The woman who can do this is always cherished and adored.

YOUR MANNERS IN THE DATING GAME

Though many girls are kind to old ladies and have impeccable behavior in most social matters, they may sometimes treat the men in their lives in an offhand, inconsiderate way. Courtship customs, though they deny the girl the right to ask a man for a date, set her up as the ruling majesty once the courtship is under way. Such power must be used thoughtfully and kindly. Its abuse quickly affects her popularity, to say nothing of her rating as a humane individual. To check yourself, see how well you would do in the following instances.

If you are not particularly enthusiastic about a date, do you ever keep him dangling in hopes something better will come along?

It's only fair to give him a definite answer the first time. If you play for time, you not only increase the hurt of your refusal, but the delay may spoil his chances with the girl who might be his second choice.

Do you encourage boys to call you at the office?

This is never good policy. Boy-girl telephone chitchat sounds very out of place in a business office, to say nothing of the inconvenience it can cause to your boss and your work. If a man calls you at work, keep your remarks brief and as impersonal as possible.

Do you ever break a date to accept another?

Not if you value your social life. Not only is it unfair, but boys talk to each other, too, and the word travels fast when a girl heartlessly juggles dates.

If you don't want to accept a date, can you do it kindly and without getting yourself involved?

The best strategy is to say simply that you'll be busy or have other plans. Don't trip yourself up by offering any concrete explanation that may keep you from accepting another date should another man call.

🌺 If you already have a date when a second offer is made, can you refuse it without appearing smug?

When you're already booked, don't rub it in, especially if you want to encourage the second fellow. Tell him you're very sorry you can't go (try to avoid mentioning the previous date) and, if you like him, suggest that perhaps you can make it some other time.

🌺 If a fellow who seems nice but travels in a fast crowd asks you for a date, would you be wise to accept?

"Birds of a feather flock together"—and even if they don't, others will think they do. He may turn out to be quite all right—and he may not—but, regardless, as his girl you're likely to be dubbed with a fast reputation that will be rather difficult to undo. As another saying goes, "There are plenty of fish in the sea."

🌺 If another girl wants you to go on a blind date, should you accept?

Judge by the person who wants to introduce you and the caliber of the company she keeps. If you don't know the person very well or have any doubts about her, better refuse.

🌺 Are you ready when your date arrives?

Any man appreciates promptness. He came to see you, not to sit around reading your magazines—or, worse yet, to make idle conversation with your roommates, parents, or kid sister.

🌺 How considerate are you of his money?

Would a ten-minute walk, rather than a ride, upset your cheery disposition? Do you always have a few suggestions for free fun if he's financially embarrassed? When he suggests coffee after a movie, do you immediately mention an elaborate sundae or pizza? Do you suggest quarters or dimes for the juke box? When you give presents are they in a reasonable price range?

Although a man wants to show his date a good time, he has financial goals, too. He wants a vacation trip, a car, a nest egg that will enable him to start off a marriage. A girl with expensive tastes scares a man off. Help him save his money and he may pop the question that much sooner.

🌺 At a party do you ever cling to your date? Or do you flirt with every man in sight in an effort to make your date jealous?

While you want to circulate at a party so that he has a little freedom, too, the girl who encourages the competition to too great a degree antagonizes not only her escort but also every other girl there. Since your date brought you to the affair, you owe him the courtesy of the major portion of your time and attention.

�}); Do you purposely bring another man's name into your conversation with a date?

There are times when you would naturally speak of other men, but don't drag in other men and other date activities in a desire to impress him, or he may decide to leave you to the others.

🌺 Do you resist the urge to tell him how great you are at this, that, and the other thing?

Men dislike the girl who's filled with her own importance. He'll be duly impressed with how wonderful you are if you tell him how wonderful he is. Your talents and abilities have a way of making themselves apparent; you won't have to tell him—he'll soon find out for himself.

🌷 When you're out with a mixed group, are you cool to the other women?

Men often judge a woman on how well she gets along with other women. Even if your worst enemy is among those present, do your best to be pleasant and charming to all. Snide remarks about another girl will quickly plummet your rating, no matter how clever they are.

🌷 Do you tend to talk more about things and people you dislike than about things you like?

We all have things we dislike, but it's not very pleasant to listen to someone expounding on how terrible everything is, especially if her partner doesn't happen to agree.

Enthusiasm and appreciation are positive thoughts and are always attractive. Too much negativism repels.

🌸 At a party does your laughter sound a little too loud to you? Do you feel your antics might not be appreciated?

If in doubt, lower the lid. Gaiety and high spirits add much to the party, but even Alice-sit-in-the-corner is more highly regarded than the girl who overdoes the clowning bit.

🌸 When it comes to the big questions—drinking, parking, necking, petting—can you refuse without sounding like a prude?

You will probably meet your share of smooth operators, the boys who have all the arguments right at hand—and how convincing some of them can sound to the gullible girl when she is feeling more than a little bit in love or afraid that she will lose him. Just remember that men who try to seduce every girl they date are not capable of a deep and long-lasting love.

You have to be ready to recognize that behind those rationalizations is only one objective—and that is a selfish one. When a boy really cares for you, when he is thinking seriously about you and your feelings, he will not try to take advantage of you. If, on the other hand, he is just testing you (and his own powers of persuasion as well), your response will go a long way in determining what your mutual future will hold.

Everyone has to set up her own standards of conduct. The right boys will respect and admire you all the more if you maintain high standards and have the courage to stick to them. You don't need a long sermon to explain your stand; a tactful, polite—but firm—refusal will do. Never be afraid to be a little different from the crowd when you know you're right. If you've a pleasant personality, you'll always be popular.

🌸 Are you afraid *not* to go steady?

The girl who goes steady has the assurance that she won't have to sit home with a book on Saturday nights. But unless she's played the field a good bit previously, she may never know what she's missing. For a girl, it's especially advisable to know as many types of men as possible and to acquire experience in getting along with many different types of dates so that she will be better able to judge the right man for marriage. Our personalities grow with each new close friendship. It's possible to love several dates, each for a different reason. When you're ready for marriage, you will probably select someone who is a composite of all these; and you will have the experience to spot him and to appreciate him.

 FOLLOW-UP

1 If you are going steady and can see no rosy future in the relationship, don't let it drag on any longer. This is the time to meet new men and to know as many as possible so that you can make the right permanent choice when the time comes.

2 If you would like to meet new men, see what activities you could join in your town or in nearby areas so that you could make new friends.

3 Experiment with ways to change your hairdo to make it a bit more festive for a prom date.

Once you've charmed the man of your choice into giving you his name, you'll probably take on the double job of marriage *and* a career. Then, more than ever, you'll need to apply all your techniques of charm and efficiency to keep life running smoothly. Your days will move at a swifter pace than ever before, but they can also be tremendously satisfying and purposeful.

Not too many years ago the married woman hesitated to work for fear that her action would be interpreted as a slur on her husband's earning power. But times have changed. Society has come to recognize that perhaps a woman might prefer to be active in the business world—she might like being good at something in addition to her house-keeping. Many women find that their jobs bolster their egos and give them a sense of importance and accomplishment that they never could achieve around the house. Work also has overcome the problem of loneliness and gives women the opportunity for companionship with people who have the same interests and who talk the same language.

Today almost one out of every three married women has a job. A girl no longer bids the boss good-bye just because she's taken a trip to the altar. She realizes that her education and skills can be put to good use to help finance the type of home and furnishings she wants and to accumulate savings for the advent of children. Even after the children arrive, she doesn't necessarily resign herself to becoming a permanent homebody. Many young wives take part-time positions once the children reach school age, and an increasing number of women return to full-time employment when their children are grown.

29

MARRIAGE AND YOUR CAREER

CAREERS ARE FOR KEEPING

With many work years added, it is possible for a woman, as well as a man, to have a worthwhile career. A job is no longer a brief stopgap between school and marriage. This makes it all the more important to secure a good education and to train yourself well so that you can take part in work you will like. When you are planning a life career, selecting a job becomes more than a matter of taking whatever is most convenient. The long-term view should be considered if you want a job you might keep after marriage and perhaps return to in later years. You'll also want to grow and advance in your work so that if you return to business after an interlude of child rearing, you'll be eligible for a satisfying, well-paying position that will be worth the amount of extra effort required to handle two jobs.

JUGGLING TWO JOBS ISN'T EASY

Keeping both a boss and a husband happy and satisfied is likely to keep a career woman on the run. She owes definite responsibilities to each and cannot neglect one at the expense of the other. The married career woman has to stretch her talents so that she can juggle both jobs with equal dexterity. She can't be too tired if her husband wants to go out at night; she can't let him run out of clean shirts or socks. Neither can she let her household concerns take so much of her attention that she becomes inattentive at the office. She will have to keep up a pretty swift pace, perhaps sacrificing lunch-hour gab sessions to grocery shopping and household errands. If overtime is required, her husband may not be very appreciative.

Much has been written about the pitfalls of a too-early marriage. For the married working girl, extreme youth only compounds her problems. Many young couples figure that they can manage if the wife works for a while to help the marriage get on its feet, but some younger girls find this much more difficult than they had expected. Here are factors every young girl would do well to consider before she decides to become a working wife.

�*/ A youthful marriage has greater financial pressures at the beginning. If *both* the husband and wife are young, they won't have the higher salaries that more job experience brings. Money will be scarce and they won't be able to afford many of the timesaving appliances and other conveniences that make a wife's work easier. Life is much smoother for the couple who can save a little nest egg before marriage. Then, too, the arrival of a baby will not be such a financial catastrophe.

🌼 A working girl has a multitude of responsibilities. The married career girl no longer has Mother to handle household chores and to help care for her clothes. Even with a roommate, housekeeping is a 50-50 proposition. After marriage she must not only keep her job running smoothly but she is in full charge of caring for herself and her wardrobe and is also taking on the additional responsibilities of full care for her home and her husband. There will be *his* suits to press, *his* buttons to sew on, *his* laundry to do, as well as her own. The home must be kept attractive. Meals must be planned, shopped for, and prepared well; this alone can be a bit of a problem for the bride who hasn't had much experience in putting meals together.

🌼 You may be forced to grow up too fast. Looking back, some girls who married young are a little resentful. They find themselves tired, suffering from nervous strain, and feeling a little sorry for themselves, especially if they weren't able to finish their education. An early marriage and the responsibility it entails deprives them of some of the fun they feel they ought to be having while they're young. They find themselves cleaning house and pinching pennies while their single friends are buying glamorous clothes and going on festive dates. Of course, marriage has many compensations, but the contrast may still hurt.

Some girls are ready for marriage earlier than others, but statistics prove that if a girl waits until she's 23 or 24, the odds for happiness are much greater. By this time she

457

has had a chance for a little fling at life. When she settles down, she isn't afraid she may be missing her share of the fun of life. And neither will her husband.

🌼 Much self-discipline is demanded. The wife who works has great need for well-controlled emotions and adult acceptance of responsibility. Youthful impulsiveness and rash behavior can wreck her chances for happiness.

Her husband also must be mature and understanding. She probably won't have time to cook and care for him as elaborately as his mother did. In fact, he will probably find that in order for them to have time for any fun together, he'll have to help with some of the household chores, too. Should he feel this to be beneath his masculinity, his bride will have a difficult time.

If the husband's education had to be cut short, he may later be resentful when he realizes that he could have gone much further had he been able to finish. If he does try to continue his studies at night, this puts an even greater strain on the overworked household, because he will have little time to help his wife in any way and there will be less chance for relaxation and recreation together. The cost of tuition and books may also be a strain on the slim budget.

The couple who can hold off wedding bells until they have finished their education and have had time for both emotional and financial preparation are more likely to live happily ever after. Any new marriage takes a bit of doing; but when there is a little more time, money, and experience to give love a lift, marriage is more likely to become the wonderful, satisfying relationship it should be.

HOW TO SWING IT

The most important rule for success is to avoid trying to tackle too much—either too strenuous a job or too great a household load. If the job requires too much overtime or is so hectic that you come home exhausted, perhaps you had better try to find a less strenuous position. At home you'll have to accept the fact that there may sometimes be a little dust around, that meals won't be as elaborate as you'd wish, and that you won't have time for all the baking, curtain making, and other household fussing you might like. You may also have to get used to paying for some services you'd normally do yourself. Your time and energy are in great demand and you will need to spend them where they will provide the most benefit.

Many noted career women have found that one of the best ways to combine a successful career with a successful marriage is to form a definite separation between the two. Home problems shouldn't infringe on the job, and office problems shouldn't be brought home. Give your career its full due, but close the door promptly at quitting time and let your wifely concerns have full attention until you leave for work next morning. At home be careful not to monopolize the conversation with talk about *your* day. Your husband will be more appreciative if you listen instead to *his* office adventures.

Despite your busy schedule, your home must run as smoothly as possible. The working wife should try to provide appetizing meals, and they should be served on time. This may involve doing extra cooking on weekends or the night before and learning clever

459

tricks with leftovers. A steady supply of TV dinners and delicatessen specialties is not only expensive but unappealing. Much as you're tempted to make excuses for yourself or to tell yourself you're too busy, don't. This won't pass with others. You'll have to budget each minute carefully so that you can find time to do the thoughtful little acts that make life more pleasant.

Maintaining your high grooming and beauty standards will also be more difficult. Many married women save time by resorting to simpler hairdos and by skipping nail polish for daily wear. Perhaps your beauty routine will need to be streamlined in a similar manner, but you must be careful that none of the important aspects of grooming e neglected. A good appearance is so vitally important both to success on the job and pleasing a husband that no woman can ever afford to let down.

A good job is stimulating, it's true, but a well-rounded personality needs many interests. Your tight schedule may crowd out some of your former activities, but don't just bury your head in a hole of work, work, work. Take time for fun, spending your free moments carefully on worthwhile activities that give you a lift.

Although you will have to keep your social life within bounds, be ready for fun when your husband wants to go out or invites friends to drop in. Find some easy recipes for entertaining so that having company won't be too involved. (Or, better yet, search out a store where you can buy something spectacular.) You won't be at your social best that night if you get up at 5 a.m. to prepare some special delicacy before leaving for the office. Simplicity must be the rule in the working wife's household—simplicity of routine, simplicity of furnishings, simplicity of upkeep.

The person who can learn the trick of relaxing completely whenever she has an opportunity can do much to conserve her energy supply. If you commute to and from work, use this time to shut out all thoughts and to let your mind and body relax as completely as possible. When you get home, perhaps you can find fifteen minutes to lie down. Stretch out, close out the world, let yourself go limp, and imagine that your body feels very, very heavy. Some people use the trick of relaxing their bodies section by section: start with your left foot and concentrate on relaxing it completely; then do your calf, your knee, your thigh, then the other leg, and so on up your body until you are completely relaxed. Usually this will put you to sleep, so you had better set the alarm if your time is limited. Even a fifteen-minute catnap of this sort can be very refreshing and can make the evening a time you will enjoy.

When you are tired, give in to yourself and rest. With so much responsibility, you can't afford to let your health suffer. If you become ill, doctor bills can eat up a large chunk of the profits from your labors.

Above all, avoid developing a hurried, harried look. The truly charming woman maintains an air of calm serenity. She is never so rushed that she is brusque or thoughtless, that she skips the niceties of grooming or good manners, or that she cannot take a moment to be kind. You may be as busy or busier than anyone else, but try to conceal the pressure. Your accomplishments will be heightened by your untroubled look of peace and well-being—and you will seem all the more lovely.

HANDLING THE FINANCES

Two paychecks are quite pleasant. With a double income, the young couple will soon be able to buy many of the things they might otherwise have to wait years to afford. If the wife is planning to work for only a limited time after marriage, however, it's a good idea to set aside her earnings for some special purpose—furnishings, appliances, a car, a house, children—and to live on the husband's salary alone. Otherwise it's all too easy to develop extravagant habits that may be more than his salary can stand. Unless this is done, there will be the unpleasant shock of having to trim their standards to manage on one paycheck when the wife retires. It's always easy to move up the financial scale, but hard to come down. "Expenditure rises to meet income" is a rule of thumb.

462

If you become very successful and earn more than your husband, you must be careful not to let this make him feel inferior. One girl whose student husband worked only part time explained that they overcame this unequal income problem by lumping their earnings together and setting up a budget that allotted them each enough for their particular needs. She was careful that the term *our* money was always used, never *my* money.

Difficult though the career-marriage combination may be, thousands of women have mastered the techniques. It is a tribute to the modern woman that she has been able to do so much so well. A good part of her success can undoubtedly be ascribed to her charm. This all-important element plays a key role in her success both at home and in the office. Without it, neither job can bring the rewards it should.

 FOLLOW-UP

Talk to some married couples who work full time. Find out what both the husbands and wives think of the arrangement. What problems and advantages result from the wife's job? How do they manage to have time for the details of home life and for fun together?

ANOTHER LOOK

As you come to the end of these pages, pause for a moment to analyze the progress you've made so far. During this short time you have learned many ways to make yourself more beautiful, more appealing. If you have applied what you've learned, you are already enjoying a lovely improvement. Deep down inside, there is also the blissful assurance that you are more confident, more poised, more happy with yourself. You are well on your way to a charmed life.

Beauty and charm are not easy goals to grasp. You must keep striving day after day until their good habits are so deeply ingrained that they become a natural part of you. Now that you have made such a good start, keep up your progress. Constantly check your posture, your speech, your grooming, your attitudes. When necessary, turn back and reread pages that may help you.

Don't be discouraged, either, if your progress hasn't been all you wished. Some girls move ahead faster than others because they have more natural advantages to start with. Perhaps, for instance, your figure isn't yet a model's dream. Unfortunately, different molds were used to make some of us. Although you may never be the perfectly proportioned sylph you'd like to be, don't give up until you are convinced that you've done the very best you can with what Nature gave you. Then concentrate all the more on superb posture and the selection of the most flattering clothes you can find. Many beauties have merely learned well the tricks of diminishing less than perfect features and focusing attention where it does the most good.

Keep in mind that your aim is to create the best possible YOU—to develop your own individual capacities, talents, and assets . . . to perfect your own personal flair. Let this be expressed in your clothes, your grooming, your whole personality. Be the woman who is noted for exquisite taste: dramatic color combinations, clothing with an individual difference that is unfalteringly correct for her personality. Carry this personal flair through to your movements, your speech, your thoughts. Constantly strive to improve in every way possible, whether it be in exposing yourself to stimulating, vital thoughts, in moving ahead on the job, or in cultivating your capacity to give and receive love. Try to enjoy to the fullest everything you do so that your countenance will be brightened by the better-than-beauty sparkle of a flashing smile and a vivacious zest for living. Cherish your own individuality and you can never be a pale carbon copy of the crowd—or, worse yet, a phony distortion of someone else. You will have a personal magnetism that will enhance your beauty and attract others to you.

HAPPY ENDINGS

Although this book may go back on your shelf, your progress in beauty and charm does not end here. You know the rudiments; true mastery comes only through your own repeated practice. The most gratifying part about a quest for charm and beauty is that the more you work at it, the greater are the miracles that will be worked for you.

to be
continued
– by you!

INDEX